SURVEYING IN THE SIXTEENTH CENTURY. *From Hulsius'* De Quadrante Geometrico.

NATIONAL COUNCIL OF TEACHERS OF MATHEMATICS, Nineteenth Yearbook

Surveying Instruments

THEIR·HISTORY and CLASSROOM USE

EDMOND R. KIELY, Ph.D.

Bureau of Publications, Teachers College
Columbia University, New York
1 9 4 7

MANUFACTURED IN THE UNITED STATES OF AMERICA

TO
MY FATHER

Editor's Preface

This is the nineteenth of the series of Yearbooks started in 1926 by The National Council of Teachers of Mathematics. The titles of the preceding Yearbooks are as follows:

1. A Survey of Progress in the Past Twenty-Five Years.
2. Curriculum Problems in Teaching Mathematics.
3. Selected Topics in the Teaching of Mathematics.
4. Significant Changes and Trends in the Teaching of Mathematics Throughout the World Since 1910.
5. The Teaching of Geometry.
6. Mathematics in Modern Life.
7. The Teaching of Algebra.
8. The Teaching of Mathematics in the Secondary School.
9. Relational and Functional Thinking in Mathematics.
10. The Teaching of Arithmetic.
11. The Place of Mathematics in Modern Education.
12. Approximate Computation.
13. The Nature of Proof.
14. The Training of Mathematics Teachers.
15. The Place of Mathematics in Secondary Education.
16. Arithmetic in General Education.
17. A Source Book of Mathematical Applications.
18. Multi-Sensory Aids in the Teaching of Mathematics.

The present Yearbook represents a very important addition to the volumes that precede it and is the forerunner of the Twentieth Yearbook, which will deal with the broad topic of measurement, with special emphasis upon the value of the metric system.

As editor of the Yearbook, I wish to express my personal appreciation to Brother Edmond R. Kiely, the author, for his painstaking care in helping to see the Yearbook through the press.

W. D. REEVE

Author's Preface

Twelve years' experience with the teaching of high school mathematics and a similar term of experience with the early stages of the education of engineers form the background from which the author offers this work to the interested reader. It is hoped that the book will be of benefit to those engaged in similar duties and that it contains sufficient relevant material which, up to the present time, has not been readily available. The needs of the mathematics teacher for the information contained in the following pages are detailed in the fifth chapter and require no reiteration here. It is sufficient to state that practically all leading authorities on mathematical education recognize that such information is part of the necessary professional equipment of the well-qualified teacher. For some years those charged with the formulation of the educational policies of engineering colleges have recognized the need for an increase in the cultural subject matter of engineering curricula. It is scarcely controvertible that an engineering education which does not include the history of the particular branch of engineering being pursued is incomplete. For this reason the material of the first four chapters should be of use to the educators of future civil engineers.

The author wishes to offer his sincere thanks to many friends for their aid and cooperation in the collection and arrangement of the material: in particular, to the superiors of the Congregation of the Christian Brothers of Ireland for affording the opportunity to carry on the work; to Professor J. K. Finch, Dean of the Engineering College, Columbia University, well known for his interest in the history of engineering, under whose guidance the first four chapters took shape; to Professor J. R. Clark of Teachers College, Columbia University, an experienced teacher of high school mathematics, for his advice on the development of Chapters V and VI; to the members of the mathematics faculty of Teachers College and contemporary students for constructive criticism on various topics; to Professor O. Neugebauer of Brown University, foremost authority on the history of Babylonian mathematics, for checking the material of the first chapter; to Professor R. S. Kirby of Yale University, Professor C. N. Shuster of Teachers College, and Dr. A. Bakst for reading the manuscript and offering helpful criticisms; to Br. P. B. Doyle of Iona College for aid in deciphering some passages from the *Lingua Latina;* to my friend of the camera, Br. J. F. Hamill, who has since passed on to a better world, for many hours spent in making reproductions from the old books; to Br. J. R. O'Farrell of Dublin for much assistance in research on a topic which unfortunately still defies a definite solution; to Miss M. S. Newell for a critical reading of the manuscript; to the librarians of Columbia University and the New York Public Library for their cooperation in locating many rare books; to the publishers, societies, and individuals who kindly gave permission for reproductions and quotations; to Miss C. Foss of the Bureau of Publications for carrying out efficiently the tasks of preparing the manuscript for publication and reading the proofs; and finally, but not least, to Professor W. D. Reeve and the Board of Directors of The National Council of Teachers of Mathematics for the honor they have conferred in adopting this work as their Nineteenth Yearbook.

E. R. K.

Iona College
Lá 'le Columcille, 1947

Contents

Surveying
Instruments

Dimensionis disciplina artes singulas adjuvat, vix enim quidpiam agere possumus sine mensura.

PATRIZI

Per varios usus artem experientia fecit, exemplo monstrante viam.

MANILIUS

I am sure no subject loses more than mathematics by any attempt to dissociate it from its history.

GLASHIER

I

BEGINNINGS in Egypt, China, and Babylonia

THROUGHOUT the centuries, the history of mankind shows an ever-present desire to attain truth in its multifarious forms. In few fields is this better illustrated than in that of mathematics, which as an abstract science has taken man beyond the bounds of earth and helped him form a fair picture of the infinite, and as an art is fundamental to all human effort in measurement. The need for measurement must have been felt from the very beginning of human existence. The first steps in this art were naturally crude and slow. The methods employed have not been recorded, except insofar as we can surmise from relics unearthed from time to time by the antiquarian. Adding this hypothetical information to what we have in recorded history, we see in retrospect a long, slow struggle in the refinement of ways and means of measuring, which has gradually built up the foundation of the precise art of measurement of which we are so proud in this era of ours.

A few years ago Henry D. Hubbard of the United States Bureau of Standards paid a glowing tribute to this fundamental art:[1]

Down the ages from prehistoric times came the art of measuring by which things are dimensioned for utility, by which time and space are measured for every fact and act of life. The measuring stick is the scepter in the hand of science; a tool of discovery, a means of record and an example of the use of exact knowledge. The gradual rise in the art of measurement gave no sign that in this century it would reach a commanding place in human affairs.

A study of the history of any art usually affects us at first with wonder because of the slowness of its early developments, but the final impression produced is a high esteem for the progress

[1] H. D. Hubbard, "The Romance of Measurement," *Scientific Monthly*, October, 1931, p. 356. By permission of The Science Press.

1

achieved by our ancestors, for the ultimate triumphs of persever-
ance and genius. The history of the Egyptian *harpedonaptae,* the
Roman *agrimensores,* and the others whose lineal descendant is
the modern surveyor offers nothing very spectacular; it is rather
the record of a slow and sometimes hesitant onward march of
achievement and progress. As might be expected, at certain intervals down the ages the chain of development seems to be
broken, owing to the vagaries of human nature. Nevertheless,[2]

all through the ages the surveyor has been not only an essential figure
to the progress of civilization, the maintenance of property rights and
the building of engineering works, but due to the fact that he dealt with
careful measurements and facts, he has had a steadying influence on
man's efforts to advance.

Our knowledge of the instruments used by the people of any
particular place or period must depend primarily on the two
chief sources of historical evidence; namely, the relics of instruments, either real or diagrammatic, and the written documents
which have survived the ravages of time. From three other, but less
reliable, sources we may also legitimately draw conclusions: first,
the remains of monumental edifices, roadways, water-supply systems, canals, and in general what we now term civil engineering
projects, for the construction of which, knowledge of the use of
some form of surveying instruments was of paramount importance;
secondly, the attainments of a people in any branch of knowledge
basic to the art of surveying, particularly mathematics; finally, the
traditions handed down from later periods.[3] An attempt will be
made in the remainder of this chapter to indicate briefly the more
important features of our present-day evidence as to the attainments in surveying of what are commonly considered the three
most important of the ancient cultural groups; namely, the Babylonians, Egyptians, and Chinese. Unfortunately for our reconstruction of the attainments of these three peoples, basic evidence
in the form of relics of instruments is practically non-existent;

---

[2] J. K. Finch, "Our Indebtedness to the Old Surveyor," *The Military Engineer,*
July-August, 1925, pp. 320-325. By permission of the author.
[3] The danger in using these three secondary sources of evidence is that they
may lead to some wishful thinking. For example, see F. Schmidt, *Geschichte der
geodätischen Instrumente und Verfahren im Altertum und Mittelalter* (Neustadt an
der Haardt, 1935) on early forms of plumb-bob levels (p. 55) and on the symmetrical
construction of a right angle by means of cord (p. 95).

Figure 1. EGYPTIAN HARPEDONAPTAE OR ROPE-STRETCHERS.
From Wreszinski's Atlas zur altägyptischen Kulturgeschichte. *Reproduced
by permission of J. C. Hinrichs & Co., Leipzig.*

this is naturally to be expected, since such instruments were probably made of perishable materials.

In the cuneiform clay tablets of Babylonia and the hieroglyphical inscriptions and diagrams on Egyptian papyri and monuments
we have direct contemporary evidence, but here again, unfortunately, the amount of such evidence is very meager. Among the
Babylonian tablets have been discovered several primitive maps[4]
in which land divisions are carefully delineated, but no Babylonian
tablet has yet been discovered which describes a surveying process
or gives a diagram or description of a surveying instrument.[5] By
comparison Egyptian hieroglyphical evidence is far more abundant, and from it we have the earliest diagrams of surveying instruments and scenes depicting the harpedonaptae at work (Figure 1).
Although Babylonian and Egyptian civilizations are probably
much older than the Chinese, their historical records are far more
authentic because of the durability of the materials on which these
records were written. The few accounts from ancient China, which
deal with surveying methods and instruments, are probably of
much later origin than the dates traditionally assigned to them.[6]
The oldest Chinese document which carries information on sur-

[4] The oldest known Babylonian map tablet dates from about 2500 B.C. See E.
Raisz, *General Cartography* (New York, 1938), p. 10.

[5] Fragments of Babylonian clay astrolabes have been discovered, but these are generally considered to have been used solely in astronomical work. See E. Weidner,
Handbuch der babylonischen Astronomie (Leipzig, 1915), Vol. 1, pp. 62 ff.

[6] About 1000 B.C. is now considered probable. See D. E. Smith, "Unsettled Questions
Concerning the Mathematics of China," *Scientific Monthly*, Vol. 33, 1931, pp. 244-
250. L. van Hee, S.J., "The Great Treasure House of Chinese and European Mathematics," *American Mathematical Monthly*, Vol. 33, 1926, pp. 502-506.

veying is the *Chou-pei*.[7] Its author and date are both unknown,
and there is reason to believe that it has undergone considerable
change since it was first written. Nevertheless, it is probably a fair
record of Chinese surveying practices at the beginning of the
second millennium B.C. The only other important Chinese documents that give any information bearing on the subject are the
K'iu-ch'ang Suan-Shu[8] and the *Chou-Li*.[9]

The evidence of extensive undertakings for which surveying was
necessary forms our most important clue, up to the present time, to
the fact that surveying, sometimes of a surprising degree of accuracy, as will be shown later, was carried on by these peoples. This
fact makes it all the more regrettable that our evidence both as regards instruments and written records is so meager. Before considering the details of the direct evidence, it is well to review briefly
what is known of the attainments of these peoples in the field of
geometry.

Mathematical Attainments

Our knowledge of Egyptian mathematics depends in the main
on the contents of two papyri.[10] As far as we know, there is no
proof from this period of the existence of any kind of deductive
geometry. Whatever geometrical knowledge existed seems to have
been acquired by empirical processes. The opinions of the foremost authorities on Egyptian mathematics are well summed up in
the words of Thomas:[11]

[7] E. Biot, "Traduction et examen d'un ancien ouvrage chinois intitulé Tcheou-pei," *Journal Asiatique*, Series 3, Vol. 11, 1841, pp. 593-639.
[8] D. E. Smith, *History of Mathematics* (Boston, 1923), Vol. 1, pp. 31-33.
[9] E. Biot, *Tcheou-Li ou rites de Tcheou* (Paris, 1851).
[10] The Ahmes or Rhind papyrus (*c.* 1550 B.C.) was found in Thebes. Purchased in 1858 by A. H. Rhind, it is now in the possession of the British Museum. The first important study on this papyrus was that of A. Eisenlohr, *Ein mathematisches Hand-buch der alten Ägypter* (Leipzig, 1877). In recent times two important works on this papyrus have been published; namely, *The Rhind Mathematical Papyrus*, by B. T. E. Peet (Liverpool, 1923); and *The Rhind Mathematical Papyrus*, by A. B. Chace, H. P. Manning, and R. C. Archibald (Oberlin, Ohio, 1927). The Golenishchev or Moscow papyrus (*c.* 1850 B.C.) is now in the possession of the Moscow Museum of Fine Arts. The only complete study of it so far published is that of W. W. Struve, "Mathematischer Papyrus des staatlichen Museums der Schönen Künste in Moskau," *Quellen und Studien zur Geschichte der Mathematik*, 1930, Abt. A, Bd. 1.
[11] W. R. Thomas, "Moscow Mathematical Papyrus, Problem 14," *Journal of Egyptian Archaeology*, Vol. 17, 1931, p. 52. By permission of the Egypt Exploration Society.

The Egyptian, according to the two papyri, had explored nearly the whole field of mensuration, and had arrived in every case at correct results of general application. The whole system of deductive "analysis" as the word is understood today, appears to have been outside his ken, both in its geometrical and its algebraical form; at all events there is no indication of such a method in the papyri, and we must still be content to assign its discovery to the Greeks and the Arabs. There remains only, according to logicians, the inductive method of trial, hypothesis, classification and verification used alike by the modern scientist and prehistoric man.

In the Rhind papyrus there are nineteen problems of a geometric nature; namely, numbers 41-46 and 48-60. In the first three, on the volumes of cylindrical granaries, π is indirectly given the remarkably close approximation of 256/81 or 3.1605. The same value is also to be found in the Golenishchev papyrus. Contemporary with these papyri the Babylonians were using $\pi = 3$. Problems 44-46 deal with volumes and dimensions of parallelopipedal granaries. Problems 48-55 are concerned with areas; while 56-60 are the so-called pyramid problems. In Problems 51-53 the area of a triangle is determined by multiplying one-half of its base, and of a trapezoid by multiplying one-half the sum of its bases, by the length of a line called the *meret*, which may be taken either as a side or as a line representing the altitude. The indefiniteness of the papyrus as to the meaning of the word *meret* has given scope for much controversy over what the Egyptians really used. Chace concludes:[12]

It does not seem probable that the author had much conception of different kinds of triangles. We may suppose that he has in mind a piece of land, of a certain width at one end and coming to a point, or at least narrower at the other end. Thus to get the area he thinks of a rectangle with the average width of the piece of land.

Gunn and Peet summarize our information on Egyptian knowledge of triangles as follows:[13]

[12] Chace, Manning, and Archibald, *op. cit.*, p. 37. By permission of The Mathematical Association of America. See also B. G. Gunn, in review of Peet's edition of the Rhind papyrus, *Journal of Egyptian Archaeology*, Vol. 12. 1926, p. 133; and K. Sethe, in review of the same edition, *Jahresbericht der deutschen mathematiker Vereiningung*, Vol. 33, 1925, pp. 139-143.

[13] B. G. Gunn and B. T. E. Peet, "Four Geometrical Problems from the Moscow Mathematical Papyrus," *Journal of Egyptian Archaeology*, Vol. 15, 1929, p. 176. By permission of the Egypt Exploration Society.

(1) [It is] certain that the Egyptians of the [Middle Kingdom] period knew of the properties of the isosceles triangle which we should express by the following equations: (a = area, h = height, b = base)

$$a = h\frac{b}{2}; \quad h = \sqrt{2a\frac{h}{b}}; \quad b = \frac{b}{h}\sqrt{2a\frac{h}{b}}$$

(2) There is nothing to show that these calculations were restricted to isosceles triangles. In the formulation of the problems the general word "spdt," "triangle" is used and the solutions, both in the terms used and the methods employed, apply equally well to any sort of triangles.

As to methods of calculating the areas of quadrilaterals, we find no record in the two papyri; our first evidence comes from a much later period. In the inscription on the temple at Edfu,[14] built about 100 B.C., reference is made to a large number of four-sided fields. If the sides are named in order a, b, c, d, then these areas were determined by the formula $1/2 \ (a + c) \cdot 1/2 \ (b + d)$, which except in the case of the rectangle gives erroneous results. Strange to say, we find this same formula still in use nearly a thousand years later, side by side with the correct formula.[15]

The pyramid problems of the Rhind papyrus deal with the ratio of the lengths of two sides of a right triangle corresponding to the cotangent of the angle which a face of a regular pyramid makes with its base. This ratio was known as the *seked* (*seqd*) of the pyramid.[16] Gandz explains its significance:[17]

The pyramids were built in decreasing layers or stories of stones. In order to obtain an even slope and a smooth surface in filling out the corners, the inlaying stones must have the same slope or the same ratio between the base and the height. This was in all likelihood the *seqd*. But it would be a great mistake to assume that the ancient Egyptians actually measured angles or computed their cotangents. They only had the practical rule and some vague idea, as all the primitive people engaged in building would have, that the slope of a pyramid is determined by the ratio of half the side of the base to the height.

[14] K. R. Lepsius, "Über eine hieroglyphische Inschrift im Temple von Edfu," *Preussische Akademie der Wissenschaften zu Berlin. Abhandlungen,* 1855, pp. 69-114.
[15] For example, in the writings of Bede and Gerbert. See Chace, Manning, and Archibald, *op. cit.,* p. 132.
[16] T. Heath, *A History of Greek Mathematics* (Oxford, 1921), Vol. 1, pp. 127-128, 130-131. L. Borchardt, "Wie wurden die Boschungen der Pyramiden bestimmt," *Zeitschrift für ägyptische Sprache,* Vol. 31, 1893, pp. 9-17.
[17] S. Gandz, "The Origin of Angle-Geometry," *Isis,* Vol. 12, 1929, p. 460. By permission of the Editor, G. Sarton.

There is no direct evidence that the Egyptians knew the formula for the volume of a pyramid, yet it is most probable that they did, since the pyramid played an important role in their lives, especially during the Third Dynasty. Vogel remarks:[18]

From the fact that Democritus (c. 500 B.C.) "found" the formula (1/3 bh) for the pyramid, we may perhaps conclude that this was a piece of wisdom brought from Egypt, for his visit to that country is authenticated, and he prides himself upon a geometrical knowledge equal to that of the Egyptians.

The remarkable work in Problem 14 of the Golenishchev papyrus is equivalent to finding the volume of a truncated regular pyramid of square base, using the formula $V = (h/3) (a^2 + ab + b^2)$.

The study of Babylonian mathematics has been given great impetus within recent years, owing chiefly to the research work of Neugebauer.[19] In the light of his recent findings, our knowledge of the early history of mathematics has undergone a profound change. Mathematical ideas which were formerly thought to have originated among the Greeks are now known to have existed at least fourteen hundred years earlier. From clay tablets, the earliest of which date from about 1800 B.C., we have numerical operations which imply correct knowledge of the following geometric facts,[20] all of which would have been useful to the surveyor: areas of (1) rectangle, (2) right triangle, (3) trapezoid with one side perpendicular to the parallel sides; volumes of (1)

[18] K. Vogel, "The Truncated Pyramid in Egyptian Mathematics," *Journal of Egyptian Archaeology*, Vol. 16, 1930, p. 243. By permission of the Egypt Exploration Society.

[19] In 1929 Otto Neugebauer founded the periodical *Quellen und Studien zur Geschichte der Mathematik* for the dissemination of the results of research in the history of ancient mathematics. In "Mathematische Keilschrift-Texte," Parts I and II (1935), Part III (1937), *Quellen*, Abt. A, Bd. 3, are to be found the most important results of Neugebauer's own work on Babylonian mathematical tablets. Other important works of his are: "Vorlesungen über Geschichte der antiken mathematischen Wissenschaften," Vol. 1, "Vorgriechische Mathematik," *Die Grundlehren der mathematischen Wissenschaften*, Vol. 43, 1934; and "Die Geometrie der ägyptischen mathematischen Texte," *Quellen*, 1929, Abt. B, Bd. 1, pp. 413-451. For the latest information on Babylonian mathematics, derived chiefly from the Yale University collection of Babylonian tablets, see *Mathematical Cuneiform Texts*, Edited by O. Neugebauer and A. Sachs (New Haven, Conn., 1945).

[20] R. C. Archibald, "Babylonian Mathematics," *The Mathematics Teacher*, Vol. 29, 1936, pp. 209-219. The footnotes in this article give references to the evidence which Neugebauer adduces in his works to establish the truth of these facts. See also E. T. Bell, *The Development of Mathematics* (New York, 1945), Ch. 2.

rectangular parallelopiped, (2) right prism with trapezoidal base, (3) right circular cylinder, using $\pi = 3$; also (1) proportionality of corresponding sides of similar right triangles, (2) bisection of base by the perpendicular from the vertex of an isosceles triangle, (3) inscription of a right angle in a semicircle, and (4) finally but not least, the Pythagorean theorem.

Of the Chinese documents already mentioned the only one that gives any worth-while information on geometry is the *K'iu-ch'ang Suan-Shu*. The first section of this work relates to surveying "with correct rules for the area of the triangle, trapezium and circle $(1/2 \ c \cdot 1/2 \ d$ and $1/4 \ cd)$ and with the circle approximations $3/4 \ d^2$ and $1/12 \ c^2$ where π is taken as 3." [21] The ninth section deals with simple cases of the Pythagorean theorem. In arithmetical computations all three peoples, like the Greeks and Romans of later times, were under a tremendous handicap by comparison with the users of the Hindu-Arabic number system.

Fundamental Problems

The old adage "Necessity is the mother of invention" is undoubtedly as true here as in any other sphere in which the ingenuity of man has been called upon to solve a problem. Herodotus' attribution of the beginnings of geometry among the Egyptians to the annual overflow of the Nile may be equally well applied to the peoples dwelling in the valleys of the Tigris-Euphrates and the Yangtze. But before man acquired a method of estimating areas, he went through, in prehistoric times, a series of operations in which through trial and error he acquired knowledge of methods of measurement as such measurement became necessary. As to what instruments were first used, we can only surmise from what we find in historic times. There can be little doubt that parts of the human body were set up as standard units at an early age; we still have vestiges of this practice in our system of measurement. Analogies between parts of instruments and the eye, hand, and foot can be so easily made that it is safe to conclude that the human body, by means of which man made his first rough estimates, was taken as the archetype in instrument design and that instruments and parts of instruments were developed as aids to

[21] Smith, *History of Mathematics,* Vol. 1, p. 32.

these organs in sighting, pointing, measuring, and setting up on a firm base. Among man's first intuitive ideas of practical geometry must have been those of the straight line, the vertical line, and the horizontal plane. In nature he saw these exemplified in many ways. From the combination of the latter two there developed the idea of the right angle and rudimentary notions of symmetry.[22] From the right angle came the square as the fundamental unit of area.

Instruments Needed

The instruments developed by these three peoples depended naturally on the needs for them. These needs may be placed in four categories. We know that in all three countries taxes were imposed in proportion to the land holdings; therefore means of measuring lengths and areas had to be developed. Irrigation works were of primary importance; this naturally led to the development of some form of leveling device. The *plumb line* was the natural outcome of the need for erecting vertical walls. Finally, for the orientation of important buildings, and the setting out of ground plans in general, some means of laying out one line at right angles to another was necessary.

DIRECT MEASUREMENT INSTRUMENTS There is evidence showing that for the direct measurement of distances ropes or cords were used by the Egyptians and most probably also by the Babylonians and Chinese. Several scenes have been discovered on the walls of Egyptian tombs depicting surveyors in the act of measuring with cords which appear in some diagrams to be marked off at regular intervals.[23] That measuring cords were used by the Babylonians may be inferred from the phrase "stretching a field," which they used to denote "measuring a field." [24] We may assume that care was taken in the making of such ropes to ensure that they would neither shrink nor lengthen. Of the process of manufacture we

[22] Gandz, *op. cit.* E. Fettweis, "Über die erste Entstehung der einfachten geometrischen Formen," *Archiv für Geschichte Mathematik, Naturwissenschaften und der Technik,* New Series 3, Vol. 12, 1929, pp. 117-119.

[23] W. Wreszinski, *Atlas zur altägyptischen Kulturgeschichte* (Leipzig, 1923), Vol. 1, Pls. 11, 189, 191, 231, 232, 243, 424, etc.

[24] Neugebauer, "Mathematische Keilschrift-Texte," Part II, p. 15a. F. Thureau-Dangin, *Rituels accadiens* (Paris, 1921), p. 49 (14).

have no early account, but it was probably somewhat along the lines described later by Heron of Alexandria:[25]

The rope is stretched taut between two stakes, and after it has been kept in this position for a considerable length of time it is stretched again. When the process has been repeated several times, the rope is rubbed with a mixture of beeswax and resin. It is better, however, instead of stretching the rope between two stakes to suspend it vertically for a long time with a sufficiently heavy weight attached to it.

On the subject of rope measures a well-known authority says:[26]

A well made rope, (such as a patent wove line woven circularly, with the strands always in the line of the strain) when stretched wetted, and allowed to dry with moderate strain, will not vary from a chain more than one foot in 2000, if carefully used.

LEVELING INSTRUMENTS   In considering this type of instrument two operations are here understood by the term *leveling:* first,

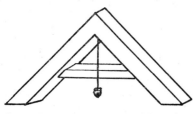

Figure 2.   EGYPTIAN PLUMB-BOB LEVEL

the determination of a horizontal line or plane; second, the determination of the difference in height between two points. These two operations, which originated from early human necessities, must have been carried on by man from prehistoric times. The first was needed whenever buildings with any pretense toward stability and beauty of design were conceived, whether temples, monuments, or dwellings. The needs of irrigation and water supplies for populous communities gave rise to the second operation. Unfortunately, although there are many traces of ambitious irrigation schemes in the three countries under consideration,[27] and although there are a few records of some types of instruments used, there is no extant account of the methods employed. More surprising still is

[25] Quoted by A. de Rochas in "Geodesia," in Daremberg and Saglio, *Dictionnaire des antiquités grecques et romaines* (Paris, 1837).

[26] W. M. Gillespie, *A Treatise on Surveying* (New York, 1904), p. 15. By permission of D. Appleton-Century Co., Inc.

[27] J. H. Gandolfo, "Tracing the Engineer in Early Egypt and Assyria," *Civil Engineering*, Vol. 1, 1931, pp. 632-637. E. W. Lane, "Ingenuity of the Ancient Chinese," *Civil Engineering*, Vol. 1, 1931, pp. 17 ff.

the fact that there is no indication in either Babylonian or Egyptian records of any type of *water level* or *leveling rod;* only from China have come some vague hints as to their use.[28] We know that plumb-bob levels were in use among the Egyptians. They were in the form of a capital **A** (Figure 2), probably made of wood, the plumb line hanging from the apex and the crosspiece carrying a mark with which the plumb line coincided when the instrument rested on a horizontal surface.[29] The making of such an instrument implies at least a practical knowledge of the properties of the isosceles triangle.

SIGHTING INSTRUMENTS For the establishment of verticality there is no record of the use of the plumb bob among the Babylonians, but its use in building is so fundamental that we can scarcely conceive of their not employing it. The earliest recorded use of the plumb bob is by the Egyptians. By them it was used in combination with a split palm leaf for star observation in connection with the measurement of time and also for the determination of the meridian line used in the orientation of temples and pyramids[30] (Figure 3). This combination

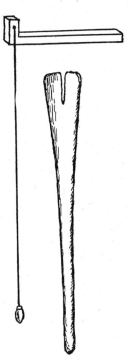

Figure 3. EGYPTIAN SIGHTING INSTRUMENT, THE MERCHET. *After Borchardt.*

[28] Biot, "Traduction et examen d'un ancien ouvrage chinois intitulé Tcheou-pei," "What is horizontal must coincide with the water surface" (p. 481). "When a city is to be planned out, the surveyors level the ground with water, with which they employ the hanging cord" (p. 553).

[29] L. Borchardt, "Längen und Richtungen der vier Grundkanten der grossen Pyramide bei Gise," *Beiträge zur ägyptischen Bauforschung und Altertumskunde,* Vol. 1, 1926, p. 9. It is interesting to note that the miner's "triangle" used until recent times was practically identical in form. McCullough says: "The early miners in California set grade pegs on hundreds of miles of ditches and roads with this primitive instrument." E. McCullough, *Practical Surveying* (New York, 1915), p. 74. By permission of D. Van Nostrand Co.

[30] L. Borchardt, "Ein altägyptisches astronomisches Instrument," *Zeitschrift für ägyptische Sprache,* Vol. 37, 1899, pp. 10-17; and "Die altägyptische Zeitmessung," *Die Geschichte der Zeitmessung und der Uhren,* Edited by E. von Bassermann-Jordan, Vol. 1, 1920, pp. 52 ff.

instrument, known as the *merchet,* is of special interest since it is the earliest record of a method of sighting and the forerunner of the slit and hair utilized in the Renaissance. The use of the plumb bob is recorded by the early Chinese.[31]

RIGHT-ANGLE INSTRUMENTS   Throughout the history of surveying the right angle has played an important role in its development. In fact, the right angle has been the dominant characteristic

Figure 4. EGYPTIAN SQUARE. *From Wilkinson's* Manners and Customs of the Ancient Egyptians.

of the surveying not only of the period now under discussion but also of the Greek and Roman period which followed, and the methods which evolved during these periods survived in Europe until the Renaissance. The reason for the predominance of this right-angle surveying lay in the fact that the right angle is the simplest relation between two directions and that the square is the simplest division of a horizontal surface. To carry on right-angle surveying it was necessary to have instruments for laying out horizontal right angles. The commonest group of instruments used for the purpose of laying out or verifying a right angle by contact is generally designated in English as *squares.* Throughout history, their forms and applications have changed but little; as far back as we can go to the origin of these instruments, we find them in quite common use. The form of early squares we know through mural diagrams, such as Figure 4. This diagram is from a mural on a tomb at Thebes. It depicts a joiner's workshop and is considered to date from about 1450 B.C.[32] Although no diagram or mention of the square has been found in Babylonian records, there is every probability, judging by their knowledge of geometry, that the Babylonians made use of some form of square in order to set up right-angle boundaries for their lands, as the Romans did later. Babylonian survey maps, some of

[31] Biot, *Tcheou-Li ou rites de Tcheou,* p. 545.
[32] J. Wilkinson, *Manners and Customs of the Ancient Egyptians* (London, 1878), Vol. 2, pp. 198-199. For other diagrams showing the square, see Wreszinski, *op. cit.,* Pls. 310, 314, 315.

which antedate 2000 B.C., show many sections of land composed of irregular polygons subdivided into right triangles, rectangles, and trapezoids, whose dimensions and areas are indicated.[33] The square is mentioned in the Chinese writings. "Knowledge originates from the square, the square from the right triangle; the right triangle with numbers regulates and governs all things." [34]

An unverified tradition that has long been a source of controversy among the historians of mathematics credited the harpedonaptae with the construction of the right angle by means of a cord marked off in intervals proportional to 3, 4, and 5.[35] But nothing in Egyptian documents warrants the certainty of this tradition.[36] The possibility of the use of such a method is acknowledged because of the appearance on an Egyptian papyrus[37] of four sets of Pythagorean triplets derived from the primitive 3, 4, and 5; but whether the Egyptians were acquainted with the Pythagorean theorem is still unknown. On the other hand, there is no longer any doubt that the Babylonians were well acquainted with the Pythagorean theorem about 1800 B.C., although there is no documentary evidence as to the extent to which they made use of it in their surveying. The same situation appears in Chinese records of about the period 1000 B.C.

The probability of the use of some form of *surveyor's cross* by these peoples has been increased within recent years by the dis-

[33] F. Thureau-Dangin, "Un cadastre chaldéen," *Revue d'assyriologie*, Vol. 4, 1897. V. Scheil, O.P., *Une saison de fouilles à Sippar* (Paris, 1902), Tablets Nos. 178, 180, 199, 718. P. Deimal, "Die Vermessung der Felder bei den Sumeren um 3000 v. Chr," *Orientalia*, Vol. 7, 1924, pp. 1-43; Vol. 5, 1922, pp. 56-63. L. Speleers, *Recueil des inscriptions de l'Asie antérieure des musées royaux du cinquantenaire à Bruxelles* (Brussels, 1925), No. 195.

[34] Biot, "Traduction et examen d'un ancien ouvrage intitulé Tcheou-pei," p. 602.

[35] For recent popular propagations of this tradition, see L. Hogben, *Mathematics for the Million* (New York, 1940), p. 61. A. Hooper, *The River Mathematics* (New York, 1945), p. 170. F. W. Kokomoor, *Mathematics in Human Affairs* (New York, 1946), p. 3. Bell, *op. cit.*, p. 68.

[36] Peet, *op. cit.*, p. 32. "Nothing in Egyptian mathematics suggests that the Egyptians were acquainted even with special cases of Pythagoras' theorem concerning the squares on the sides of a right-angled triangle." By permission of the University Press of Liverpool. See also S. Gandz, "Die Harpedonapten oder Seilspanner und Seilknüpfer," *Quellen und Studien zur Geschichte der Mathematik*, Abt. B, *Studien*, Bd. 1, Heft 3, 1930, pp. 256 ff. W. Lietzmann, "Über einige 'Legenden' aus der Geschichte der Mathematik," *Zeitschrift für mathematischen und naturwissenschaftlichen Unterricht aller Schulgattungen*, Vol. 71, 1940, pp. 22-30.

[37] The Berlin papyrus from Kahum. See J. Tropfke, *Geschichte der Elementar-Mathematik*, Vol. 4, 1923, p. 139.

covery in 1925 of what is considered to be part of an Egyptian instrument of this type.[38] If such was used, it fulfilled the need for an instrument in the laying out of long lines at right angles to each other and was the forerunner of the *groma* of Roman times and the surveyor's cross of later times. This interesting relic (Figure 5) has been described as follows:[39]

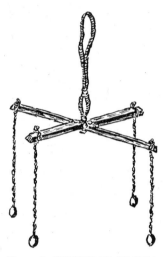

It consists of two pieces of palm-leaf rib, 352 mm. and 342 mm. long respectively, which are tied together at right angles with a piece of palm fibre cord. The upper rod has a part of the rounded "keel" of the palm rib cut away so as to form a stop against which the lower rod rests when it is in the correct position. The plumb-lines and plummets were missing but the upper part of each rod is deeply notched at 12 and 15 mm. from its ends for the attachment of the plumb-lines. The instrument was evidently made by some landowner or cultivator for his own needs.

Figure 5. EGYPTIAN GROMA.
After Sloley.

A loop left in the cord at the intersection of the two crosspieces shows that the instrument was intended to be suspended, probably by hand. This specimen of an Egyptian groma is considered to be of a late period. How far back its use goes we do not know, but since the Egyptians were employing the plumb line at a very early date, it is probable that this instrument was also long in use.

STAFF COMBINATIONS   Staffs, now used occasionally for ranging in a line, have been associated, along with the plumb line, with surveying from the dawn of history. Probably the oldest recorded use of the vertical staff is in connection with the time-measuring devices used by the Egyptians;[40] and among the Baby-

---

[38] This was accidentally discovered in a storeroom of the British Museum after it had been lying for years unrecognized among a quantity of other antiquities which had been transferred from the Fayum district in 1899. See R. W. Sloley, "An Ancient Surveying Instrument," *Ancient Egypt*, Vol. 3, 1926, pp. 65-67.

[39] H. Lyons, "Ancient Surveying Instruments," *The Geographical Journal*, Vol. 69, 1927, p. 140. By permission of The Royal Geographical Society.

[40] Borchardt, "Ein altägyptisches astronomisches Instrument," p. 52.

lonians it was used for a like purpose.[41] Since they were acquainted with the properties of similar right triangles, the Babylonians may have also used the vertical staff for the indirect measurement of heights, but of this there is no record. Thales learned this method in Egypt at a much later date, but there is no early Egyptian record of its employment. Horizontal rods may have been used in the measurement of short distances, but of this, likewise, there is no record.

Evidences of Early Surveying

The most abundant evidence which we have today that surveying instruments, with which a most surprising degree of accuracy was sometimes attained, were used by these ancient peoples, is to be found in the ruins of engineering and architectural enterprises that have survived through the intervening ages.[42] Probably our most ancient Egyptian record of surveying is to be found on the Palermo stone, which records river gauge readings and tells of the "numbering of gold and lands" in the period about 3000 B.C. From the inscriptions on this stone and other evidence Lyons concludes:[43]

Such a "numbering" of the royal possessions made every two years throughout the land by the officials of the Treasury, would be a sort of verificatory survey of State property which doubtless included herds as well as land, and this biennial census was so regular a procedure of the administration in these early times that events in the reign of the king were dated with reference to it.

Throughout ancient times the placing of boundary stones was accompanied by religious rites; such stones were looked upon as sacred monuments, the removal or desecration of which was a crime subject to severe punishments.[44] Breasted records that a set of such boundary stones was erected on both sides of the

[41] E. Weidner, "Ein babylonisches Kompendium der Himmelskunde." *The American Journal of Semitic Languages and Literature,* Vol. 40, 1923, pp. 198-200.

[42] For descriptive accounts of some of these projects, see, besides the articles mentioned in note 27, R. S. Kirby, "Some Engineering Beginnings," *Civil Engineering,* Vol. 7, 1937, pp. 735-739; and "Specifications and Plans of Ancient Times," *Civil Engineering,* Vol. 11, 1941, pp. 393-396.

[43] Lyons, *op. cit.,* p. 133. By permission of The Royal Geographical Society.

[44] See Deuteronomy XXVII, and the extract, "Ex libris Vegiae arrunti veltymno" in F. Blume, K. Lachmann, and A. Rudorff, *Die Schriften der römischen Feldmesser* (Berlin, 1852), Vol. 1, p. 350.

Nile Valley by King Ikhnaton of the Eighteenth Dynasty in order
to define his possessions. Part of the inscription on one of these
stones reads as follows:[45]

. . . from the southern landmarks on the eastern mountain of Akhetaton [the town], it makes, 6 iter, 1 khet, 1/2 khet, 1/4 khet and four
cubits. Likewise, from the S-W landmark of Akhetaton to the N-W
mark on the western mountain of Akhetaton amounting to 6 iter, 1
khet, 1/3 khet, 1/4 khet and 4 cubits, . . area within these four landmarks, from the east mountain to the west mountain of Akhetaton . . .
opposite, it belongs to my father, Aton.

In 1909 Montagu, as a result of a triangulation survey which he
conducted in this district, where some of the boundary stones still
stand, concluded that the Egyptians were able to lay out and
measure distances of considerable length (c. 15,000 meters) with
a very creditable accuracy.[46]

As an example of the accuracy attained in the orientation of
buildings by means of the merchet, Cole[47] states, as a result of his
survey, that the azimuth of the N-S axis is only 3' 06" to the west
of the true north. In the building of this pyramid the outer portion of the base rock was first leveled.[48] In checking the horizontality of this base, Cole found slopes of 6 mm. from east to west
and 14 mm. from north to south, representing slopes of approximately 1 in 38,000 and 1 in 16,500.

Because of the nature of the materials which the Babylonians
had to use, their engineering projects deteriorated much more
rapidly than those of the Egyptians and hence have not been sub-
jected to the same close scrutiny. All we have today are the crum-
bling remains, often buried deep in desert sands, of what must
have been colossal buildings,[49] and faint vestiges of what must have
been at one time an intricate system of canals. Lyons, describing

[45] J. H. Breasted, *Ancient Records* (Chicago, 1906), Vol. 2, p. 398. By permission of
the University of Chicago Press.
[46] C. F. Montagu, "Survey of the Boundary of Stelae Tel-El-Amara," *Cairo Scientific
Journal*, Vol. 3, 1909, p. 80.
[47] J. H. Cole, "Determination of the Exact Size and Orientation of the Great Pyramid of Giza," *Survey of Egypt* (Cairo, 1925), Paper No. 39.
[48] For a description of the probable method of leveling such an extensive rock surface, see S. Clarke and R. Engelbach, *Ancient Egyptian Masonry* (Oxford University
Press, 1930), pp. 62 ff.
[49] J. A. Hammerton, *Wonders of the Past* (New York, 1924).

a tablet from Tello now in the Museum of Constantinople, says that it[50]

bears a dimensioned plan of royal property of which the area was about 515 acres. The fields were measured with a cord just as in Egypt and the land-measurer is referred to in the land charters, known as "Boundary Stones," as the "dragger of the rope."

Neugebauer has shown that several problems to be found in the cuneiform tablets relate to engineering projects, such as the cross-sectional area of a canal, estimation of excavation for a building, and the cross-sectional area of a dam.[51] If the Babylonians were capable of planning their projects to such an extent as these problems would suggest, then it is all the more regrettable that we have so little real information as to their instruments and methods of surveying. The advancement of our knowledge within recent times with regard to Egyptian and Babylonian mathematical attainments leaves us with the hope that the time is not too distant when more satisfactory evidence can be produced as to the surveying practices of these peoples.

[50] Lyons, *op. cit.* By permission of The Royal Geographical Society.
[51] Neugebauer, "Mathematische Keilschrift-Texte," Part I, pp. 165, 167 ff., 243, 508; Part II, p. 52; Part III, p. 32.

II

DEVELOPMENTS in Greece
and Rome

FOR a clear understanding of the contributions of this period to the development of surveying instruments it is essential to bear in mind the contrasting attitudes of the Greeks and Romans toward mathematics and scientific research.

The history of Greek thought may be conveniently divided into three periods. First came the Pythagorean, initiated by the philosopher-mathematician Thales. This period emphasized man's relation to his physical surroundings and sought mystic meanings in physical phenomena and mathematics, as may be seen in the philosophical contributions of Pythagoras, Anaximander, Heraclitus, Anaxagoras, and Democritus. It was climaxed by the golden age of Greek art and architecture.

The second period, ushered in by Socrates, represents the golden age of Greek thought, distinguished by such great minds as Plato, Aristotle, and Eudoxus. Man and his relationship to his fellow man formed the main theme of philosophic thought. According to Plato, mathematics is essentially a branch of philosophy. To him geometry is important not because of its practical uses but because "it would tend to draw the soul to truth, and would be productive of a philosophic attitude of mind, directing upward the faculties that now wrongly are turned earthward." [1] Aristotle classified the practical uses of geometry under the title of *geodaisia* and set it up in sharp contrast with pure geometry. The latter has for its field the immaterial; the former, the material.[2] The lack of all evidence as to what instruments and methods were in

[1] Plato, *The Republic*, Loeb Library Edition, Translated by P. Shorey (Cambridge, Mass., 1935), Vol. 2, Bk. VII, pp. 171-173. By permission of the Harvard University Press.

[2] Aristotle, *Metaphysics*, Loeb Library Edition, Translated by H. Tredemick (Cambridge, Mass., 1933), Bk. 3, Ch. 2, par. 25, p. 113.

use among the Greeks throughout most of their history must be ascribed to the fact that, in keeping with the spirit of the Platonic school, the practical applications of mathematics were held in contempt, as something unworthy of great minds, and their records were not considered worth preserving. For this reason the question of what methods were employed by the Greeks in setting out their wonders of architecture must remain unanswered.

The third and most important period, so far as this work is concerned, began after the conquest of Egypt by Alexander and the founding at Alexandria of the first institution worthy of the name of university.[3] From Alexandria and under Egyptian influences the Greeks dominated the mathematical and scientific world for over five hundred years. The outstanding names of this school are Euclid, Archimedes,[4] Apollonius, Heron, Pappus, Eratosthenes and Diophantes. What we owe to this period has been well summed up by Heath:[5]

Acquaintance with the original work of the Greek mathematicians is necessary for any mathematician worthy of the name. Mathematics is a Greek science. So far as pure geometry is concerned, the mathematician's equipment is almost wholly Greek. The Greeks laid down the principles, fixed the terminology and invented the methods *ab initio;* moreover, they did this with such certainty that in the centuries which have since elapsed there has been no need to reconstruct, still less to reject as unsound, any essential part of their doctrine.

Heron of Alexandria is the outstanding exception to the general Greek tendency, in that his writings for the most part deal with practical applications of mathematics. What Euclid did for pure geometry, and Galen for medicine, Heron did for the art and theory of surveying. His contribution was to systematize the knowledge of surveying by sifting the mass of traditional material, which must have been predominantly Egyptian in origin, since from the time of Thales it was the custom of the Greek scholars to spend some time among the Egyptians in pursuit of knowledge.

Diametrically opposed to the Greeks' spirit of knowledge for

[3] G. Sarton, *Introduction to the History of Science* (Baltimore, 1927), Vol. 1, pp. 150, 156.
[4] Archimedes did most of his work at Syracuse and probably never lived in Alexandria, but his work was in the spirit of the Alexandrian school.
[5] T. Heath, *The Legacy of Greece,* Edited by R. Livingstone (Oxford, 1921), p. 98. By permission of The Clarendon Press.

knowledge's sake was the Roman attitude of interest only in what
was of practical value. By some outstanding individuals this attitude was bewailed;[6] nevertheless it remained a characteristic of
Roman life. The real reason for this lack of interest among the
Romans in the scientific attitude of mind lay in their predom-
inating philosophy of Stoicism. In comparison with the Greeks
the Roman Empire produced no outstanding scientist or mathematician, notwithstanding the fact that Hellenism began to influence Roman thought about the time of the Second Punic War,
c. 214 B.C. How slight was the mathematical knowledge absorbed
by the Romans from the Greeks may be judged from the works of
Boethius, who has been styled "the last of the ancients." And as
the Romans seem to have rejected the advanced mathematics of
the Greeks, so, too, the work of Heron seems to have been neglected, for there is no instrument comparable to Heron's *dioptra*
to be found in the history of the Roman surveyors. The agrimensores of the Empire, instead of taking their clue from Greece,[7]
preferred to use simpler instruments which in some cases were
only slightly modified forms of those indigenous to the country
and developed by their ancestors, the Etruscans.

Leveling Instruments

WATER LEVELS   Ancient water levels, by which a horizontal
direction was determined by means of a still, free water surface,
were of two kinds: the first and simplest was usually in the form
of a long, narrow, open trough; the second consisted of two trans-

---

[6] Cicero, *Tusculanarum Disputationum,* Bk. 1, Ch. 2. "In summo apud illos [Grae-
cos] honore geometria fuit; itaque nihil mathematicis illustrius; at nos metiendi ra-
tiocinandique utilitate huius artis terminavimus modum." Seneca, *Epistulae,* No. 90.
Referring to some building improvements: "Vilissimorum mancipiorum ista com-
menta sunt: sapientia altius sedet nec manus edocet: animorum magistra est . . . non
abduxit, inquam, se (ut Posidonio videtur) ab istis artibus sapiens, sed ad illas
omnino non venit."

[7] On the question as to how much the Roman agrimensores depended on Heron,
see W. Schmidt, "Haben Vitruv und die römischen Feldmesser aus Heron geschöpft?"
Bibliotheca Mathematica, 1900, pp. 297-318. The author of this interesting article
shows that to answer the question we must examine not only what there is in the
Roman writings which corresponds with the methods of Heron but also what meth-
ods have been handed down by the Romans which are not found in Heron. "When
Agrippa undertook the survey of the Empire [see p. 40] he had to bring in Alex-
andrian specialists, though the nominal superintendent was a Roman." J. L. Heiberg,
Mathematics and Physical Science in Classical Antiquity, Translated by D. C. Mac-
Gregor (Oxford, 1922), p. 61. By permission of The Clarendon Press.

parent receptacles connected by a long tube. The oldest descriptions we have of such instruments are those of Heron[8] and Vitruvius.[9] Heron's level belongs to the second class. The surprisingly well-finished instrument—if we may judge by the descriptions in the manuscripts; no diagrams by Heron have come down to us—the numerous applications, and Heron's own assertions force us to the conclusion that many useful forms of this type of instrument may have existed, but unfortunately no accounts of them have been transmitted. Heron's level was set up by removing from the top of its Doric column the sighting mechanism of his dioptra and replacing it by the leveling tube. The column was secured in the ground by three short legs and made vertical by means of a plumb bob. The level consisted essentially of a long bronze tube which rested in the groove of a wooden block about six feet long. Two glass tubes about ten inches long were connected at right angles to the ends of the bronze tube by wax or other binding material. According to Schöne's reconstruction (Figure 6), two small boxes were attached near the ends of the wooden block to house the vertical glass tubes. Grooves with sliding plates were built into the box ends. These sliding plates touched the glass cylinders and carried horizontal slots which aided in sighting across the surfaces of the water in the two vertical glass tubes. The up-and-down movement of these slotted plates was regulated by a screw mechanism. In use the tubes were partially filled with water so that the water surfaces were visible in

[8] Heron belongs to the Alexandrian school. His work differs essentially from that of the other Greek mathematicians in that he emphasizes the practical uses of mathematics. Much doubt exists as to the period in which he lived. Estimates vary from 100 B.C. to A.D. 200. The most probable estimate places him in the last half of the first century B.C. See D. E. Smith, *History of Mathematics* (Boston, 1923), Vol. I, p. 125; and F. Cajori, *A History of Mathematics* (New York, 1922), p. 43. There are three incomplete manuscript copies of his treatise *On the Dioptra* in existence. One copy is part of the Greek manuscript No. 2430 of the Bibliothèque Impériale, Paris; a second, known as c. III 6, belongs to the library of the Protestant Seminary at Strasbourg; the third and least complete is in the National Library at Vienna. A partial text was published in Italian by J. B. Venturi, *Il Traguardo di Erone* (Bologna, 1814); a full text by A. J. H. Vincent, "Le Traité de la dioptre de Héron d'Alexandrie," *Notices et extraits des manuscrits de la bibliothèque impériale*, Vol. 19, 1858, Part 2. A complete German text was published in later times by H. Schöne, *Herons von Alexandria Vermessungslehre und Dioptra* (Leipzig, 1903).

[9] Marcus Vitruvius Pollio wrote *De Architectura Libri Decem* about 15 B.C. Quotations used here are from the translation by M. H. Morgan (Cambridge, Mass., 1914). By permission of the Harvard University Press.

the glass sections. The line of sight across the water surfaces, made more distinct by means of the slit disks, was the required horizontal sight. Other simpler reconstructions such as those of

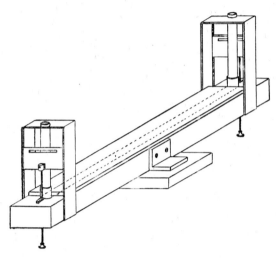

Figure 6. HERON'S LEVEL. *Reconstruction by Schöne. Reproduced by permission of B. C. Teubner & Co., Leipzig.*

Venturi and Vincent (Figure 7) are probably closer to the original.

Much simpler than Heron's level is that described by Vitruvius in his chapter, "Leveling for Water Conduction and the Connected Work." [10] Here he mentions three seemingly different levels; namely, dioptra, *libra aquaria,* and *chorobates.* Only the last is described, and he gives it preference to the other two.[11] Whether his dioptra was fashioned after Heron's is problematic. Leveling of the chorobates (Figure 8) could be accomplished in two ways, as we note from the following description:[12]

The chorobates is a straightedge about twenty feet long. At the extremities it has legs made exactly alike and jointed on perpendicularly to the extremities of the straightedge, and also crosspieces, fastened by tenons, connecting the straightedge and the legs. These crosspieces have vertical lines drawn upon them, and there are plumb-lines hang-

[10] Vitruvius, *op. cit.,* Bk. 8, Ch. 5, p. 242.
[11] *Ibid.* "Libratur autem dioptris aut libris aquariis aut chorobate, sed diligentius efficitur per chorobatem, quod dioptrae libraeque fallunt."
[12] *Ibid.,* Bk. VIII, Ch. 5.

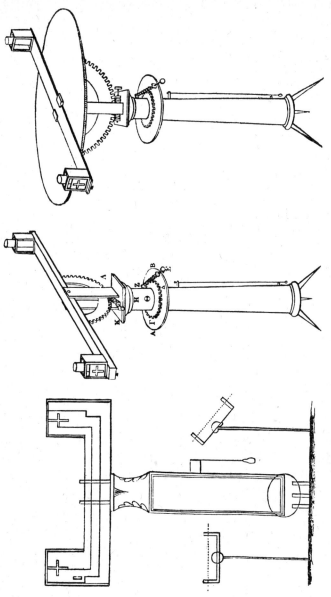

Figure 7. HERON'S LEVEL. *Manuscript diagram and reconstructions by Venturi and Vincent.*

ing from the straightedge over each of the lines. When the straightedge is in position, and the plumb-lines strike both the lines alike and at the same time, they show that the instrument stands level.

But if the wind interposes, and constant motion prevents any definite indication by the lines, then have a groove on the upper side, five feet long, one digit wide, and a digit and a half deep, and pour water into it. If this water comes up uniformly to the rims of the groove, it will be known that the instrument is level. When the level is thus found by means of the chorobates, the amount of fall will also be known.

The greater length of the plane by which the surveyor directed his line of sight may have been, in the estimation of Vitruvius, the reason for his preference of the chorobates, or again it may

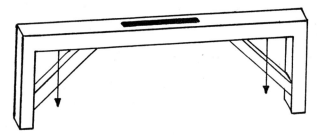

Figure 8. THE CHOROBATES OF VITRUVIUS

have been that Heron's dioptra level was too complicated both in construction and in use. At all events the Roman agrimensores seem to have taken their cue from Vitruvius and discarded the Heron level for simpler forms. Notwithstanding Vitruvius' enthusiasm for the chorobates, it must have been quite cumbersome and awkward to handle. It could be brought into adjustment only by slowly and cautiously wedging up one end till the plumb lines finally settled over the vertical marks on the side of the braces. Furthermore, it would have to be readjusted whenever two or more sights were taken from the same station at different angles. Notwithstanding these difficulties, levels of this type were quite common all through the Middle Ages, while the results of Heron's mechanical ingenuity were neglected.

PLUMB-BOB LEVELS   Heron often calls the horizontal difference between two points "the difference of the plumb-bob levels," but in no place does he describe such a level.[13] Vitruvius' description of his chorobates is the oldest we have of such instruments. The chorobates was an advance on the simple plumb-bob levels of the Egyptians because of its double control. Vitruvius' original diagrams are lost; because of this many variations of his instrument have appeared. The brief accounts of leveling instruments by various Roman surveyors, such as that of Columella, do not make clear whether they are water or plumb-line instruments.[14] Diagrams of small Roman plumb-bob levels, together with other evidence of their handicraft, have been found on the gravestones and murals of the Roman builders. They are generally in the forms shown in Figure 9.

Figure 9. ROMAN LEVEL AND SQUARE. *Reproduced from Smith's* History of Mathematics, *Vol. II, by permission of Ginn and Co., Publishers.*

LEVELING RODS The rod (Figure 10) which Heron describes was practically as good as the common type in use at the present day.[15]

Two pieces of wood are cut which are 10 cubits long, 5 digits wide and 3 digits thick. In each is cut a dovetailed groove down the whole length of the broad side, the short side of the dovetail being outside. In this groove a tenon runs freely without coming out, carrying a circular disc, ten or twelve digits in diameter; which is divided by a straight line perpendicular to the end of the rod, into two semi-circles, one of which is painted black and the other white. To the tenon is attached a cord

[13] Vincent, *op. cit.,* Vol. 19, Part II, pp. 52-54.

[14] L. J. M. Columella, *De re rustica,* Bk. III, Ch. 13. Quoted by M. Cantor, *Die römischen Agrimensoren und ihre Stellung in der Geschichte der Feldmesskunst* (Leipzig, 1875), Note 182. Columella here speaks of using a level in combination with the groma.

[15] Vincent, *op. cit.* Translation by Skyring-Walters in "Greek and Roman Engineering Instruments," *Transactions, The Newcomen Society for the Study of Engineering and Technology,* Vol. 2, 1921, pp. 51-52. By permission of The Newcomen Society.

which passes over a pulley on top of the staff and goes down the other side of the staff remote from that of the disc. Now, if one holds the staff in a vertical position and pulls the cord from behind, one makes the disc rise; if, on the contrary, one loosens the cord the disc will descend by its own weight, especially if there has been nailed a plate of

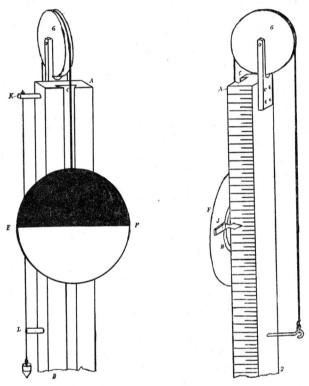

Figure 10. HERON'S LEVELING ROD. *Reconstruction by Schöne. Reproduced by permission of B. C. Teubner & Co., Leipzig.*

lead at the back of the disc, for this will cause it to move more quickly. Consequently by means of the cord, the disc can be manipulated to any desired part of the staff. It is necessary to divide the length of the staff, from the bottom, into cubits, palms and digits. At these divisions lines are drawn on the side of the staff to the right of the disc. The disc carries a pointer on the back in line with the diameter, which points to the graduated divisions marked on the side of the staff. The staff must be held in a truly vertical position. This is ensured by there being fixed [on the plain side opposite the graduated side, i.e., the left side of the disc] a small rod about three digits long, at the end of which is a vertical hole, through which a string passes carrying a weight. Near the bottom of the staff is another small rod of length equal to the distance of the hole from the staff on the top and on the end of this is marked a vertical line. When the plumb-line coincides with this line, it will show that the staff is truly vertical.

Like his level, Heron's rod also found no favor among the Romans. The type in common use may be better judged from simpler forms of later times. Vitruvius has left no description of a rod. Simple rods are briefly described by Sextus J. Africanus[16] and by Heron of Byzantium.[17]

Right-Angle Instruments

SQUARES AND ROPES Pliny has preserved the tradition that the square and other tools of architecture were invented by the Greek Theodorus of Samos about 600 B.C.[18] In contradiction to this is the fact that Thales of Miletus and many other Greeks had sojourned in Egypt and had acquired knowledge of the building methods and surveying instruments employed by Egyptians. Diagrams of Roman squares (normae) of various shapes have been preserved.[19] That large forms of these were sometimes used by the agrimensores for laying out right angles in the field, we know from the writings of Nipsus.[20] According to Nipsus the norma was laid on the ground and the direction of the legs produced as required by means of ropes and pegs.

It is natural to expect that Grecian surveyors made use of the two propositions of Euclid[21] on the construction of a perpendicular to a line from points on and outside the line; they may also have used the symmetrical construction,[22] although none of these are mentioned by Heron. Neither are they recorded by any Roman surveyor, and since the symmetrical construction made its first European appearance early in the Middle Ages, it was probably transmitted not by the Romans but by the Muslims. From

---

[16] Vincent, op. cit., p. 415.
[17] Ibid., p. 351.
[18] Pliny, Natural History, Translated by Bostock and Riley (London, 1855), Bk. 7, p. 57.
[19] See Figure 9, a Roman tombstone.
[20] Cantor, op. cit., p. 112.
[21] Euclid, Elements, Bk. I, Props. 11, 12.
[22] See Chapter VI, pp. 277, 279.

the time of the publication of the Pythagorean theorem, there is no reason why the Greeks should not have used the rope method which naturally follows from it; the semicircular construction was also within their grasp, but again we are left in darkness by the

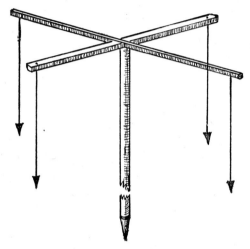

Figure 11. THE GRECIAN STAR

historians as to whether or not these methods were used. We know from the writings of Balbus[23] that the Romans made use of the last-mentioned methods.

STAR   In order to emphasize the good points of his own dioptra, Heron compares it with what he calls "the so-called Star" instrument,[24] which he says was then in use for nearly all the operations for which he proposes to use the dioptra. As to the construction of the *Grecian star* and its uses, we can only surmise from the indirect testimony of Heron. It appears to be the next stage in the development of the groma from the Egyptian instrument mentioned on page 14. In order to provide a better support for the instrument the Greeks seem to have set it up on a vertical staff.

[23] F. Blume, K. Lachmann, A. Rudorff, *Die Schriften der römischen Feldmesser* (Berlin, 1852), Vol. 1, p. 108. "Nam quod ad extremam lineae normationem pertinet, vulgaris consuetudinis est sex, octo et decem; haec de qua supra disputavimus circuli ratio magis artificialis est, quae numeros non praefinit; habemus enim apud Euclidem, quocumque loco ad circumferentur lineam ex signis dimensiones duae lineae concurrerint, normam facturas.

[24] Heron, *op. cit.*, Ch. 32. Schöne Edition, p. 289.

They also provided, according to Heron, hollow wooden tubes to shield the plumb bobs from the wind. It is generally believed that the form of the star (as shown in Figure 11) was that usually associated with the Roman groma before the discovery of Della Corte in 1912. The cross was placed horizontally at about eye level on the vertical staff. The pair of plumb lines on each cross-piece determined a vertical plane, and both vertical planes intersected at right angles. Sighting diagonally across the plumb lines was impossible because of the interference of the vertical staff; therefore the plumb lines had to be spaced equally from the intersection of the arms, thus determining four external vertical planes, each perpendicular to two others and parallel to the fourth. These external planes must have been the ones employed in sighting, although the criticisms of Heron would tend to show that he had in mind sighting across the arms and not across corners.[25] Heron also emphasizes the fact that the crossarms should be set up horizontally, but as to the method of doing this he is silent. If the staff was joined to the crossarms at right angles, a plumb line on the staff would suffice for the proper setting up.

GROMA The instrument most commonly used throughout the whole Roman period was the groma, which differed fundamentally from the Grecian star only in one respect, which was that the cross was carried on a swinging arm (*umbilicus soli*) instead of being attached directly to the top of the staff. Although the groma was mentioned frequently in Roman writings, no detailed description was given, and until the second decade of the present century the work of reconstructing[26] depended on the slight information handed down in writing and the conventional diagrams which had been found on some Roman tombs.[27] However, in 1912 the office of a Roman surveyor, still containing many of the

[25] F. Schmidt, *Geschichte der geodätischen Instrumente und Verfahren im Altertum und Mittelalter* (Neustadt an der Haardt, 1935), p. 109.
[26] The principal previous reconstructions were those of Venturi, *op. cit.*; G. Rossi, *La groma e lo squandro ouvero storia dell'agrimensura italiana* (Torino, 1877); E. N. Legnazzi, *Del catastro romano e di alcuni strumenti antichi di geodesia* (Padua, 1885); Fabricus, for whom see article, "Groma," by Schulten in Pauly-Wissowa, *Realenzyklopädie der klassischen Altertumwissenschaften* (Stuttgart, 1912), Vol. 7, p. 1882; C. G. de Montauzan, *Essai sur la science et l'art de l'ingenieur aux premiers siècles de l'empire romain* (Paris, 1909), p. 49.
[27] Smith, *op. cit.*, Vol. 2, p. 361.

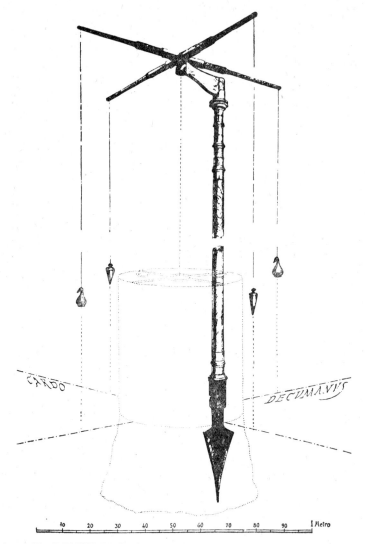

Figure 12. **ROMAN GROMA.** *Reconstruction by Della Corte. Reproduced by permission of the Accademia Nazionale dei Lincei, Rome.*

instruments of his profession, such as poles (*metae, signa*) and large measuring rods (*perticae, decempedae*), was discovered among the ruins of Pompeii. Only the metallic parts of the groma were found, the wooden sections having disintegrated through the intervening centuries. The reconstruction (Figure 12), carried out by Della Corte[28] with the aid of the remaining metal parts, is now considered our best estimate as to what the groma actually looked like. The swinging arm overcame two obstacles met with in the Grecian star: first, it served to avoid the already mentioned hindrance to sighting diagonally; and secondly, it simplified the placing of the center of the cross over a mark.

The following characteristics are important in comparing the old diagrams with the reconstruction of Della Corte. The arms of the cross were about 92 cm. in length. They were made of wood and held together with iron plates. The plumb lines (*fila, nerviae, perpendiculi*) hung near the ends about 80 cm. apart. The bobs (*pondera*) on one arm were conical in form; on the other they were pear shaped. As to the possibility that the weights were allowed to dip into water in order to steady the plumb lines, Nowotny[29] remarks that the pear shape of the bobs was probably the result of such a practice. Otherwise there is nothing to show that the line was in any way protected against the wind. There were no traces of any arrangement by which the cords were tied to the arms. The foot of the pole (*ferramentum*) was partly ornamented and terminated in a pointed shoe with four large flukes. The upper end of the staff was topped by a swivel peg. On the latter the swinging arm was held by a bronze screw. On the other end of the arm was a bronze pin on which the cross rested. It was therefore possible to move the arm round the standard and to revolve the cross around the peg on the arm.

The instrument was set up as follows: the ferramentum was stuck in the ground so far from the required mark that the cross-point of the arms could be brought over the mark by turning the swinging arm. For exact setting, a bob from the center of the cross was necessary; this was missing in the Pompeiian remains. Heron's warning about the necessity of a horizontal setting for the Grecian star applied also to the groma, but it is not mentioned by any of the Roman writers. Apparently they were satisfied to have the main pole perpendicular.[30]

---

[28] M. Della Corte, "Monumenti antichi," *Reale accademia nazionale dei lincei*, Vol. 28, 1922, pp. 1-50. For commentary on Della Corte's work see F. W. Kelsey, *Classical Philology*, Vol. 21, 1926, pp. 259-262.

[29] E. Nowotny, "Groma," *Germania*, Vol. 7, 1923, Part 1, pp. 22-29.

[30] M. J. Nipsus in Blume, Lachmann, and Rudorff, *op. cit.*, pp. 287-288. "Cum ita

Whether the groma, which was used principally in order to set out lines at right angles to each other, was derived from the Grecian star or from some earlier Etruscan instrument cannot be definitely stated. Those who favor the latter assumption remind us of the fact that the orientation of important buildings was a much more general practice among the Etruscans than among the Greeks or Egyptians. This practice can be traced back to the earliest Etruscan history, as the right-angled land divisions on the tablet of Herakleia[31] bear witness; many Roman writers also speak of the Roman method of orientation as being of·Etruscan origin.[32] This orientation consisted in staking out the east-west line—the *decimanus*—by the rising and setting of the sun and establishing the north-south line—the *cardo*—by means of the groma.[33] Since this operation gave the true directions only at the time of the equinox, we find in the writings of the agrimensores recommendations to establish these lines from the shadow of the sixth hour—the meridian line.[34]

DIOPTRA   The culmination of Greek ingenuity in the making of surveying instruments was reached in Heron's dioptra. The dioptra was a compound instrument which by the interchange of

feceris, figes ferramentum ad lapidem ita ne in rigore limites figas. Fixo ferramento convertes umbilicum soli supra punctum lapidis et sic perpendes ferramentum. Perpenso ferramento ab umbilico soli emittes perpendiculum ita ut in puncto lapidis cadat. Comprehendes quattuor signa ea quae posuisti in limitem. Aliis corniculis tenebis alium limitem."

[31] K. O. Müller, *Die Etrusker* (Stuttgart, 1877), Vol. 2, p. 159.

[32] Thus Frontinus, "Limitum prima origo, sicut Varro descripsit, a disciplina Etrusca." Blume, Lachmann, and Rudorff, *op. cit.*, p. 27.

[33] Frontinus, *ibid.*, p. 28. "Ab hoc fundamente maiores nostri in agrorum mensura videntur constituisse rationem. Primo duo limites duxerunt; unum ab oriente in occasum, quem vocaverunt cardinem. Decimanus autem dividebat agrum dextra et sinistra, cardo citra et ultra."

[34] Hyginus in Blume, Lachmann, and Rudorff, *op. cit.*, p. 170. "Multi ignorantes mundi rationem solem sunt secuti, hoc est ortum et occasum, quod is semel ferramento comprehendi non potest, quid ergo? Posita auspicaliter groma, ipso forte conditione praesente, proximum vero ortum comprehenderunt, et in utramque partem limites emiserunt quibus kardo in horam sextam non continuerit, et quidam, ne proximarum coloniarum limitibus ordinatos limites mitterent, relicta caeli ratione mensuram constituerunt qua tantum modus centuriarum et limitum longitudo constaret, quidem agri longitudinem secuti: et qua longior erat fecerunt decimanum, quidam in totum converterunt, et fecerunt decimanum in meridianum et kardinem in orientem: sicut in agro Campano qui est circa Capuam." For further details see M. Albricht, "Astronomische Orientierungen in der römischen Geodäsie," *Weltall*, Vol. 5, 1904, pp. 53-63.

parts could be used either as a level or as an instrument for laying off right angles. We have already described the dioptra as a level (p. 21). In the introduction to his description of the dioptra Heron states that other forms of dioptras already existed but that they had not proved successful. He now offers a combination instrument with the guarantee that it can be used to solve all known problems. After a description of the instrument he goes on to show how various problems are solvable. In passing we may remark that this set of surveying problems by Heron exercised as much influence on the theory of surveying for the next fifteen hundred years as did Euclid's *Elements* on the content of our school geometries up to the beginning of the present century.

The name *dioptra* was applied by the Greeks to various types of measuring instruments; it was probably originally used in connection with astronomical instruments.[35] Neither Heron nor any other Greek writer has left us a description of the early forms of dioptra used in surveying. Doubtless they were some form of cross which made use of fixed sights so as to eliminate the disadvantages of the swaying plumb lines of the star.

As to the general uses of the dioptra Heron speaks as follows:[36]

It is easy to say in a few words what the application of the dioptra does in the way of solving many practical problems. Thus, it is advantageously employed for the setting out of water-channels, ramparts, harbors and buildings of every kind. It is used for many astronomical purposes in connection with the observation of the sky, such as the measurement of distances which separate stars, their size and the determination of the distances and the eclipses of the sun and moon. Again it is used for geographical or surveying purposes, and for the determination of the relative positions of islands and seas and, generally, for the estimation of distances between inaccessible points. It is useful to know a distance over inaccessible ground, for often an obstacle stands in the way which prevents us from measuring it directly, such as an enemy in possession of the country or an inaccessible or impassable land having some physical peculiarity such as a rapidly flowing river. How many times in an attack of a stronghold have we arrived at the foot of the ramparts and found that we had made our ladders and other necessary

[35] This was true of the dioptra of Hipparchus (*c.* 180-125 B.C.), described by Claudius Ptolemy. For reconstruction see F. Hultsch, "Winkelmessungen durch die Hipparchische Dioptra," *Abhandlungen zur Geschichte der Mathematik*, Vol. 9, 1899, p. 120.

[36] Heron, *op. cit.*, Ch. 11. Vincent Edition. Translation by Skyring-Walters, *op. cit.* By permission of The Newcomen Society.

implements for the assault too short, and have consequently been defeated for not knowing how to use the dioptra for measuring the heights of walls; such heights having to be measured out of range of the enemy's missiles.

The following is Heron's incomplete description of his dioptra. It is given in full because of the historical importance of the instrument and also that we may be able to form a discriminating estimate of the various reconstructions[37] that have been made.[38]

A stand is made resembling a small column which has on the top a cylindrical pivot. On this pivot is fixed, concentrically, a small circular copper plate. Higher up the pivot, is a copper sleeve which turns easily on it; at the bottom, this sleeve is fixed to a toothed wheel which is smaller than, and rests upon the copper plate; and on the top, for appearance, is a plinth of a small Doric column in the form of a miniature capital. Gearing with the toothed wheel is a small worm whose bearings are fixed to the copper plate. A groove wider than the width of the teeth is cut in the worm so that if one turns the latter until the groove is opposite the teeth, the toothed wheel will be quite free to turn; and having thus put the wheel roughly in position, the worm can be turned until its thread gears with the teeth of the wheel, which is thereby locked. On the plinth, two vertical uprights, made of copper, are fixed at a distance equal to the thickness of another toothed wheel whose axle passes through them and on the same plinth between these two large uprights is a movable worm [here there is a gap in the text; supply "to turn the toothed wheel in a vertical circle"] whose small bearings are attached to the plinth. Between these two parallel uprights is the axle, four digits above the top of the plinth.

That the two vertical uprights served as a support for a toothed semicircular disk may be seen from the following excerpts from the text in connection with the exercises: "The semi-circle is turned while the other parts of the instrument remain at rest." [39] "The semi-circle is lowered to a point . . . which is visible through the line of sight." [40] The diameter of the semicircular disk must have had attached to it the crossplate with the sighting apparatus, as seen from the following: "The sighting-line is now

[37] Unfortunately, in no one of the existing mss. is this description complete. Where gaps occur in the texts, reconstructors have sought to complete the picture from the various operations which Heron describes in his exercises. Herein lies the source of divergencies and controversies.

[38] Translation by Skyring-Walters, *op. cit.* By permission of The Newcomen Society.

[39] Heron, *op. cit.*, Ch. 8, Schöne Edition. Schmidt, *op. cit.*, pp. 117-118.

[40] Heron, *op. cit.*, Ch. 9.

turned on the large circular plate";[41] ". . . until the point becomes visible by turning the line of sight through a right angle";[42] and ". . . the circular disk about which the line of sights moves."[43] Revolving on the circular disk were two diametrical arms at right angles to each other. One arm, the *alidade,* carried a pair of vertical sights at its extremities; the other was shorter and terminated in arrow-shaped indicators, as may be inferred from the following quotations: "The dioptra will be moved along the line until the point on the existing line is seen through the other." [44] "I then go to the other end of the sighting line." [45] Lastly, the circular disk was divided into 360° (these divisions were used only in astronomical work). "We have described on the surface of the large circular plate a circle at its mid-point and so large that the point of the marker attached to the line of sight touches it. This circle is divided into 360 degrees." [46] Two diametrical lines perpendicular to each other were used in surveying. For use as a level, the casing containing the tubing, already described on p. 21, replaced the circular disk above the vertical semicircle.

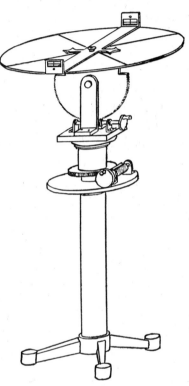

Figure 13. HERON'S DIOPTRA. *Reconstruction by Schöne. Reproduced by permission of B. C. Teubner & Co., Leipzig.*

The reconstruction by Schöne (Figure 13) [47] adds only the crosswire sights to those parts which are mentioned in the manuscripts. The actual dioptra of Heron must have been a far cruder instrument than this reconstruction

[41] *Ibid.,* Ch. 8.
[42] *Ibid.,* Ch. 9.
[43] *Ibid.,* Ch. 17.

[44] *Ibid.,* Ch. 10.
[45] *Ibid.,* Ch. 8.
[46] *Ibid.,* Ch. 32.

[47] *Ibid.,* pp. 192, 193, 198, 199.

would lead us to believe. The technical difficulties of making the required parts and then fitting them properly together must not be forgotten. The material used, except where copper is specifically mentioned, was probably hard wood. The making of gear wheels and worm screws which would work together with the necessary precision required the highest available technical ability of the times. Perhaps this is the most important reason why such a theoretically advanced instrument was allowed to lapse into oblivion by Heron's successors. Even with all our modern technical aids, Lancaster-Jones[48] has shown that it was impossible to produce from the working drawings of Schöne a satisfactory model of the dioptra for the British Museum. For more simplified reconstructions which would seem to resemble more closely the instrument of Heron see Figure 7 (p. 23).

For the ordinary purpose of setting out lines at right angles to each other, the dioptra was set over the point of intersection and the circular plate made horizontal—Heron does not state by what method. Then the alidade was set on one of the diametral lines, and the plate turned by means of the horizontal worm wheel until the line of sight coincided with the given direction. The alidade was then turned through $90°$; that is, until it coincided with the other diametral line. By a sight taken through the alidade a stake was set down in the direction of the required line. So far as surveying practice was concerned the vertical, toothed semicircular disk does not seem to have played any essential part. It may have been used in the leveling of the instrument. At most it was used only to allow the sights to follow a vertical plane, but this had already been accomplished in a much simpler fashion by the plumb lines of the Grecian star and the Egyptian merchet. We are tempted to think that such an arrangement for changing the vertical angle of the line sights may have been used in order to reduce inclined lines to the horizontal, but Heron has left no record of such. This vertical gear seems to have been built into the instrument especially for astronomical observations, and for the same purpose the circular plate was divided into $360°$ in accordance with Babylonian astronomical usage.

[48] E. Lancaster-Jones, "Criticism of Heron's Dioptra," *The Geographical Journal*, Vol. 69, 1927, p. 140.

Staff Combinations

INDIAN CIRCLES   One important surveying operation involving the use of a vertical staff was the determination of the north-south direction or the meridian line by the process commonly known in later times as the *Indian circles* method.[49]   The importance of this operation was due to the fact that the orientation of temples, palaces, and monumental tombs was common among many ancient civilizations and was employed extensively by the Romans, who when possible orientated their cities, camp sites, and land divisions. We have already seen how this orientation was accomplished by the Egyptians employing the merchet. Whether the Egyptians or Babylonians used the Indian circles method is unknown. It is described by Proclus Diodochus,[50] who attributes its use to the astronomer, Ptolemy. In his *Syntaxis* Ptolemy himself probably had in mind this operation when he speaks of "fixing the meridian line at a given point." [51]   Among the Romans, Vitruvius[52] and Hyginus[53] give clear descriptions of the use of the Indian circles method; the first for the establishment of street lines; the second in connection with work on the determination of boundaries. Hyginus recommends the use of three staffs of different lengths. The operation he describes implies such geometrical difficulties that the method must have been of Greek origin and not suited to the simplified practical work of the Romans.[54]

INDIRECT MEASUREMENT   We now turn to the application of combinations of straight staffs to indirect measurement. This operation depended on the theory of similar triangles and formed a very important step in the early development of instruments. Herein we meet not only single staffs used in perpendicular and horizontal positions, but also simple measuring instruments con-

[49] Details on the early history of this method will be found on p. 61. The earliest description of the method is given on p. 281.

[50] Proclus Diodochus, *Hypotyposis Astronomicarum Positionum*, Edited by C. Manitius (Leipzig, 1909), p. 50.

[51] Claudius Ptolemy, *Handbuch der Astronomie*, Edited by C. Manitius (Leipzig, 1912), p. 42.

[52] Vitruvius, *op. cit.*, Bk. 1, Chs. 6, 12.

[53] Blume, Lachmann, and Rudorff, *op. cit.*, p. 188.

[54] Cantor, *op. cit.*, pp. 68-70.

sisting of assembled staffs, especially the combination of a perpendicular and a horizontal in the form of a "square," and staffs used as sighters in combination with plumb lines.

The use of such a combination as a *shadow staff* or *gnomon* and the length of the shadow cast by the sun for time measurement is older than its use for height determinations in surveying, since calculation of time was a more fundamental human need.[55] As soon as people observed the relation between the length of the gnomon and its shadow, the first application would naturally suggest the second. Probably about the same period, namely, the beginning of the sixth century B.C., which is given for the setting up of the shadow-reckoner by Anaximander of Miletus,[56] another native of Miletus, Thales, according to numerous accounts, had learned in Egypt the application of the shadow staff to measurement of the height of an object. In this historic operation we have the first important step in the development of indirect measurement.

According to two accounts Thales used the shadow of his own body; according to a third, he used that of a staff. The oldest account comes from Jerome of Rhodes, a pupil of Aristotle, and is related thus by Diogenes Laertius: "Hieronymus also says that he [Thales] measured the Pyramids; watching their shadow and calculating when they were of the same size as that was." [57] The second account is that of Pliny.[58] It agrees with the first and was probably copied from it. Plutarch's account[59] in "The Banquet of the Seven Wise Men" is much later. In this he speaks of the use of a vertical staff.

The use of two vertical staffs probably soon arose from the methods developed by Thales and his immediate successors. The first account of this combination is to be found in the work of Heron.[60] Essentially, the method consists in placing two vertical

---

[55] L. Borchardt, "Ein altägyptisches astronomisches Instrument," *Zeitschrift für ägyptische Sprache,* Vol. 37, 1899, pp. 40 ff.

[56] Diogenes Laertius, *The Lives and Opinions of Eminent Philosophers,* Translated by C. D. Yonge (London, 1853), Bk. 2, Ch. 1, p. 57.

[57] *Ibid.,* Bk. 1, Ch. 1, p. 16.

[58] Pliny, *op. cit.,* Bk. 36, Ch. 17.

[59] C. A. Bretschneider, *Die Geometrie und die Geometer vor Euklides* (Leipzig, 1870), p. 45.

[60] Heron, *op. cit.,* Schöne Edition, Chs. 12, 14.

staffs of unequal height such a distance apart that by sighting along the tops one sees the point whose height is required.[61]

For more accurate and convenient measurement with staffs, there gradually evolved a combination resembling an enlarged "square" in which the horizontal, usually the shorter, was permanently attached to the vertical and carried a scale. There are many accounts of measuring with wooden triangles or "squares," which are practically identical with this combination of staffs, to be found in the writings of the Roman agrimensores.[62] In the Middle Ages the use of various combinations of staffs was quite common, as we shall see later. The importance of these staff instruments in ancient surveying is clear from the number of applications that have been handed down in books on practical geometry. The more important of these applications are given in Chapter VI.

Landmarks of Greek and Roman Surveying

In the history of Greek architecture the work of the surveyor has been almost entirely neglected. In our rapture over the beauty of form and simplicity of line we have overlooked the part played by those whose business it was to lay out the foundations and check on the alignment of the building as it developed. For this historical lacuna the Greeks themselves are to blame, since they have handed down little or nothing of information relative to the actual practices of their surveyors. As we view the Acropolis of Athens, with its numerous ruins of what were once the gems of Greek architecture, such as the Parthenon, the Erechtheum and the Theater of Dionysius, we realize the fund of information on surveying practices of which we have been deprived.

Slight information has been handed down to us on a few large engineering projects of the Greeks. One was the remarkable aqueduct built at Samos about 500 B.C. Herodotus describes it:[63]

The first is a mountain, 150 orgyae in height; in this is dug a tunnel, beginning from the base, with an opening at each end. The length of the excavation is 7 stades, and height and breadth 8 feet each; through

[61] For details see Chapter VI, p. 288.
[62] Cantor, *op. cit.*, p. 112.
[63] Herodotus, *History*, Translated by H. Cary (London, 1847), Bk. III, p. 60.

the whole length of it is dug another excavation 20 cubits deep, and 3 feet broad, through which the water conveyed by pipes reaches the city, drawn from a copious fountain. The architect of this excavation was a Megarian, Eupalinus, son of Naustrophus.

This remarkable tunnel about 3,000 feet long was discovered in 1882, and a detailed survey of it was made the next year by the German archaeologist Fabricus.[64] It seems to have been dug from both ends, but the sections failed to meet because of incorrect alignment amounting to about twenty feet; there was also a difference in elevation of about eight feet.

Another remarkable engineering feat of early Greece was the building of a canal about six miles long through the Mount Athos peninsula in order that Xerxes might have a convenient passage for his war boats.[65] About a hundred years earlier Periander contemplated building a similar ship canal through the Isthmus of Corinth but did not carry out the project. Under Roman rule, six hundred and fifty years later, the same project was proposed by Nero. When the work was partly developed, it was abandoned because the Roman engineers concluded that the sea was higher on one side of the isthmus than on the other and that if the canal were completed the island of Aegira would be washed away. Not until 1893 was this canal completed; it now follows practically the same course as that mapped out by Nero's engineers.

Vestiges of Roman surveying are much more numerous than those of Grecian. If we are indebted to the Greeks for the development of the fundamental theory, we owe a debt of gratitude to the Romans for the remarkable skill they have shown in engineering practice. The most ambitious Roman project was the construction of a complete map of the Empire. This was proposed by Caesar but carried out in the reign of Augustus under the supervision of his son-in-law, M. Vispanius Agrippa. The work took nearly thirty years to complete. Such a huge-scale survey was possible because of the well-defined system of roads developed in different sections of the Empire and the skilled body of agrimensores which had been built up and fostered under imperial auspices. From the data collected a huge map was constructed on

[64] A. C. Merriman gives a synopsis of the findings of Fabricus in "A Greek Tunnel of the Sixth Century B.C.," *School of Mines Quarterly*, Vol. 6, 1885, pp. 264-275.

[65] Herodotus, *op. cit.*, Bk. VII, pp. 22-24.

a wall of the Porticus Octaviae, especially built for that purpose by order of Augustus.[66] This was the prototype of all large strategical maps. A copy of a later map, known as the Peutinger table, which was first made about A.D. 250, shows clearly the army routes throughout the Empire. The whole map is greatly distorted in the E-W direction; evidently the methods (if any) used for locating relative latitude and longitude were not sufficiently accurate for cartographical purposes on such a large scale.

The ability of the Roman surveyors to prolong a straight line over a large stretch of rough country has been investigated by Hammer.[67] His investigations were carried out on that portion of the Empire boundary which stretched almost in a straight line from the River Rems in Württemburg to the district of Wallfum in Baden, a distance of about 80 km. For a portion amounting to 29 km. he found the mean error of a point on the boundary was 2 m., which indicates a surprising accuracy considering the period. Hammer concludes that the Romans must have fixed a few principal points in prominent positions by signals at night, although there is nothing in Roman writings to confirm this, and then interpolated intermediate points, since the observed accuracy could never have been attained, in his opinion, by prolonging a line.

Most of our information on the methods of surveying employed by the Romans has been acquired through the manuscript known as the *Codex Arcerianus*[68] now preserved in the municipal library of Wolfenlaüttel, South Germany. It contains excerpts from the writings of the outstanding Roman agrimensores, or *gromatici,* on surveying practices and the legal aspects of property rights and boundaries. The most important sections are those from Fronti-

---

[66] Of this map Cassiodorus records, "Augustus made a complete survey of the whole Orbis Romanus in order that each tax-payer should know exactly his resources and obligations. The results of this survey were tabulated by the author Hyrummetricus." *Variarum Epistularum, Libri XII,* Translated by T. Hodgkin (London, 1886), Bk. III, No. 52. F. Philippi, *Zur Reconstruction der Weltcarte des Agrippa* (Marburg, 1880).

[67] E. Hammer, "Über die Genauigkeit einiger antiker Absteckungen," *Zeitschrift für Vermessungswesen,* Vol. 40, 1911, pp. 573-586.

[68] This *Codex* is one of our oldest extant Latin manuscripts, dating probably from the seventh century, and transcribed in the Irish monastery of Bobbio, founded in 613 by St. Columban. There are two modern studies of this *Codex.* To the first we have already referred several times; namely, the work of Blume, Lachmann, and Rudorff. A more recent study with corrections and additions to the above is that of C. Thulin, *Die Handschriften des Corpus Agrimensorum* (Leipzig, 1913), Vol. 1, Facs. 1.

nus, Hyginus, Balbus, and Nipsus. From this codex we know that, wherever possible, cities, colonies, and military camps as well as main roads were all carefully laid out on systems of rectangular coordinates. The boundaries of agricultural holdings were also carefully marked out according to the same plan, and hence the normal shape of the fields was rectangular, with sides parallel to the roads.[69] It is interesting to note that this Roman plan of co-ordinate layout according to the decimanus and cardo axes was essentially that adopted by the United States Department of Surveys after the Revolutionary War for the delimitation of all new states, counties, and townships.[70]

From 313 B.C., when the construction of the Aqua Appia and the Via Appia was undertaken by Appius Claudius Grassus Caecus,[71] Roman engineering ingenuity excelled in the building of roads and aqueducts, the remains of which are to be found all over the Empire. In the building of the aqueducts, mountains were often negotiated by tunnels, and valleys by large masonry structures, so as to preserve a proper gradient. The following inscription, discovered in 1886, will give some idea of the difficulties encountered by the Romans in connection with their engineering projects:[72]

Varius Clemens to Valerius of Etruria: The illustrious state of Saldi-tana and I, myself, together with the people of Salditana, beseech thee, Lord, to urge Nonius Datus, the surveyor, veteran of the III legion of Augusta, to come to Saldae to complete the remaining portion of his undertaking. [The difficulties of the surveyor are next described by Nonius:] After setting out I suffered from robbers on the way, . . and naked and wounded I escaped with my [companions]. I arrived at

[69] For a good analysis of Roman surveying methods, see E. Stoeber, *Die römischen Grundsteuervermessungen* (Munich, 1877), Ch. 4. "Fields laid out in centuriae, or 100 lot plots, each field measuring about 2370 ft. x 170 ft. (this last = 10 Roman perches) may still be seen near Bologna, having still the precise boundaries given them by the Roman surveyors and thus presenting the same appearance from the surrounding mountain tops that they disclosed 1800 or 1900 years ago." Quoted by C. Herschel, in *Frontinus and the Water Supply of the City of Rome* (Boston, 1913), p. 121, from *Nouvelle géographie universelle*, by E. Réclus (Paris, 1876), Vol. 1, p. 344. By permission of Longmans, Green & Co.

[70] C. Whittlesey, "Origin of the American System of Land Surveys," *Journal of the Association of Engineering Societies*, July, 1883, Vol. 3, pp. 275-280.

[71] Frontinus, *De Aquis Urbis Romae*, in C. Herschel, *op. cit.*, p. 7.

[72] *Corpus Inscriptionum Latinarum* (Berlin, 1863 *et seq.*), Vol. 8, No. 2728, p. 323. Inscription discovered in October, 1886, by M. Medan. Latin text in Appendix, p. 361.

Saldae and interviewed Clemens, the procurator. He conducted me to the hill, where those doubtful of the undertaking were lamenting over the tunnel which they thought would have to be abandoned, because the boring of the tunnel work had been made longer than the length of the hill. It looked as if the borings had wandered from the right direction to such an extent that the upper boring verged towards the South to the right and the lower likewise verged towards the North to the right; thus both sections having wandered off the true direction were diverging. Moreover, the true direction had wandered over the hill from East to West. Lest any reader be in doubt as to the borings, that which is designated "upper" and "lower" must be thus understood: The "upper" is that section where the tunnel receives the water, the "lower" where [the water] rushes out. Having planned the work, so that they might know what share of the borings each had [to perform], I assigned the carrying out of the work to the marines and the spear men, and thus they began upon the boring of the hill. And so I, who was the first to carry out the leveling, to lay out the direction, and to arrange its being carried out according to the plan, which I had handed over to Petronius Celerus, the contractor, completed the work. When the work was complete and the water sent through, Varius Clemens, the procurator, dedicated the work.

That my work in connection with this tunnel at Saldae may be clearer, I have added a few letters. Porcus Vetustinus writes to Crispinus: Dear Lord, you have acted very generously in keeping with your wonted kindness and benevolence, in sending me the ex-legionary Nonius Datus, so that I might discuss with him the work he had undertaken to look after. And so, though time pressed and I was hastening to Caesarea, yet I hurried to Saldae and examined the aqueduct [which was] well under way but a big undertaking. A task which cannot be completed without the skill of Nonius Datus, who faithfully and diligently handled it. And so I am asking your permission for him to stay some months with us to execute the undertaking, unless he has fallen into ill health contracted from his labors.

It is fitting to close this section with a quotation from a statesman and scholar of the period when the Roman Empire was in a state of disintegration. Cassiodorus, writing about A.D. 540, gives us a picture of the high place the surveyor occupied in Roman life even in this period:[73]

The professors of this science [of land surveying] are honored with a more earnest attention than falls to the lot of any other philosophers. Arithmetic, theoretical geometry, astronomy, and music are discoursed

[73] Cassiodorus, *op. cit.*

upon to listless audiences, sometimes to empty benches. But the land surveyor is like a judge; the deserted fields become his forum, crowded with eager spectators. You would fancy him a madman when you see him walking along the most devious paths. But in truth he is seeking for the traces of lost facts in rough woods and thickets. He walks not as other men walk. His path is the book from which he reads; he shows what he is saying; he proves what he hath learned; by his steps he divides the rights of hostile claimants; and like a mighty river he takes away the fields of one side to deposit them on the other.

III

CONTRIBUTIONS of Medieval Europe, Islam, and India

THERE are many aspects of the general European history of the medieval period which it is well to bear in mind in order to get a comprehensive picture of the influences which either accelerated or retarded developments in the topics under discussion. At the beginning of this period the Western Roman Empire had practically disintegrated; new kingdoms, the prototypes of our modern European nations, were being established by those peoples whom the Romans had contemptuously styled the "barbari." The early centuries of this period have been commonly known as the Dark Ages, but as Sarton well remarks, "those ages were never so dark as our ignorance of them." [1] For the widely propagated pessimistic picture of the early medieval period certain writers on the history of mathematics and science are particularly at fault, since their narrow viewpoint of the scope of human progress makes it synonymous with scientific progress. These centuries have too long been depicted by the Rationalistic school as a time of ignorance, tyranny, and stagnation.[2] But this is to forget that the peculiar interest of the early Middle Ages

lies in the spectacle of a civilization struggling to the birth amidst a welter of barbarism; of a gradual conquest of brute force by right,

---

[1] G. Sarton, *Introduction to the History of Science* (Baltimore, 1927), Vol. 1, p. 54.

[2] As an example of this school of thought, the following from a recent history of engineering is typical. "For ten centuries human energy was to lie practically dormant. Progress had been arrested. The history of these centuries is a record of corruption, waste, and a succession of ignoble squabbles, with but a few uncorrelated events to relieve the monotony. The wresting of the Magna Charta from King John and the defeat of the Saracens at Tours by Charles Martel, the one guaranteeing liberty and the other saving what was left of European culture, are the best of the few glories that illuminate the Middle Ages." W. B. Parsons, *Engineers and Engineering in the Renaissance* (Baltimore, 1939), p. 3. By permission of The Williams and Wilkins Co.

anarchy by law, instinct and passion by reflective intelligence and rea-
soned purpose; above all, of an ardour of aspiration which, in face of
facts that seem at every point to give the lie to the ideal, kept its gaze
firmly fixed on the spiritual goal of human life.[3]

Judged by Greek standards the mathematical attainments of
early medieval Europe were of a low order. For this there were
justifying causes, not the least of which was the failure on the part
of the Romans to transmit the Greek legacy. Other contributing
causes would seem to be the barrier of isolation which gradually
separated Eastern Europe from the West, and the secondary status
of material progress in an age whose dominant ideal of progress was spiritual. Nevertheless, it is an error—one which has
been altogether too commonly repeated—to restrict the discovery
of ancient learning to the fifteenth and sixteenth century Renaissance.[4] European interest in the revival of classical knowledge
began with the foundation of the Carlovingian schools in the
ninth century. During the next four centuries there is no period
that does not record the achievements of some outstanding
scholars in many branches of knowledge. By the thirteenth century the medieval world had reached the zenith of its attainments;
it has been titled, with good reason, "the greatest of the centuries."
To this climax of European medieval culture contributions came
from three distinct sources, which we shall now briefly examine,
with special emphasis on their effect on the development of instruments and methods of measurement. These sources were first, the
residue of classical knowledge preserved from the Roman debacle
and disseminated chiefly through the monastic schools; second, the
Muslim reservoir of Greek and Oriental knowledge, initiated
under the aegis of the eighth-century caliphs of Bagdad, by which
European mathematical knowledge was revitalized two centuries
later; and third, the Byzantine depository of the original Greek

[3] W. G. de Burgh, *The Legacy of the Ancient World* (New York, 1924), p. 363.
[4] "Candid inquirers are becoming increasingly convinced that the true Renaissance
occurred around the twelfth rather than the fifteenth century, that medieval Latin
and Scholasticism possessed great merits, that Gothic painting has been neglected
just as Gothic architecture and sculpture once were, that democracy and popular
education declined rather than advanced in early modern times, that organized
charity and care for public health received much attention in medieval towns, whose
unsanitary streets seem largely a figment of the modern imagination." L. Thorndike,
Science and Thought in the Fifteenth Century (New York, 1929), p. 10. By permission
of the Columbia University Press.

attainments which was to remain almost a secret to Western
Europe until the end of the Middle Ages. From the viewpoint of
mathematical progress, undoubtedly the most important contributions came from the Muslims, but the other two sources must
not be entirely overlooked.

The Carlovingian schools had their origin in the monastic
movement. There were for a time in Western Europe two sources
of this movement, which later merged into one. The first was of
Roman origin and dates from the foundation of Monte Cassino
and the Benedictines in 529; the second originated in Ireland,
which became during the sixth and ensuing centuries a fountainhead of great intellectual activity. Ireland's participation in the
intellectual revival of Europe[5] began with the foundation by St.
Columban of the monasteries of Luxeuil and Bobbio. How much
of this intellectual activity carried on by the monastic establishments was concerned with mathematics and science is rather difficult to estimate. Certain it is that in the pursuit of their mission
of Christianization the monks taught the useful arts, among which
must have been some elementary methods of surveying. Evidence
from Latin manuscripts before the end of the first millennium is
very meager with the sole exception of the *Codex Arcerianus* of
Bobbio.[6] There remains the possibility of the existence in Continental libraries of manuscripts in medieval Irish which have not

[5] On the work of the Irish missionaries and schoolmen, Zimmer says, "Aber als
Lehrer auf allen Gebieten des damaligen Wissens, als Inhaber und Träger einer
höheren Cultur als zu jener Zeit auf dem Continent heimisch war, haben sie in
erster Linie die Grundsteine der abendländischen Cultur auf dem Continent gelegt,
an der wir Theil nehmen und auf denen unsere Zeit fortbaut." H. Zimmer, "Über
die Bedeutung des irischen Elements für die mittelalterliche Cultur," *Preussiche
Jahrbücher*, 1887, p. 59.

[6] See p. 41. The existence of this codex in Bobbio leads to the assumption that
knowledge of Roman methods of surveying existed in at least all the larger monastic
establishments. E. Dümmler in his extracts from the history of the monastery of
St. Gall—an offshoot of Bobbio—quotes the following to show that the distinction
between pure and applied geometry was appreciated. "Geometria abstracte quanti-
tatis est cujus pars tamen est ars calculatoria, ut in calculis videatur, quid abstrahatur,
ut in hoc quadrato abjectis calculis cubus surgit perfectus contemplative speculandus."
Ekkehart IV von St. Gallen, *Zeitschrift für deutsches Altertum und deutsche Litteratur*, Vol. 14, 1869, p. 23.

G. R. Zimmermann in his study of the life of Ratpert, educated at St. Gall, concludes that "Die Geometrie wurde nicht nur in der Schulstube, sondern am liebsten
im Freien studiert . . . es wurde die Höhe von Erdboden bis zum Kirchturnhahn
gemessen, oder ein jünst dem Kloster vermachtes Gut wurde abgesteckt." *Ratpert,
der erster Zürcher Gelehert* (Basel, 1878), pp. 43 ff. Referring to the plans for a new

yet been brought to light and which should help clarify our knowledge of the standard of practical mathematics attained in the monastic schools.[7] The fragmentary information which we have from the writings of Bede, Alcuin, Aldhelm, Hrabanus Maurus, and others does not do justice either to the spirit of the times or to the curricula and teachers of the schools they attended.[8]

Turning to the East, in the early centuries of this period we find another movement getting under way that was destined finally to make the greatest contribution to the knowledge of mathematics and science of medieval Europe. In a few years—from 622 till his death at Mecca in 632—Muhammad had established the political unity of the nomadic tribes of Arabia. By the end of the seventh century the followers of Muhammad not only had conquered Syria, Mesopotamia, and Egypt but had also penetrated eastward beyond Persia to the boundaries of India, while westward their conquering hordes overran all North Africa, crossed over to Spain, overthrew the Kingdom of the Visigoths, and established the seat of their Western government at Cordova. In the East the only power to keep them at bay was Byzantium, while in the West a final stop was put to their military encroachment on Europe when they were defeated at Poictiers by the Franks under Martel in 732. The widespread political power of Islam, consolidated in such an amazingly short time under two dynasties—the 'Abbāsid in the East with Bagdad as focus of political and intellectual activity, the Umayyad in the West with headquarters at Cordova—embraced within its fold peoples of many races and religious beliefs, chief among whom, so far as the intellectual renaissance of the Muslims is concerned, were the Syriac Christians and the Persians.

From the middle of the eighth century there developed a real intellectual revival in the East under the guidance of a group of 'Abbāsid caliphs, the most outstanding of whom were al-Masūr,

monastery at St. Gall under the abbot Gozpert or Hartmuot, S. Günther remarks, "Ein Architekt der einen solchen Riss anzufertigen vermochte, hatte nicht nur unbewusst die Regeln der darstellenden Geometrie angewandt, sondern er musste sich auch auf Vermessungskunde verstehen." *Geschichte des mathematischen Unterrichts im deutschen Mittelalter bis zum Jahre 1525* (Berlin, 1887), p. 114.

[7] See the introduction to the translation by Maura Power of a medieval Irish treatise on the astrolabe, *Irish Texts Society*, Vol. 14, 1912.

[8] On the work of the "Perigrini Scotti" see Dom Louis Gougaud, O.S.B., *Gaelic Pioneers of Christianity*, Translated from the French by V. Collins (Dublin, 1923);

Hārūn-al-Rashīd and al-Mamūn.[9] Muslim mathematical activity got under way with the introduction from India of the Hindu number system and the astronomical-mathematical work, the *Siddhānta*,[10] which was translated into Arabic by the Persian al-Fazārī. From then until the end of the eleventh century Arabic was destined to be the pre-eminent language of science.[11] From the Hindus, through the Persians, the Arabs imbibed their knowledge of arithmetic, algebra, trigonometry, and astrology, while at the same time, using the Syrian Christians as intermediaries, they became acquainted with the philosophy, geometry, astronomy, and medicine of the Greeks. Not only did the Muslims master the

B. Fitzpatrick, *Ireland and the Foundations of Europe* (New York, 1927).

[9] Al-Mamūn's reign was contemporaneous with that of Charlemagne, but unfortunately the centers of learning set up by these two patrons had almost no contact.

[10] D. E. Smith, *History of Mathematics* (Boston, 1923), Vol. 1, p. 167.

[11] "The Arabic-writing scientists elaborated algebra (the name is a telltale) and trigonometry on Graeco-Hindu foundations; they constructed and developed—though, it must be said, very little—Greek geometry; they collected abundant astronomical observations and their criticism of the Ptolemaic system, though not always justified, helped to prepare the astronomical reformation of the sixteenth century; they enriched enormously our medical experience; they were the distant originators of modern chemistry; they improved the knowledge of optics and meteorology, the measurements of densities; their geographical investigations extended from one end of the world to the other." G. Sarton, *History of Science and the New Humanism* (New York, 1931), p. 102. By permission of Henry Holt and Co.

In this movement the work of the following individuals is of importance insofar as the history of measuring instruments is concerned: al-Fazārī (*fl.* 760), credited with being the first Muslim maker of astrolabes; ibn-'Īsā al-Astrolābī (*fl.* 800), another early maker of astrolabes; Māschāllāh (*fl.* 800), Jewish writer of an important treatise on the astrolabe; al-Chwārizmī (*fl.* 820), developer of the Hindu number system and algebra; al-Kindī (*fl.* 850), styled "the philosopher of the Arabs"; Tābit ibn-Qorra (*fl.* 870), Persian astronomer; al-Battānī (*fl.* 900), Sabian, "the greatest astronomer of his race and time"; ibn-Jūnus (*fl.* 990), "next to al-Battānī, the most famous astronomer among the Arabs"; al-Bīrūnī (*fl.* 1020), Persian, "one of the very greatest of all times"; ibn-Sīnā (Avicenna) (*fl.* 1020), Persian, "the most famous scientist of Islam"; Abū'l Wefā (*fl.* 980), one of the greatest Muslim mathematicians; al-Zarqālī (*fl.* 1060), Spanish Muslim, who made an important change in the construction of the astrolabe; Abū'l Salt (*fl.* 1130), important Western astronomer; ibn-al-'Auwām (*fl.* 1130), writer on agriculture; al-'Urdī and Nāsir al-Dīn al-Tusī, astronomers in the 1200's.

There is still a great dearth of research in the English language on the history of Muslim science and mathematics. Early in the nineteenth century the two Sédillots blazed the trail for the Continental work on this subject. (See notes 38 and 91.) In more recent times, most important work has been carried on by students of Erlangen University under the leadership and guidance of Professor E. Wiedemann. Wiedemann's own contributions are to be found in various "Beiträge zur Geschichte der Naturwissenschaften" in *Sitzungsberichte der physikalisch-medizinischen Sozietät in Erlangen* (hereafter contracted to *Beitr. Sitz. Ber.*). Among those who have worked in this group and whose contributions are mentioned hereafter are J. Frank, H. Seeman, C. Schoy, J. Drecker, P. Schmalzl, and M. Meyerhoff. Special mention must be

knowledge transmitted to them, but in most cases they also made important improvements.

Because of its constant contact with the East for commercial and religious reasons, the western section of the Muslim empire was well informed on the scientific knowledge which radiated from Bagdad. How much of this Islamic culture seeped into northern Europe before the twelfth century is a matter of conjecture.[12] That students from the northern countries made frequent visits to the intellectual centers of Spain is well known.[13] So far as the subject matter of this work is concerned, the visit of Gerbert is important, since in all probability it was during his sojourn in Spain[14] that he acquired much of the information on practical geometry which he afterward used in the oldest known medieval European treatise on the subject.[15] But it was not until after 1085

made of the important historical work of H. Suter of Switzerland, "Die Mathematiker und Astronomen der Araber und ihre Werke" published in *Abhandlungen zur Geschichte der mathematischen Wissenschaften,* Vol. 10, 1900. It is a compendium of the lives and works of all known Islamic scholars of mathematics and astronomy. English works so far published have been mostly descriptions of existing instruments, the following being of most interest: W. H. Morley, *Description of a Planispheric Astrolabe* (London, 1856); and *Description of an Arabic Quadrant* (London, 1860); L. Evans, "Some European and Oriental Astrolabes," *The Archaeological Journal,* Vol. 58, 1911; R. T. Gunther, *The Astrolabes of the World* (Oxford, 1932).

[12] "I am convinced that the schools of Lorraine in the last half of the tenth century were the seed-plot in which the seeds of Arabic science first germinated in Latin Europe, from which the knowledge radiated to other parts of Germany—witness Hermann Contractus in Reichenau—to France, and especially, owing to the preference of Knut the Great for Lotharingian clergymen, into England. And yet, until Adelard of Bath, Arabic learning was still so little cultivated in western Christendom that Guibert de Nogent could write, 'Scientia scilicet astrorum quae apud occidentales tenuior extat et rarior, eo apud orientales ubi et originum habuit, continuo usu ac frequenti memoria magis fervere cognoscitur' (Recueil des croisades, Hist. occident IV, 246. Cf. III 814; IV 193), a declaration remarkable for its recognition of the value of the new learning and its tribute to the Arabs." J. W. Thompson, "The Introduction of Arabic Science into Lorraine in the Tenth Century," *Isis,* Vol. 12, 1929, p. 191. By permission of the Editor, G. Sarton.

[13] M. C. Welbon, "Lotharingia as a Center of Arabic Influences," *Isis,* Vol. 16, 1933, pp. 188-189.

[14] C. H. Haskins, *Studies in the History of Medieval Science* (Cambridge, Mass., 1924), p. 8.

[15] *Gerberti . . . Geometria,* Edited by P. B. Pez, Published in Migne, *Patrologiae Cursus Completus,* Vol. 139, 1853. Gerbert, born in Aurillac, France, 950, became a Benedictine monk, after spending some time in Spain, taught at Rheims, and was elected Abbot of Bobbio, Archbishop of Rheims, Archbishop of Ravenna, and finally Pope under the title of Sylvester II (999-1003). For bibliography of his work as a mathematician see Smith, *op. cit.,* Vol. I, p. 195. Regarding Gerbert's dependence on Muslim sources, see J. Würschmidt, "Geodätischen Messinstrumente und Messmethoden bei Gerbert und bei den Araben," *Archiv der Mathematik und Physik,* Series 3,

when Toledo, the greatest center of Muslim learning in the West, was recaptured by the Spanish Christians, that intellectual contact on a large scale came into being.[16] The intermediaries, at this period, between those who spoke Latin and those whose language was Arabic were the Spanish Jews.[17]

The two most prominent Europeans who worked at Toledo on translations were Adelard of Bath and Gerard of Cremona.[18] The most important treatise on practical geometry that came from Spain at this time was the *Liber Embadorum*.[19] In this work there is very little reference to particular instruments; it deals chiefly with the underlying geometric facts required for finding lengths, heights, and areas. About the same time appeared Hugo Physicus' *Practica Geometriae*,[20] mainly a repetition of Gerbert's work.

The influence of Byzantine scholarship on Western Europe

Vol. 19, 1912, pp. 315-320. The practical geometry of Gerbert was followed soon afterward by a similar work, which shows distinct Muslim influence, written by another Benedictine, Hermann Contractus. See J. Drecker, "Hermannus Contractus, über das Astrolab," *Isis*, Vol. 16, 1933, pp. 200-219. Hermann's treatise, edited by Pez, published in Migne, *op. cit.*, Vol. 143, pp. 379-412.

[16] From about the middle of the eleventh century another center of contact between Christian and Muslim was set up in Sicily when that island was taken over by the Normans from the Arabs. From this center came nothing worth while in the mathematical line. See C. H. Haskins and D. D. Lockwood, "The Sicilian Translators of the Twelfth Century," *Harvard Studies in Classical Philology*, Vol. 21, p. 75.

[17] "The scientific life which expanded in Toledo during the twelfth century is reminiscent in many ways of the translation period of Baghdad three centuries before. Just as the Caliph al-Mamūn installed the 'House of Wisdom' so Archbishop Raymond founded, under the direction of the Archdeacon Dominico Gundisalvi, a school of translation which flourished in Toledo until the thirteenth century. The part of the polyglot Christians and Sabian translators of Baghdad was played in Toledo by the Jews who spoke Arabic, Hebrew, Spanish and sometimes Latin." Max Meyerhoff in "Science and Medicine," *The Legacy of Islam*, Edited by T. Arnold and A. Guillaume (Oxford, 1931), p. 347. By permission of The Clarendon Press. For a detailed account of the part played by the Jews at this period see M. Steinschneider, "Die Mathematik bei den Juden," Part I, *Bibliotheca Mathematik*, New Series 10, 1896, No. 3 (continued in later numbers).

[18] Smith, *op. cit.*, Vol. 1, pp. 202-203.

[19] Written by a Spanish Jew, Abraham bar Chiia, commonly known as Savasorda (c. 1070-1136), translated into Latin by Plato of Tivoli. Latin text with German translation edited by M. Curtze in *Abhandlungen zur Geschichte der mathematischen Wissenschaften*, Vol. 12, 1902.

[20] Edited by M. Curtze in *Monatschefte für Mathematik*, Vol. 8, 1897. Of the same character is the *Practica Geometriae* of Dominicus Parisiensis. See M. Curtze, *Zeitschrift für Mathematik und Physik*, Vol. 40, Hist. Liter. Abt., p. 161. Another work which, though written shortly after the end of the period under consideration, belongs in the same category is the *Practica Geometriae* of Mainardi of Cremona; German translation by M. Curtze in *Abhandlung zur Geschichte der mathematischen Wissenschaften*, Vol. 13, 1902.

played but a minor role until direct contact was established
through the Crusades, especially after the occupation of Constantinople in 1204. Even then its chief contribution was that of
being the depository of the original Greek classics, which European scholars were already studying through Latin translations of
Arabic translations of Syriac translations from the Greek. Although the opportunity was now at hand for the dissemination of
Greek mathematical thought through Europe, very little use was
made of it, chiefly because the custodians of this Greek depository
were themselves for the most part unacquainted with its contents.
The Byzantine world had made little use of its Greek legacy in
mathematics and science. Further developments having been rare
and of minor importance, retrogression had been inevitable. For
this phenomenon the Roman rulers of the East must be held responsible. "Roman insistence upon the material conditions of
stability was so strong that the Greek tradition of disinterested
research was stifled." [21] By comparison with Muslim activity,
Byzantium was practically dead so far as the advancement of
science was concerned. There is no record of any work of mathematical importance stemming from this source.[22] It was not until
the sixteenth century that the mathematical works of the Greeks
began to be known in Western Europe in their original form.
The outlying provinces seemed to fare somewhat better. By the
middle of the sixth century the school of Alexandria was Chris-
tianized, and it was partly through the Christian commentators
of Alexandria that the Greek legacy was transmitted to other
Christian communities of the East, notably the Syrians and Ar-
menians, by whom it was finally handed on to the Muslims.
Shortly before the Muslim invasion, we find one important document from Alexandria which serves to trace the history of the
astrolabe to Greek sources. This oldest account we have of the
astrolabe, written by John Philoponus,[23] shows clearly that the

[21] Sarton, *Introduction to the History of Science,* p. 10. By permission of The Williams and Wilkins Co.
[22] Psellus is supposed to be the author of some minor works in mathematics. See
Smith, *op. cit.,* Vol. 1, p. 197.
[23] "Joannis Alexandri, cognomine Philopoi, de usu astrolabi eiusque constructione
libellus." Edited by H. Hase in *Rheinsches Museum für Philologie,* Vol. 6, 1839. German translation by J. Drecker, "Des Johannes Philoponus Schrift über das Astrolab,"
Isis, Vol. 11, 1928, pp. 15-44.

astrolabe was in use from the time of Ptolemy and was a well-known instrument in the sixth century. This is further corroborated by the treatise on the astrolabe by the Syrian bishop Severus Sebokt of the seventh century, based wholly on Greek sources.[24]

Discussing a fine Byzantine astrolabe, known as the Brescia astrolabe, Dalton summarizes the status of Byzantine science thus:[25]

The evidence of Byzantine literature seems to show that science in the East-Roman Empire underwent a long eclipse from the beginning of the Saracenic wars to the close of the thirteenth century, a period of 500 years. Though this evidence is negative, resting on the absence of scientific literature, it probably accords in the main with fact. But the existence of the Brescia Astrolabe suggests that the eclipse was not total during the period of the Macedonian and Commenian dynasties. We know that the traditions of Alexandrian astronomy were still alive in the second half of the seventh century. It would now appear that they did not then vanish from their proper territory and that the Arabs, though supreme, had no absolute monopoly in astronomical knowledge throughout the earlier centuries of the Middle Ages.

Early in the thirteenth century Fibonacci (Leonardo of Pisa) wrote his *Practica Geometriae;*[26] although his Muslim contacts were other than through Spain,[27] he seems to have drawn heavily from the *Liber Embadorum.*[28] Practically the same problems are dealt with in each work, though Fibonacci is more specific on the use of instruments. An important treatise which shows the extent to which a knowledge of the Muslim *quadrant* had been absorbed by the Europeans in the thirteenth century is that of Robert Anglicus, *Tractatus Quadrantis.*[29] There are many other treatises dealing more particularly with astronomy and astrology, in which we find detailed accounts of the astrolabe and the quadrant,[30] all

[24] M. F. Nau, "Le Traité sur l'astrolabe plan de Sévère Sebokt," *Journal asiatique,* Series 9, Vol. 13, 1899, pp. 56-101, 238-303. In this treatise we find mention of the Hindu-Arabic numerals for the first time in a European language.

[25] O. M. Dalton, "The Byzantine Astrolabe at Brescia," *British Academy Proceedings,* Vol. 12, 1926, pp. 133-146. By permission of The British Academy.

[26] *Scritti di Leonardo Pisano,* Edited by B. Boncompagni (Rome, 1862), Vol. 2.

[27] Smith, *op. cit.,* Vol. 1, pp. 214-217.

[28] M. Curtze, *Abhandlungen zur Geschichte der mathematischen Wissenschaften,* Introduction.

[29] "Le Traité du quadrant du maître Robert Anglais," Edited by P. Tannery, *Notices et extracts de la bibliothèque nationale,* Vol. 35, 1897, Part 2.

[30] For example, treatises by Sacrobosco, Richard of Wallingford, Roger Bacon, Alexandre de Villedieu, Jordanus Nemorarius, Albertus Magnus, Alfonso X of Castile, and John of Montpellier.

of which go to show that by the climax of the Middle Ages the Muslim instruments and Muslim trigonometry were well known in the intellectual centers of Europe. Little was produced during the fourteenth and the first half of the fifteenth centuries to advance the development of measuring instruments. The only important innovation of this time was the introduction of the *baculum* or *Jacob's staff* by Levi ben Gerson (1288-1344); this instrument, however, did not come into general use until much later. Another instrument, the use of which in surveying does not seem to have developed to any great extent before 1500 but whose origin in all probability dates from the early Middle Ages, is the *magnetic compass*. As regards methods of surveying in vogue toward the end of the Middle Ages, the only important documents are an anonymous English manuscript on mensuration[31] and the *Geometria Culmensis*.[32] This last century and a half was a period of much strife and misery throughout Europe. Besides the Hundred Years War and the Black Death, there were frequent uprisings[33] among the lower classes against their feudal lords. These local rebellions were ruthlessly crushed, but the seed was sown by which the right of the individual to the ownership of land was established—the death knell of feudalism was sounded, and the day was at hand when the surveyor was to be called upon to exercise his art to an extent heretofore unknown.

Leveling Instruments

WATER LEVELS   There has been very little on the use of water levels handed down to us by the Muslims; it would seem that they were unacquainted with the instruments of Heron and Vitruvius,[34] or else because of the cumbersomeness of these instruments they preferred levels which depended on the principles of the plumb bob. Ibn-Lujūn and al-Tignarī [35] describe the use of an

---

[31] *Rara Mathematica*, Edited by J. Halliwell (London, 1839), pp. 56-71.

[32] *Geometria Culmensis, Ein agronomischer Traktat aus der Zeit des Hochmeisters Conrad von Jungingen (1393-1407)*, Edited by M. Mendthal (Leipzig, 1886). Latin and German texts.

[33] Chief among these were the Jacquerie Revolt in France, 1358; Tyler's Rebellion in England, 1381; Flanders Revolt, 1323.

[34] H. Schneller, "Beiträge zur Geschichte der Technik in der Antike und bei den Araben," *Abhandlungen zur Geschichte der Naturwissenschaften und der Medizin*, Heft 6, 1922, p. 36.

[35] Wiedemann, *Beitr.* 10, *Sitz. Ber.* 38, 1906, pp. 316-317.

open vessel with rim parallel to the base, which was filled with water. If the water remained even with the rim the vessel rested on a horizontal plane. As an aid to better sighting a flat board (al-qubtāl) was placed across the rim of the vessel (Figure 14).

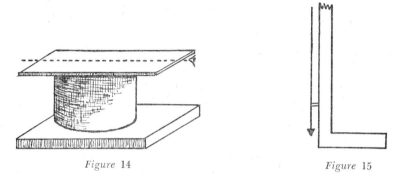

Figure 14   Figure 15

Strange to say, there is no mention of any type of water level in the writings of Gerbert. The use of the astrolabe and the *geometric square* as levels, which were introduced by the Muslims, seems to have supplanted in medieval Europe the use of the more natural water levels developed by the Greeks and Romans. Not until the Renaissance was the water level in common use again.

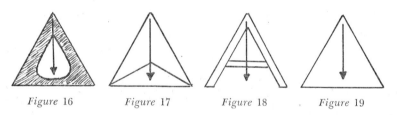

Figure 16   Figure 17   Figure 18   Figure 19

PLUMB-BOB LEVELS   Instead of the water level, the Muslims made use of many forms of plumb-bob levels. A simple carpenter's square with plumb bob attached was in common use (Figure 15). Among the many who mention it are al-Battānī and ibn-Sīnā.[36] Several forms of simple isosceles-triangular levels are described by the Muslims, such as those in Figures 16-19.[37] In all these forms

[36] *Al-Battānī sive Albatenii, Opus Astronomicum*, Edited by C. A. Nallino (Mediolani, 1903), Part I, p. 143. E. Wiedemann, "Avicennas Schrift über ein von ihm ersonnenes Beobachtungsinstrument," *Acta Orientalia*, Vol. 5, 1927, p. 104.

[37] E. Wiedemann, "Al-Mīzān," *Encyclopaedia of Islam* (Leyden, 1913), Vol. 3, pp. 530-539.

the plumb line was dropped from the apex of the triangle, which was usually made of wood, bearing a mark or line indicating the direction of the perpendicular when the triangle stood on a level surface. The wood was usually partly cut away to accommodate the

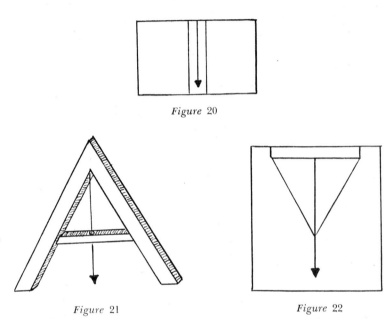

Figure 20

Figure 21   Figure 22

bob. Another form, used chiefly by builders, is described by ibn-Lujūn and al-Tignarī. It consisted of a rectangular piece of wood bearing two parallel lines perpendicular to its base (Figure 20). Between these lines hung the plumb line. Two distinctive types are described by al-Marrāquschī.[38] The first consisted of three rods placed together as in Figure 21. The crosspiece had a hole through which the plumb line hung. The second was known as the *murdjīkāl* (the bat); it consisted of an inverted suspended isosceles triangular form which was hung from a stretched cord. The plumb line was fixed at the center of the base line and hung over the apex of the triangle when the apparatus was level (Figure 22).

Besides actual leveling instruments, the Muslims describe various devices by which the levelness or straightness of parts of instru-

[38] J. J. Sédillot, *Traité des instruments astronomiques des Arabs* (Paris, 1831), p. 376.

ments might be tested.[39] That a ruler had a straight edge was tested by applying a stretched thread along it. When one straight edge was determined, others were tested by placing them side by side with the standard one. The planeness of a surface was tested by applying a straight edge to it in various directions and observing whether any light penetrated between the edge and the surface. The levelness of a plane surface was proved either by the primitive method of pouring water on it and observing whether it flowed equally in all directions or by placing on the surface a plate or dish of water, whose edge was parallel to its base; the surface was level if the water touched the top rim of the vessel all round. To test the smoothness of large metal rings which he used on his astronomical instruments, al-'Urdī proceeded as follows: The ring to be examined was first made horizontal by means of a level. A circular gutter of potter's clay was then built round the inside of the ring. The outer edge of this clay ring was on the same level as the surface of the metal ring, while its inner edge was made somewhat higher. The gutter was then filled with water on which were scattered light ashes. If the water flowed over the ring any depressions in it would be filled, while the ashes would remain in the raised parts of the metal, thus bringing out the irregularities of the ring surface.[40]

The first of the medieval European writers to mention the use of the plumb-bob level is Leonardo of Pisa.[41] His level consisted of an isosceles-triangular piece of wood with a lead bob. He describes its use in the *cultellare* process, that is, finding the horizontal area of a sloping piece of ground, a process already described by the Roman agrimensores (see Figure 157). The other Latin works on practical geometry referred to at the beginning of this chapter omit completely to mention anything connected with leveling, so that we have no direct information as to what proc-

[39] These are taken from Wiedemann, "Al-Mīzān."

[40] H. Seemann, "Die Instrumente der Sternwarte zu Marāgha nach al-'Urdī," *Sitzungsberichte der physikalisch-medizinischen Sozietät in Erlangen,* Vol. 60, 1928, pp. 47-48.

[41] Leonardo Pisano, *op. cit.,* Vol. 2, p. 108. "Est enim archipendulus instrumentum ligneum habens formam trianguli equicruij; et ab uno angulorum pendit filum cum plumbo; cumque posueris basem ipsius archipenduli super perticam, et ab angulo superiori plumbum cum filo ceciderit super dimidium basis ipsius; tunc pertica stabit equidistanter illj plano."

esses were used; however, we are probably safe in the assumption that European methods followed closely those of the Muslims.

LEVELING RODS   There is very little mention of any form of leveling rod in this period; the only two Muslim writers who give any details of such rods are al-Chāzinī [42] and ibn-al-'Auwām.[43] From these accounts we see that their rods were much inferior to that of Heron. Leveling at night with the aid of a torch or lamp is also described by ibn-al-'Auwām.[44] The light was usually carried on a long pole of known length, and the person carrying it went downhill from the sighting instrument until the light was on the line of sight.

A common method of finding the difference in level between two points was to suspend a light triangular level from the middle of a cord stretched from rods which were held vertically over the points. The position of the cord on one or both rods was changed until the plumb line showed that the cord was level. The difference in the readings of the cord positions gave the required difference in level. Such a method is described by al-Chāzinī.[45] Because of the sag in the cord, the distance between the rods had to be kept short. Gandz[46] describes a more primitive form of the same method, which he says was employed by the early Jews. In this case the rods were replaced by human bodies. One person held

[42] N. Khanikoff, "Analysis and Extracts of the Book of the Balance of Wisdom by al-Chāzinī," *Journal of the American Oriental Society*, Vol. 6, 1860, pp. 1–128.

[43] The following is a translation of Wiedemann's German quotation from ibn-al-'Auwām, *Beitr*. 10, *Sitz. Ber*. 38, 1906, pp. 318-319. "A good horizontal board is placed by the mouth of the well or the opening of the cistern. The astrolabe is placed on it, so that the alidade is on the upper half and the sights correspond with the opening of the well or the outlet of the reservoir. The line of sight coincides with the direction in which it is desired to run off the water. A square board is then prepared. On one side large tangential circles are drawn. Every two adjacent [circles] have either different colors or distinguishing marks at their centers, which are plainly visible from the distance. These 'signal-rods' are then set up and sighted on, through the astrolabe, by the observer placing his cheek on the ground between the astrolabe and the outlet, and his eye as near as possible to the instrument. He determines the circle on which he sights . . . ," etc. By permission of Erlangen University. A practically similar process from ibn-al-Saffār (d. 1035) is given in *Beitr*. 18, *Sitz. Ber*. 41, 1909, p. 72.

[44] Wiedemann, *Beitr*. 10, *Sitz. Ber*. 38, 1906, p. 318.

[45] Khanikoff, *op. cit.*

[46] S. Gandz, "Die Harpedonapten oder Seilspanner und Seilknüpfer," *Quellen und Studien zur Geschichte der Mathematik*, Abt. B, *Studien*, Bd. 1, Heft 3, 1930, pp. 269-270.

an end of the rope or cord against his heart, while the person at
the other end walked up the slope until the rope was found to be
level when stretched under his foot. The horizontality of the
rope depended on the judgment of a third person.

Right-Angle Instruments

SQUARES AND ROPES The square or *Kūnijā* is mentioned quite
frequently in Muslim writings; it was used principally by builders,
and several ways were given of determining the exactness of the
right angle. Abū'l Wefā (940-998) gave two important geometrical proofs,[47] the first depending on the property of an angle inscribed in a semicircle; the second, on the Pythagorean theorem.
Large wooden squares were commonly employed throughout this
period in Europe. The Roman system of right-angled division
was preserved to some extent, but the groma seems to have given
way to the large *carpenter's square*. We have no complete description of its use, but from various allusions and a few diagrams
it seems to have been generally placed on the ground and the lines
seem to have been laid out by sighting rods or extending a cord.[48]

The oldest applications which we know of the use of the cord
or rope in the construction of the right angle are to be found in
the Indian Sulvasūtras. The title signifies "rules of the cord"; it
is the name given to those portions of the Kalpasūtras—laws of
the Vedic religion—which treat of the measurements and construction of various types of sacrificial altars. The three most
important commentaries on the Sulvasūtras are those of Baudhāyana, Āpastamba, and Kātyāyana, which are believed to have
been written not later than A.D. 200. The original Sulvasūtras
probably date back to about 800 B.C.[49] How much change occurred

[47] H. Suter, "Das Buch der geometrischen Konstrucktionen von Abū-'l Wefā,"
Abhandlungen zur Geschichte der Naturwissenschaften und der Medizin, Heft 3,
1922, pp. 98-99.
[48] *Geometria Culmensis,* p. 23. Method of finding the area of a field in the shape of
a right triangle: "Habetur propositum; verbi gracia sit campus triangularis rectangulus *ABC,* sitque *B* angulus rectus, et *BC* et *BA* sint latera angulum rectum continencia.
Tunc ponat mensor gnomonem in puncto *B,* et trahatur funis a puncto *B* ad punctum
A, et sit eius longitudo 16 perticarum. Deinde gnomone manente fixo trahatur
corda de puncto *B* ad punctum *C* sitque 24 perticarum. Multiplicentur 16, que est
medietas lateris *BC,* et proveniunt 192, continencia campi dicti."
[49] A. B. Datta, *The Science of the Sūlba. A Study of Early Hindu Geometry* (Calcutta, 1932).

in them between these dates is an unsettled question.[50] If some of the rules are pre-Pythagorean and independent of Greek influence we may be fairly certain that they are not the result of any mathematical deduction. Kaye says that these Vedic rules were "primarily not mathematical, but ancillary to religious aims," and that "the ritualists who composed the Sulvasūtras were not interested in the Pythagorean theorem beyond their own actual wants, and it is quite certain that even as late as the twelfth century no Indian mathematician gives evidence of a complete understanding of the irrational."[51] However, it should be stated in passing that no modern Indian writer on the history of Indian mathematics agrees with the conclusions of Kaye.

The problems involved in the Vedic altar constructions may be summed up as follows: (1) to construct a square equal to the sum or difference of two squares; (2) to construct a square equal to a rectangle and vice versa; (3) to construct perpendiculars from, and to, a straight line; (4) to construct a straight line equal to an irrational; (5) to construct a square equal to a circle. In the solution of Problem 3, we find the simple symmetric construction with the stretched cord being employed[52] and the construction by means of arcs of circles also fully described.[53] But besides these more primitive methods, we also find instructions for laying out right angles by means of various Pythagorean triangles, including five primitive triplets; namely, 3,4,5, 12,5,13, 15,8,17, 7,24,25, 12,35,37, and the composite triplets, 15,36,39, 12,16,20, and 15,20,25.[54]

Although there is no mention of the symmetric construction with the stretched rope in Greek or Roman writings, it appears again in the Middle Ages in the work of Leonardo of Pisa.[55] The Pythagorean construction was well known in the later Middle

[50] For references on the literature of this question see Smith, *op. cit.*, Vol. 1, p. 98, footnotes.

[51] G. R. Kaye, *Indian Mathematics* (Calcutta, 1915), pp. 4, 6. For criticism of Kaye see S. Ganguli, "Notes on Indian Mathematics," *Isis*, Vol. 12, 1929, pp. 132-145.

[52] A. Bürk, "Das Āpastamba-Sūlba-Sūtra II: Übersetzung." *Zeitschrift der deutsch Morgenland Gesellschaften*, Vol. 56, 1902, p. 330.

[53] G. Thibaut, "On the Sulvasūtras," *Journal of the Asiatic Society of Bengal*, Vol. 44, 1875, pp. 249-251.

[54] The first six are to be found in Baudhāyana; see Thibaut, *ibid.*, p. 235. All but the fourth are to be found in Āpastamba; see Bürk, *op. cit.*, pp. 340-342.

[55] Leonardo Pisano, *op. cit.*, Vol. 2, p. 43.

Ages and was probably commonly employed by builders and surveyors.[56]

SURVEYOR'S CROSS   No description of an instrument modeled after Heron's dioptra or the Roman groma has come down to us from the Muslims. Not even Gerbert, who was nearest to the Romans in point of time, makes any mention of the groma. An instrument called the *crucze* is spoken of in one place in the *Geometria Culmensis* in connection with laying out a perpendicular line,[57] but no description is given of it. Because of its omission in all the medieval texts on practical geometry, we may safely assume that no form of surveyor's cross was in common use during this period.

Staff Combinations

INDIAN CIRCLES   The oldest Indian description of the establishment of the north-south line by the Indian circles method is to be found in the *Sūrya Siddhānta,* an astronomical work dating from about 400 B.C.[58] There is every reason to believe that this method was long in use among the Indians. The establishment of the meridian line by this method was very extensively used by the Muslims, both in their astronomical work and in determining the direction of Mecca for some of their religious rituals.[59] Because of its importance the Muslims introduced various refinements in the methods of observation of the meridian. Among the most important is that of al-'Urdī,[60] which consisted in describing a number

[56] In the *Geometria Culmensis,* p. 33, the right triangle of sides 21, 28, 35, is spoken of. On page 34, after stating the relationships between the sum of the squares of the sides containing a given angle of a triangle and the square of the opposite side, the author adds that this information seems to be more or less a secret among geometricians. "Et illa sunt satis secreta apud geometras." Even the great architect Leone Battista Alberti used a 4, 5, 6 combination as a right triangle. See M. Cantor, *Vorlesungen über Geschichte der Mathematik* (Leipzig, 1880), Vol. 2, p. 292.

[57] *Op. cit.,* p. 31. "Duch sal man allewege czulegen das rechte winkelmos adir crucze, wornoch man misset, wenne alle mose geen uo dem rechten winkel."

[58] Cantor, *op. cit.,* Vol. 1, p. 599. Kaye, *op. cit.,* p. 9. For translation of the original description, see p. 281. E. Burgess, "Sūrya-Siddhānta," *Journal of the American Oriental Society,* Vol. 6, 1860, p. 239.

[59] Knowledge of the direction of Mecca, or the *Qibla,* was important in Muslim religious ceremonials. In the writings of al-Chāzinī (Suter, "Die Mathematiker und Astronomen der Araber und ihre Werke," Nr. 293) the geographical positions of all important places in Iran relative to Mecca are given.

[60] C. Schoy, "Abhandlung über die Ziehung der Mittagslinie," *Annalen der Hydrographie und Maritimen Meteorologie,* Heft 10, 1922, pp. 265-271.

of concentric circles, instead of one (Figure 23). The advantage of this method was that points could be observed on the different circles at different times, and a temporary shadowing of the sun by clouds or a temporary lapse by the observer would not then vitiate the results. Of the European writers of this period, the only one who describes the Indian circles method is Gerbert. He explains its use in connection with the setting out of the cardo and decimanus.[61]

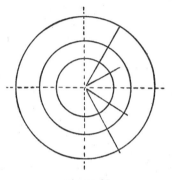

Figure 23

INDIRECT MEASUREMENT The works on practical geometry produced in this period contain many examples of the use of single staffs and combinations for carrying out indirect measurements. The use of a single vertical staff in the measuring of heights by the shadow method is recorded in the Indian works of Aryabhatta and Brahmagupta.[62] The Muslims seem to have preferred to use the astrolabe. Gerbert and other European writers describe the use of the simple staff and its shadow,[63] but in general for measuring heights they employed the astrolabe and the geometric square. The very important method [64] of measuring a height whose base is inaccessible by two observations on a vertical staff from two stations is first recorded by Aryabhatta.[65] There is also frequent mention of the use of the horizontal staff. Bhāskara uniquely applied the two positions method using a horizontal staff and a mirror to measure the height of an object.[66] The horizontal staff was used by the Muslims quite

[61] Gerbert, *op. cit.*, Ch. 94.

[62] G. R. Kaye, "Notes on Indian Mathematics," *Journal of the Asiatic Society of Bengal, New Series,* Vol. 4, 1908, pp. 128-129.

[63] Gerbert, *op. cit.*, Chs. 25 ff. Leonardo Pisano, *op. cit.*, pp. 200 ff. Hugo Physicus, *op. cit.*, pp. 204 ff.

[64] F. Schmidt, *Geschichte der geodätischen Instrumente und Verfahren im Altertum und Mittelalter* (Neustadt an der Haardt, 1935), p. 234, citing an unpublished dissertation by R. Geiger, "Indische Geodäsie im Altertum und Mittelalter" (Erlangen, 1922).

[65] For description of this and other uses of staffs, see Chapter VI.

[66] *Līlāvatī, A Treatise on Mensuration by Bhāskara,* Edited by M. S. Dvivedi (Benares, 1912). See also *Algebra, Arithmetic with Mensuration of Brahmegupta and Bhascara,* Edited by H. T. Colebrooke (London, 1817), pp. 317-318.

commonly in finding the depth of wells,[67] a problem found later in all the Medieval practical geometrics.

Combinations of horizontal and vertical staffs were numerous and were designated by various names.[68] In the earlier forms the staffs were of equal length and bound firmly together; later various ratios were used in the lengths, the common one being 3:4. Large right-triangular pieces of wood or metal were sometimes substituted.[69] In all these forms the position of the observer was controlled by a fixed line of sight. To overcome this limitation, the binding of the staffs was so arranged that the lengths could be varied; another improvement was the introduction of a third or sighting staff along the hypotenuse of the right triangle. A unique variation of the simplest combination is described by Leonardo of Pisa.[70] Using a staff of the same height as himself, the observer lies on his back on the ground and holds the rod vertically between his feet. He must choose his position so that the line of sight, from his eye to the top of the rod, meets the top of the object whose height is required. Such a rough-and-ready method was probably quite ancient; still we find it repeated in a fifteenth-century English manuscript.[71] From this combination of vertical and horizontal staffs emerged the *shadow square,* which became the most important part, so far as surveying is concerned, of the three predominant instruments of this period; namely, the astrolabe, the geometric square, and the quadrant.

[67] Wiedemann, *Beitr.* 18, *Sitz. Ber.* 41, 1909.

[68] Gerbert calls it the "skorpion," *op. cit.,* Ch. 29. The *Liber Embadorum* gives thirteen problems involving the use of this combination.

[69] Hugo Physicus, *op. cit.,* pp. 206-207.

[70] Leonardo Pisano, *op. cit.,* p. 203.

[71] Halliwell, *op. cit.,* p. 27, quotes the following from a manuscript in the British Museum: "Here foloweth a rule howe a mann stondying in a playne by a steple or such another thynge of height by lokyng uponn it it shall knowe the certentie of the height thereof. First, let a mann consider by his estimacion howe farre he stondeth from it be it XX, XXX, or XL fadam. And thereaboute as he demeth the certentie let hym stonde and there pitche a staffe the upper poynte thereof to be juste with his yie, he stondying upp righte thereby. And thann let hym leye hym down alonge upp righte beyonde the staffe from the steple warde his feet juste to the staffe, and whann the staffe so stondeth he lying as is aforesaid, as his yie on the hyghest poynte of the staffe is juste with the height of the hyghest poynte of the steple. Than the juste space from his yie as he lyith to the foote of the steple, that is to saye to that parte of the foot which is as litill as the top thereof is the juste measure of the height of the said steple. And if the staffe stonde not juste let hymnn remeve it till his yie he lying as is aforesaid with the heighest poynte of the staffe accorde with the highest poynte of the steple."

The Astrolabe and Its Derivatives

ASTROLABE Of all the measuring instruments which have come
down to us from antiquity, none was better known than, or remained in common use as long as, the astrolabe. Even today it
may still be found in use.[72] The derivation of the name from
'άστρον (a star) and λαβεῖν (to take) implies that it was originally
an astronomical instrument for finding the altitude of the stars.
The two most important types of astrolabes are the *armillary,*
which consisted essentially of three rings arranged at right angles
to each other, and the *planisphere,* which carried a stereographic
projection of the heavens on a circular plane surface. The history
of the armillary astrolabe, which was used chiefly for astronomical
purposes, does not concern us here. However, in passing, it may
be remarked that it was probably developed by Hipparchus (*c.* 140
B.C.) and further improved by Ptolemy (*c.* A.D. 150), who gives a
description of such an instrument in the *Almagest.*[73] The planisphere astrolabe carried a circle divided into 360°. Its early history,
therefore, probably dates back to Babylonian times; in fact, fragments of baked clay planispheres have been discovered in Babylonia.[74] Whether the Babylonians used it for any purposes other
than astronomical we do not know. It seems quite probable that
the Greeks derived their knowledge of the simpler forms of the
astrolabe and the fundamentals of astronomy from Mesopotamia.
As in many other fields, they soon developed this science beyond
the knowledge of their preceptors and with it advanced the intricacies of the astrolabe.

The earliest account that we have of an instrument which resembles the astrolabe is from Vitruvius[75] in his description of the
automatic timepiece, *horologium anaphoricum,* which is different
from the usual astrolabe only in that the disk corresponding to
the *rete*[76] was turned by water to simulate the daily rotation of

[72] New York *World Telegram,* April 23, 1940.
[73] Claudius Ptolemy, *Almagest,* Translated from the French by M. Halma (Paris,
1813), Bk. V, Ch. 1.
[74] E. Weidner, *Handbuch der babylonischen Astronomie* (Leipzig, 1915), Vol. 1,
pp. 62, 107.
[75] M. Vitruvius Pollio, *De Architectura Libri Decem,* Translated by M. H. Morgan
(Cambridge, Mass., 1914), Bk. 9, Ch. 8.
[76] Name of one of the parts of the astrolabe; see p. 67.

the earth. This shows that one of the most important early uses of the astrolabe was as a timepiece. In the same account, naming the inventors of various timepieces, Vitruvius speaks of the *arachne*, "which some say was invented by Eudoxus and which others attribute to Apollonius of Perga." [77] Some modern writers are inclined to question this statement of Vitruvius;[78] at the same time we know definitely that Ptolemy gave the theory of the lines of the planisphere astrolabe,[79] but he gives no indications as to the practical uses of the instrument. We have already mentioned (p. 52) the two important links which connect the Greek work on the astrolabe with that of the Muslims, by whom it was finally perfected both as an astronomical and as a surveying instrument.

Before continuing with the historical aspect of this subject it is well to have in mind a clear picture of the various parts of the astrolabe and their uses. The astrolabe was a portable instrument which, as we know from existing specimens,[80] ranged in size from two inches to two feet in diameter. The number of scales and plates of an astrolabe varied with the standard of the instrument, but the following parts, which were usually made of brass, were common to almost all of them (Figures 24, 25):

1. The astrolabe when in use was suspended from the thumb by means of a ring attached to a projection in the body of the instrument, so that it assumed a vertical position by reason of its weight. The ring was known in Arabic as *al-'ilāqa,* in Latin as *armilla suspensoria.*

2. The projecting piece to which the suspension ring was attached was called by the Arabs *al-kursijj* (the throne). In late Persian and Italian models this section was highly decorated.

3. The main part of the astrolabe was a thick circular plate with a flat raised border about half an inch wide on which were engraved the 360 divisions of a circle. Since the space enclosed

---

[77] "Arachnen Eudoxus astrologus dicitur invenisse, nonnulli dicunt Apollonium."

[78] Drecker, *op. cit.*

[79] J. Drecker, "Das Planisphärium des Claudius Ptolemaeus," *Isis,* Vol. 9, 1927, pp. 255-278.

[80] The largest collection of astrolabes is that of Lewis Evans, now housed in the Ashmolean Museum of Oxford University. For description of some of these, see Evans, *op. cit.* The Adler Planetarium and Astronomical Museum, Chicago, contains a collection of thirty-three astrolabes. Some of these are illustrated and briefly described in the Museum guidebook.

Figure 24. THE ASTROLABE—VIEW OF FRONT. *Reproduced from Sanford's* A Short History of Mathematics, *by permission of the author.*

by the rim was sunk and served as a recipient for the plates, this
part was called by the Arabs *al-um* (the mother).

4. Within the "mother" fitted the flat disks or tables, Arabic
safīha, each engraved with a stereographic projection[81] of the
sphere for use in a special latitude. As a rule the astrolabe contained from one to eleven such tables, although some astrolabes
are known to have had no recess but to have carried on the front
figures corresponding to the latitude of a particular locality. These

---

[81] On the various types of projections used, consult works on the astrolabe mentioned in this and the next chapter; and A. von Braunmühl, *Vorlesungen über
Geschichte der Trigonometrie* (Leipzig, 1900), Vol. 1, pp. 79 ff.

Figure 25. THE ASTROLABE—VIEW OF BACK. *Reproduced from San-ford's* A Short History of Mathematics, *by permission of the author.*

tables were prevented from revolving by a small projection on the edge of each fitting into a hole in the side of the rim, or by a notch engaging with a stop in the same position.

5. Over the uppermost table lay the revolvable perforated plate, known to the Greeks as the arachne (ʼαράΧνη) and to the Arabs as *al-ankabūt,* on account of its supposed resemblance to the spider,[82] but usually known in later times as the *rete* or net. Next to the mother plate, it is the most important part of the astrolabe for

[82] So stated Severus Sebokt. Later the likeness to the web of a spider was suggested, giving rise to the Latin name *aranea* and the Arabic *shabaka;* the prevalent Latin term *rete* is probably derived from this similitude. Chaucer describes the skeleton table as "shapen in the manner of a net or of a lap [spider] web."

astronomical work, and the makers spent a considerable amount of time perfecting it. The principal feature of the rete was an interior eccentric circle, the *ecliptic,* on which were engraved the names of the signs of the zodiac; to this was joined by a connected open work the external circle equal in diameter to that of the tables. Tongues or pointers, projecting in various places, indicated the position of fixed stars. The design used in placing these tongues often gives a good clue as to the country and period in which the astrolabe was made. The number of fixed stars varied in different instruments; it might have been as low as four or as high as sixty.[83]

6. Upon the surface of the rete moved the indicator (Arabic *al-muri,* Latin *ostensor*), the point of which could be turned to any part of the circumference; its length was either a full diameter or a radius.

7. The back of the "mother" was flat and usually contained a number of concentric circles (Figure 25). The outermost ring represented the horizon and was divided into four quadrants, the upper two of which were subdivided into 90°, reading from the horizontal to the vertical diameter. The other rings usually represented the signs of the zodiac, the days of the year, and the months of the year. In the lower half between the innermost circle and the horizontal diameter was inscribed the shadow square, which was the most important part of the astrolabe so far as surveying is concerned. To al-Battānī (850-929) goes the credit of introducing the shadow square on the astrolabe. The shadow square was constructed as follows: from the center of the quarter circle perpendiculars were drawn to both diameters (Figure 26); these perpendiculars were then divided usually into seven or twelve equal parts. Some astrolabes carry the shadow square in only one quarter, but in the greater number of instruments the "square" occupies the lower semicircle. The horizontal side was known to the Muslims as *al-zill al-basīt* (extended), also as *al-mustawī* (level); it was known in Latin as the *umbra recta* and *umbra extensa.* The vertical side was called *al-mankūs* (inverted) and *al-muntasib* (vertical); in Latin, *umbra versa* and *conversa.* In early English works they are referred to as the *long* and *short*

---

[83] Evans, *op. cit.,* p. 221.

shadows.[84] The upper semicircle, especially in Oriental instruments, usually carried a scale of astronomical hours and a sinical quadrant. The lower half of the outermost ring usually carried the shadow-arc scale, constructed as follows: the horizontal side of the

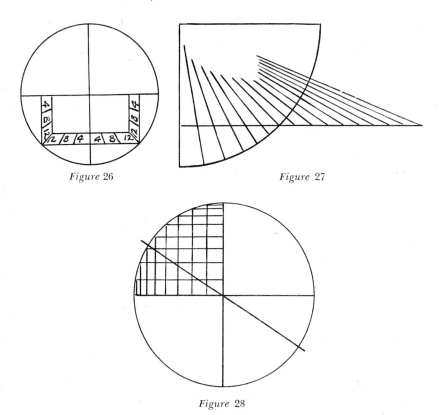

Figure 26   Figure 27

Figure 28

shadow square was produced indefinitely and marked off in the same units (Figure 27); these divisions were then projected onto the ring by radial lines. This shadow arc could be substituted for the "square," its advantage being that it gave direct readings of the length of the horizontal shadows of angles less than 45°, which could be found by the "square" only after a computation. It could

[84] This section of the instrument was known to the Muslims as *zill al-sullan*, the shadow of the rod, which points to its derivation from the staff combinations. The umbra recta corresponds to the shadow cast on the ground by a vertical staff; while the umbra versa corresponds to the shadow cast on a wall by a horizontal staff held perpendicular to the side of the wall.

also be used to find approximately the cotangents of angles. In like manner an arc of tangents could be constructed from the vertical shadow. Both are to be found side by side on a few instruments. Since the divisions on the shadow arc approach closer to each other in one direction, the angle through which it can be used is limited by the accuracy of the mode of division and the power to read these divisions. In general the angle did not go beyond 14°. The sine quadrant in the upper half was also used in surveying. It was constructed as follows (Figure 28): lines parallel to either the horizontal or vertical diameters were drawn through every fifth degree division; the distances which these lines cut off on the diameter to the center were equal to either the sine or the cosine of the angle in terms of the radius. To read these distances either the radial lines or half the altitude was usually divided into sixty parts.[85] On the back of the "mother" revolved the sighting rule or alidade (Arabic *al-ʾidāda*, Latin *mediclinium, regula*), an index arm equal in length to the diameter of the instrument, which had a vertical pierced projection near each end for taking sights.

8. The indicator, the rete, the tables, the "mother," and the alidade were all held together by a pin (Arabic *kuth,* Latin *clavus*) passing through holes in their centers.

9. Finally, through a slot near the top of the pin went a wedge, known to the Arabs as *al-faras* because it was fashioned in the likeness of a horse's head, which bound all parts together.

The Muslims came into contact with Greek knowledge of the astrolabe primarily through the Syrians. Harran in Syria seems to have been the most important center for the dissemination of this knowledge in the seventh century. By the middle of the eighth century the Muslims not only had assimilated the traditional knowledge of the Greeks but had also added to it both theoretically and practically. The first Muslim maker of astrolabes to be mentioned in history is al-Fazārī, who worked under the patronage of al-Masūr and died about 777. By the end of the eighth century a number of scholars were producing manuscripts on the astrolabe, the more famous of whom were Māschāllāh, whose work

---

[85] Wiedemann, *Beitr.* 61, *Sitz. Ber.* 52, 1920, pp. 117–118; *Beitr.* 18, *Sitz. Ber.* 41, 1909, pp. 36, 52, 58.

was. later to be the first on the subject presented to the English-speaking world, through the translation of Chaucer;[86] and al-Far-gānī, who wrote an important work on the theory of the lines of the instrument.[87] Among the early makers of the instrument were al-Merwārrudī and his famous pupil, 'Alī ibn-'Īsā, who was given the nickname of al-Astrolābī.[88] During this period al-Chwā-rizmī published a compendium of numerous problems which could be worked with the astrolabe.[89] During the next hundred and fifty years improvements continued to appear until the golden age of Muslim science was reached. Probably the most prominent figure of this period was the Persian al-Bīrūnī (973-1048), a physi-cian, astronomer, mathematician, physicist, geographer, and his-torian, who has left in his *Kitāb fi'l-istī 'āb* a complete account of the astrolabe as used at that time.[90] Another important contribu-tor to the development of the astrolabe was al-Zarqālī (1029-1087), who is responsible for a simplified method of projection for the tables. These Safīha tables of al-Zarqālī could be used over a much larger territory than the former projections.[91]

It has been estimated by Evans that there are about three hun-dred astrolabes in the different museums of Europe, the earliest dated being *c.* 950, the work of Ahmed-ibn-Khalaf. With this evidence it is not difficult to establish the variations that took place in the instrument from about the year 1000. It is our pur-pose here to confine the work to such changes on the back of the instrument as affected surveying. Because of its use in estimations of heights and depths, the angle divisions always began at the horizontal diameter and went through each quadrant to 90°. Some instruments had a set of figures starting from the vertical diame-ter; this was useful for reading directly the zenith angle of stars and reading complementary angles in connection with the sine

[86] Geoffrey Chaucer, *Tractatus de Conclusionibus Astrolabii, 1391,* Edited by W. W. Skeat (London, 1872).
[87] Wiedemann, *Beitr.* 61, *Sitz. Ber.* 52, 1920, pp. 106-109.
[88] Suter, "Die Mathematiker und Astronomen der Araber und ihre Werke," Nr. 23, p. 13; and Drecker, "Das Planispharium des Claudius Ptolemaeus."
[89] J. Frank, "Die Verwendung des Astrolabs nach al-Chwārizmī," *Abhandlung zur Geschichte der Naturwissenschaften und der Medizin,* Heft 3, 1922, pp. 1-4.
[90] Wiedemann, *Beitr.* 18, *Sitz. Ber.* 41, 1909, p. 30.
[91] L. A. Sédillot, "Mémoire sur les instruments astronomiques des Arabs," *Mémoires présentés par divers savants à l'académie royale des inscrites et belles lettres,* Series 1, Vol. 1, 1844, pp. 36-37, 182-190.

lines.[92] In the simpler, earlier forms only the upper left quadrant
—"the height quadrant"—was divided. In general Muslim astrolabes were small, so that divisions of less than a degree were
not frequent. They were usually not more than 20 cm. in diameter; there is even a record of one only 7.5 cm. in diameter
made in 1218.[93] In the division of the angle arc, every fifth or
tenth was usually denoted by a longer line. The accuracy of the
divisions naturally depended on the material used. The best astrolabes were made of bronze; some were made of wood. The
angle divisions were usually marked on a richer material which
was inlaid—silver with bronze instruments, ivory with wooden
ones.[94] Al-Bīrūnī relates measuring an angle of 34′ with the ordinary astrolabe, but this seems to be an exaggerated accuracy.[95]

The efficiency of the shadow square on the Muslim astrolabes
was greatly restricted because of the smallness of the space which
it occupied. For this reason it could not be used for accurate
surveying measurements and seems to have been inserted primarily for the determination of the various times of prayer. For
this purpose it was much handier than the Graeco-Roman method
of the gnomon. On an astrolabe of 15 cm. diameter, the usual
length of the side of the shadow square would be about 2 cm.,
which meant that each of the twelve divisions measured about 1.5
mm. In general only every second or third of these divisions was
marked. Special markings were used on some Muslim instruments
to indicate the times of prayer.[96] The shadow arc (p. 69), which
is a later form of shadow measurement derived from the shadow

[92] Al-Bīrūnī describes two such instruments. See Wiedemann, *Beitr.* 18, *Sitz. Ber.* 41, 1909, p. 30.
[93] Sédillot, "Mémoire sur les instruments astronomiques des Arabs," p. 175.
[94] For the method used by al-Bīrūnī in the division of the circle into degrees, see E. Wiedemann and J. Frank, "Vorrichtungen zur Teilung von Kreisen und Geraden nach al-Bīrūnī," *Zeitschrift für Instruments-Kunde,* Vol. 41, 1921, pp. 225-229.
[95] E. Wiedemann, *Archiv für Geschichte der Naturwissenschaften und der Technik,* Vol. 1, 1909, p. 66.
[96] In al-Bīrūnī we read: "Shadow of the 'Asr prayer. This, in the opinion of the Imāms, is the length of shadow which determines the time of the end of the early afternoon prayer Zuhr and the beginning of the late afternoon prayer 'Asr. If the length of the meridian shadow is known, called fi'l-zawāl, then the shadow is observed until it is twice as long; this is the beginning of the 'Asr, according to the Imāms of the Hijāz, and is called Ziyādah al-mithl and is marked on the instruments awwal al-'asr." *The Book of Instruction in the Elements of the Art of Astrology,* Translated by R. R. Wright (London, 1934), p. 137. By permission of Luzac and Co. See also E. Wiedemann and J. Frank, "Die Gebetzeiten im Islam," *Sitz. Ber.* 58, 1926, pp. 1–32.

square, is described in detail in the works of al-Bīrūnī.[97] Another form of shadow scale used by the Muslims is described by Dorn.[98] It was constructed on the line joining the end points of the quadrant (Figure 29) by projecting the divisions on the shadow square

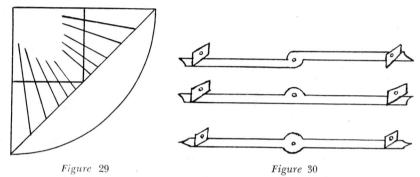

Figure 29   Figure 30

from the center of the instrument. Its advantage lay in the fact that the divisions were larger than on the square itself. Sine lines appeared early on Muslim astrolabes, but the originator of them is unknown. The Muslims must have early acquired a knowledge of the sine function from the Hindus, to whom it was known from the time of Aryabhatta (475-550).[99]

Three important types of Muslim alidades are shown in Figure 30. In the first two, the diameter coincides with an edge; this made possible readings on scales other than those on the rim, and for that reason they were the most common; they also usually carried two scales themselves, one on each half, for use with the sine lines. One scale, *al-nisf al-mugajjab,* was composed of sixty equal divisions; the other, *al-nisf al-muqawwas,* was a sine scale.[100] The other form of alidade, which was useful only for read-

[97] Wiedemann, *Beitr.* 18, *Sitz. Ber.* 41, 1909, pp. 30, 39, 40.

[98] B. Dorn, "Drei astronomische Instrumente," *Mémoires de l'académie impérial des sciences de St. Petersbourg,* 1865.

[99] Kaye, *Indian Mathematics,* p. 11.

[100] Wiedemann, *Beitr.* 18, *Sitz. Ber.* 41, 1909, pp. 36, 52-53. The following is translated from Wiedemann's quotation from al-Bīrūnī, p. 52: "The sine lines on the back of the astrolabe are drawn either parallel to the vertical or horizontal or they are both drawn at the same time. The alidade must be divided in equal parts, either into 60 parts or into 110 [?] or into 150. This [art of division] is practical but not necessary. The division into 60 parts is most commonly used. This half is called al Nisf al-mugajjab, the other half is divided into 90 parts and is called al Nisf al-muqawwas. If the sine lines are drawn parallel to the horizon or if they are marked both ways, and if the sine of an angle is required, then one goes from the end of the arc along

ings on the rim, was used on simplified instruments. The usual forms of sights employed by the Muslims consisted of small plates erected perpendicularly to the alidade near its ends. These plates were pierced usually by two sets of sight holes, a small pair for sighting the sun and a large pair for sighting stars or objects on the earth. The line of sight had to correspond with the line of the indicators on the alidade; for this reason in the first two types shown the sight plates projected over one edge of the alidade. Occasionally the sights were set in a tube, as by al-Battānī [101] and al-Bīrūnī,[102] but in general the use of such tubes was reserved for instruments in which the sights were further apart. Very seldom were point sights used.[103]

For the most part the Muslims reintroduced the astrolabe to Europe; there is, of course, also the probability that whatever knowledge the Greeks, at an earlier period, had of the instrument did not altogether die out in the intervening centuries and that such knowledge was preserved intact, if not added to, by the peoples of the Byzantine Empire.[104] The earliest description of the use of the astrolabe in Europe for surveying purposes is that of Gerbert. In his treatise he describes numerous problems worked out by means of the shadow square on the astrolabe.[105] He has left no detailed description of the instrument itself, but we may assume from the solutions of problems that Gerbert's astrolabe was a simplified form, adapted especially for surveying purposes. There is little doubt that his sources of information on the instrument were Muslim rather than Byzantine.[106] The next works

---

the horizontal line as far as the vertical and makes a mark on the latter at the point of intersection. Then one turns the alidade and observes which mark on the Nisf al-mugajjab coincides with the mark. That is then the sine. If the sine lines are vertical, then the angle e is subtracted from 90°. For the vertical line corresponding to the angle [90° — e] the point of intersection with the horizontal is found, and a mark is made, the Nisf al-mugajjab is turned until it falls on the horizontal. . . ." By permission of Erlangen University.

[101] Nallino, *op. cit.*, Vol. I, pp. 91, 272.

[102] Wiedemann, *Beitr.* 18, *Sitz. Ber.* 41, 1909, p. 38.

[103] J. A. Repsold, *Zur Geschichte der astronomischen Messwerkzeuge von Purbach bis Reichenbach, 1450-1830* (Leipzig, 1908), Vol. 1, p. 7.

[104] See p. 52.

[105] Gerbert, *op. cit.*, Chs. 16-22.

[106] Würschmidt, *op. cit.* An astrolabe made for the latitude of Rome, preserved in Florence, is thought to have belonged to Gerbert. See E. Saavedra, "Note sur un astrolabe arabe." *Atti del IV congresso internazionale degli orientalizi* (Florence, 1880).

THEIR HISTORY # THEIR HISTORY 75

on the instrument were those of Hermann Contractus.[107] One
hundred years later, Hugo Physicus wrote his *Practica Geometriae*. Both these writers seem to depend on the work of Gerbert.
Nothing new is added except the three-quadrant shadow square
of Physicus.[108] Astrolabes modeled after those of Māschāllāh and
al-Zarqālī seem to have had greatest vogue throughout the Middle
Ages. Māschāllāh's treatise was translated into Latin as early as
1140 by Johannes Hispalensis; another Latin translation was made
in the thirteenth century by Gerard of Cremona. These served
as the bases for works on the astrolabe in many lands,[109] such as
Rabbi ben Ezra's in Spain, Chaucer's in England, and an Irish
tract of unknown authorship.[110] William Anglicus introduced the
universal projection method of al-Zarqālī to the Latin-reading
world in 1231.[111] There is also a Spanish translation from the
Court of Alfonso X of the thirteenth century.[112]

GEOMETRIC SQUARE   To compensate for the limitations of the
shadow square on the astrolabe, because of the small space allowed for it, the geometric square was developed. Although our
earliest account of it comes from Gerbert, there is every reason to
believe that it was first developed by the Muslims.[113] The geometric square is really the shadow square as an independent instrument; its uses in surveying correspond to those of the shadow
square on the astrolabe; namely, the determination of what we
now denote as the tangent and cotangent of angles in terms of the
umbra recta and the umbra versa. The geometric square was usually made in the form of a hollow square of wood or metal (Figure
31). This gave more permanency to the right angle than did the
simple combination of two staffs. In order to provide sufficient

[107] Hermann Contractus (1013-1054), *De Mensura Astrolabii Liber* and *De Utilitatibus Astrolabii Libri II*. See Chapter III, note 15.
[108] *Op. cit.*, p. 201, Fig. 11.
[109] Suter, "Die Mathematiker und Astronomen der Araber und ihre Werke," p. 8.
[110] See note 7.
[111] P. Tannery, *Traité de l'astrolabe universel ou Saphea d'Arzachel par Guillaume
l'Anglais (Guillielmus Anglicus, 1231)* (Paris, 1897). See also Sédillot, "Mémoire sur
les instruments astronomiques des Arabs," p. 185.
[112] *Libros de Saber de Astronomia del Rey Don Alfonso X de Castillia*, Edited by
D. Man. Ricoy Sinohas (Madrid, 1863-1867), Vol. 3, pp. 135 ff.
[113] Würschmidt, *op. cit.* The first Muslim description of the instrument is that of
al-Bīrūnī in his *Kitāb fi'l-istī'āb*.

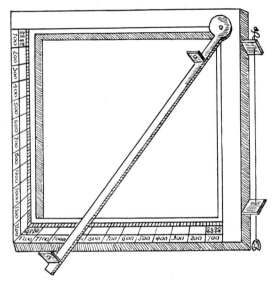

Figure 31. THE GEOMETRIC SQUARE

room for divisions, the frame was usually from two to three feet on the side and divided into twelve equal parts.

There were two types of square in use; namely, the alidade and the plumb bob. On the alidade type, two sights, usually consisting of small pierced plates, were set at right angles to the sighting rod. On the plumb-bob type the sights were carried on one side of the square. The alidade type was by far the more commonly used. So that it could be set up vertically, it carried a plumb bob on one edge. Besides its use for measuring heights and distances, the geometric square could also be used as a level; however, there are no accounts of such usage until after the Middle Ages. The square was generally employed as a hand instrument, but sometimes, in the case of extra large ones or of heavy metal models, a staff was used for support.

Gerbert's instrument was made of wood; there is no mention of divisions, but they may be inferred from his description of the operation.[114] There is very little to be found on the use of this

[114] Gerbert, *op. cit.*, Ch. 33. "Ad metiendum planum quolibet modo propositum. Si fuerit nobis propositum, quodlibet modo metiri planum, sumamus unius cubiti in longitudine lignum, cui tria alia in dimensione aequalia tali conjunctione innectantur, ut conjuncta quadrati diffinitonem suscipere videantur, quod quatuor angulis est orthogonale. Cuius unius lateris summitatibus duo semipedalia ligna erecta in-

instrument[115] until we come to the writings of Georg Purbach (1423-1461). Purbach is chiefly responsible for making an angle-measuring instrument out of it; this he used in connection with his astronomical work. Purbach subdivided each of the usual twelve main divisions of the side of the square into one hundred parts. For this purpose the sides must have been at least one meter long; the method of division is not described. For measuring angles Purbach made out a table of sines, by means of which he could read the angles directly from the divisions on the instrument.[116]

QUADRANT   The quadrant, as the name implies, usually carried a quarter-circle arc. It was used originally for measuring angles in vertical planes. The older forms of this instrument in the Middle Ages were usually quarter-circular or square in shape, with an indicator revolving from the center of the circular arc. Although the history of the quadrant primarily belongs to this period and the next, its origin goes back to the Greeks. The oldest quadrant of which we have any account is that of Ptolemy, described in the *Almagest*.[117] It consisted of a large square surface of wood or stone on which was marked a quarter circle divided into degrees (Figure 32). At the center of the

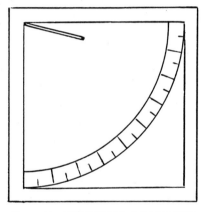

Figure 32. PTOLEMY'S QUADRANT

arc, perpendicular to the plate, there was erected a rod, whose shadow was used as an indicator. Ptolemy used this instrument to determine the height of the sun, from which he worked out the

figantur, quae in summitatibus perforara per utrumque foramen visum metientis admittere videantur. Post haec extremitati oppositi lateris mediclinium horoscopo, sic copuletur, ut, dum per oppositum sibi latus certis dimensionibus distinctum trahitur, formam orthogonii Pythagorici imitetur, vel imitari videatur."

[115] It is mentioned by Hugo Physicus, *op. cit.*; and Dominicus Parisiensis, *op. cit.* It is essentially similar to Gerbert's instrument.

[116] G. Purbach, *Quadratum Geometricum* (Nürnberg, 1516–1517), fol. A, III-V.

[117] Claudius Ptolemy, *Handbuch der Astronomie*, Edited by C. Manitius (Leipzig, 1912), p. 43.

obliquity of the ecliptic. From such a beginning the astronomical
quadrant went through many evolutions, especially in the hands
of the Muslims al-Bīrūnī and al-'Urdī and in course of time became the most important astronomical instrument of the European astronomers of the early Renaissance period.

From the large and stationary type of quadrant[118] the Muslims
early developed types which were portable and more suitable for
use in surveying. Of these there were two main classes: first, those
which used a sighting line or alidade, one edge of the instrument
being kept in a horizontal position; second, those which used a
plumb line as indicator, sighting being done along one edge of the
plate. In course of time both these classes carried not only the
fundamental angle scale, but also many others, such as the shadow
square, the shadow arc, sine lines, and other graphical aids, to
simplify computations.

The earliest indication of the use of the quadrant among the
Muslims is to be found as a short note appended to a description
of the astrolabe by al-Chwārizmī (c. 840) in his *Key to Knowledge*.[119] He writes: "The quadrant (al-rub') is another instrument like the astrolabe; it has the shape of a quarter circle; with
it, height can be determined and time ascertained." The fact that
it was used as a timepiece with inscribed hour lines goes to show
that it must have been in common use for some time; there is
nothing in Muslim writings to indicate definitely when it came
into use or who were the inventors of the various scales and
graphic tables in use up to the thirteenth century.[120] In fact,
Muslim references to the quadrant are very rare until the thirteenth century; the only two important writings on the subject
are those of ibn-Jūnus and al-Zarqālī; the reason for this seems
to be that the quadrant was overshadowed by the astrolabe. In
this century we have a complete description of a Muslim quadrant
by al-Marrāquschī.[121] On one side of this quadrant were to be
found the fundamental arc for measuring heights, the shadow
square, the shadow arc, three arcs for finding inclinations, and the

[118] For a description of such Muslim quadrants, see P. Schmalzl, *Zur Geschichte
des Quadranten bei den Araben* (Munich, 1929), pp. 18 ff.
[119] Wiedemann, *Beitr.* 18, *Sitz. Ber.* 41, 1909, p. 33.
[120] See Schmalzl, *op. cit.*, for various surmises.
[121] Sédillot, "Mémoire sur les instruments astronomiques des Arabs," pp. 2-10, 64-81.

hour circle; the other side carried the sine lines. We also have a description of a practically similar quadrant used by Alfonso X of Castile (*c.* 1254).[122]

The oldest European description of the quadrant is that of Leonardo of Pisa (*c.* 1220).[123] Here we have the simplest type of quadrant with only the graduated arc and shadow square (Figure 33). That its primary purpose was surveying, we may conclude from the exercises described by Leonardo. A much more complicated form of quadrant, with practically all the parts of the better Muslim instruments, is described in a tract written a short time later by Robert Anglicus (1231).[124] He gives numerous applications to surveying. This work became a standard for subsequent European writers on the quadrant. Another English tract from this period is that of Sacrobosco (1200-1256).[125] Among the

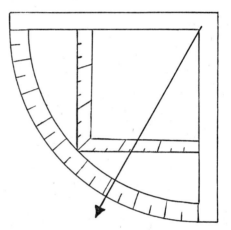

Figure 33. LEONARDO OF PISA'S QUADRANT

various uses to which he applies the quadrant is that of a timepiece.[126]

From the end of the thirteenth century there seemed to be a tendency among the Muslims to substitute the quadrant for the astrolabe in astronomical work. One reason for this was that the

[122] *Op. cit.,* Chs. 1-5.

[123] Leonardo Pisano, *op. cit.,* Vol. 2, p. 202.

[124] Tannery, "Le traité du quadrant du maître Robert Anglais," p. 34. "Est igitur quadrans quoddam instrumentum quartam partam circuli et quasdam linearum protractiones continens, per quod possumus gradum solis et eius declinationem et stellarum altitudines accipere, horas temporis discernere, rerum altitudines civitatum distancias, terrarum longitudinem, puteorum profunditatem invenire."

[125] Johannes de Sacrobosco, *De Compositione Quadrantis Simplicis et Compositi et Utilitatibus Utriusque.* For descriptions of the quadrants of Sacrobosco and other like quadrants, see R. T. Gunther, *Early Science in Oxford* (Oxford, 1923), Vol. 2, pp. 156 ff.

[126] E. von Bassermann-Jordan, *Alte Uhren und ihre Meister* (Leipzig, 1926). On pp. 18-19 is related a case of the use of a quadrant as a check on an early form of clock in the fifteenth century.

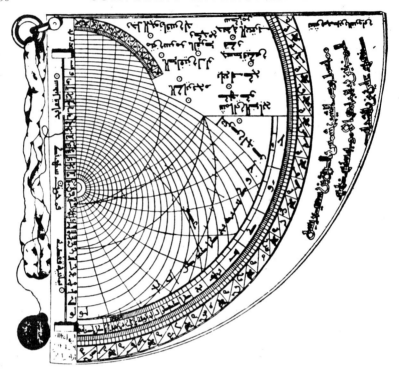

Figure 34. THE MUQANTARĀ QUADRANT. *Reproduced from Morley's*
Description of an Arabic Quadrant.

necessity for making larger instruments as an aid to more accurate
observations gave importance to the facts that for a given radius
the quadrant weighed only one-fourth as much as the astrolabe
and gave four times the space for equal weights. The result of
this tendency was the development of the *Muqantarā quadrant*
among the Eastern Muslims, first described by al-Mizzī (*c.* 1330) .[127]
Many other writings on this type of quadrant followed, of which
the more important were those of ibn-al-Schātīr (*c.* 1360), Gamāl
al-Dīn al-Māridīnī (*c.* 1390), al-Chairī (*c.* 1400) , ibn-al-Megdī
(*c.* 1430), 'Jzz al-Dīn al-Wefā'i (*c.* 1450) .[128] In the Muqantarā
quadrant (Figure 34) we find the same systems of lines for astronomical purposes as were carried on the astrolabe.

[127] Two quadrants made by al-Mizzī in Damascus are described by Dorn, *op. cit.,*
pp. 17-18. See also Morley, *Description of an Arabic Quadrant.*
    [128] For summaries of these, see the following in Suter, "Die Mathematiker und As-
tronomen der Araber und ihre Werke": Nr. 416, Nr. 421, Nr. 426, Nr. 432, Nr. 437.

The use of the plumb line as an indicator limited measurements with this type of quadrant to the vertical plane. The verticality of the plane of the quadrant was determined by the plumb
line, which usually hung from a small peg. Figure 35 shows the
relation between the angle of elevation and the angle between the
plumb line and the edge of the quadrant. The angle divisions
were numbered from the non-sighting edge. For astronomical
work many were also numbered in the other direction, so as to
give direct readings of zenith angles and also for complementary
angles in connection with calculations with the sine lines. The
position of the shadow square and its use in determining the
"shadow" of an angle may be seen in Figure 35. Sine lines were
used to a much greater extent on the quadrant than on the astrolabe to simplify the solution of various problems in similar
triangles through the line functions of angles.[129] The method of
employing them is similar to that for the astrolabe (p. 70), except
that the plumb line instead of the alidade was used in reading off
distances. Since the plumb line could not be marked off like
the alidade, the measurement on it, in any given case, had to be
determined by placing it along the scale on the edge of the quad-

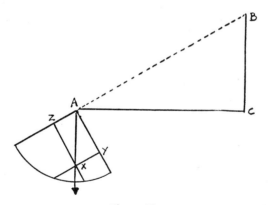

Figure 35

rant. There was usually a series of knots on the plumb line in
order to facilitate the reading of such lengths. Both edges were
usually divided into sixty equal parts from which the sine lines

[129] Wiedemann, *Beitr.* 18, p. 58; and Schmalzl, *op. cit.,* pp. 80-83.

Figure 36. PRINCIPLE OF JACOB'S STAFF. *Drawn by H. Dierkin.*

were drawn. Less frequently the lines were drawn from the degree points on the arc, in which case the edges carried ninety unequal divisions. The operation of determining the function of a given angle was as follows: the sine of an angle e or the sine of its complement $(90 - e)$ was found by going from the intersection of two lines under the line of the angle to the scale on the edges (Figure 35).

The method of using the sine lines in determining height was as follows: in Figure 35 let BC be the required height; AC the known distance to its foot; a length AY is selected so that it is a multiple of AC, then the length AZ cut off on the other edge by the sine line passing through the intersection of YX and AX is the same multiple of the required height; if the number of units of measure in AC is greater than sixty, then a half or other fraction of this is laid off along AY. From this it may be seen that the sine lines not only were a substitute for the shadow square but also simplified the computation.

Although the quadrant allowed the use of a large radius, the usual gradations were degrees. Finer gradations would have been superfluous, since the instrument was held by hand; only in a later period do we find it set up on a staff. The thickness, the

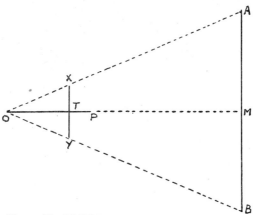

Figure 37. SIMPLE FORM OF JACOB'S STAFF

knots and the liability to stretching of the plumb line also mili-
tated against fine measurements. Unless a second observer was
present to read the intersection of the plumb line and the sine
lines, the method of determining such a point by pressing the
plumb line against the plate gave opportunity for much inac-
curacy.[130]

Jacob's Staff

The fundamental operation of the Jacob's staff is that of measuring the angle of sight of a given object. This is done by placing at
a determinable distance from the eye a suitable object such as a
short rod, so that its ends coincide with the lines of sight from
the ends of the object to be measured. The natural means of
carrying out such an operation are the outstretched arm and the
fingers of the hand held close together and at right angles to the
arm (Figure 36). At some period of man's history some unknown
individual must have noticed the relationship between the size of
the angle of sight and the number of fingers held together. If instead of varying the length determined by the closed fingers, we
change the length of the arm, the size of the angle also varies, and
this is the method used in the simplest form of Jacob's staff. In
Figure 37 the angle of sight from the object *AB* is covered by the
rod *XY*, which has been moved along the rod *OP* to *T*, at which

[130] See von Bassermann-Jordan, *op. cit.*, p. 19.

point the required conditions hold. There are, then, two similar right triangles from which $1/2\ AB = AM = (MO/OT)XT$. This combination of rods makes the simplest form of Jacob's staff, and here we have another one of those simple instruments whose applicability depends on the properties of proportion in similar triangles.

As prototypes of the Jacob's staff we have historical accounts of instruments which depended on the same principle, used by

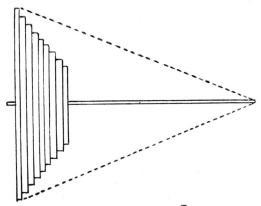

Figure 38. THE MOHĪT

Archimedes and Hipparchus in astronomical work. Indeed, these men are sometimes referred to as the inventors of the instrument.[131] An instrument much more closely related to the Jacob's staff was that used by the mariners, Muslims and Indians, on the Eastern seas. The oldest description we have of it comes from a manual on seafaring called the *Mohīt* prepared by Sidī al-Chelebri, captain of the Turkish fleet under Sultan Suleiman in 1554.[132] When and where this instrument was invented is unknown; from its method of operation we may conclude that it was a development of the use of the outstretched arm and fingers and is, therefore, in all probability quite ancient.

The instrument consisted of a long graduated rod and nine

[131] P. Ramus, *Arithmeticae libri duo, Geometricae septem et viginti* (Basel, 1559), p. 62.
[132] "Extracts from the Mohīt," Translated into English by J. von Hammer, *Journal of the Asiatic Society of Bengal*, Vol. 3, 1834, pp. 544 ff.; Vol. 7, 1838, pp. 767 ff.; and Vol. 8, 1839, pp. 823 ff.

square plates of different sizes. The plates were holed in the center so as to slide along the rod and had cords attached as a means of sliding the plates (Figure 38). The near end of the rod was held close to the eyes, and the plate was inserted at the other end. If the problem was to find the height of a star, the lower edge of the plate was kept tangent to the horizon and the plate was pulled by means of the cord until the star appeared over its upper edge. The various-sized plates had to be used because the angle of sight varied for different objects. The smallest plate was four fingers wide; the largest, twelve fingers wide. These at a distance of an arm's length (about 70 cm.) measured angles from 7° to 19°. They were used for rough calculations on a moving ship. Prinsep relates the use of the outstretched arm by an Arabic ship captain in 1836.[133] From early medieval Europe we also have accounts of the use of the hand in determining elevation. In the itinerary of Abtes Nicolaus of Puera about 1150 we read: "If a person lies down on one's back on a level field near the Jordan and raises his knee and sets his fist with thumb erect upon it, so may the Pole-star be seen, so high and no higher." [134] A similar method of determining the height of the sun is given by Priester Halldor in 1266. As an example of another primitive method of determining latitude by an observation on the polestar, mention may be made of the *calabash* used by the natives of the South Pacific islands in directing their course north to Hawaii.[135]

The earliest description of the Jacob's staff proper, as used in later times, is that of Levi ben Gerson.[136] The rod was about one

[133] J. Prinsep, "Note on the Nautical Instruments of the Arabs," *Journal of the Asiatic Society of Bengal,* Vol. 5, 1836, pp. 784 ff.

[134] J. Hoops, *Reallexikon der germanischen Altertumskunde,* Vol. 2, 1911, article "Geometrie" by A. A. Bjornbo, p. 154.

[135] H. Rodman, "The Sacred Calabash," *United States Naval Institute Proceedings,* Vol. 53, 1927, pp. 867-872. The calabash was made from a cylindrical gourd about three feet in length. Near the top were bored four holes about 90° apart on a circle whose plane was at right angles to the longitudinal axis. The calabash was filled with water up to the holes. The angle of elevation determined by sighting through a hole and over the top of the opposite rim was about 19°. When the polestar appeared on this line of sight the natives knew that they had reached the latitude of Hawaii.

[136] Levi ben Gerson (1288-1344), known as "Leo Israelita de Balneolis," was the outstanding Jewish mathematician of the fourteenth century. His work on the Jacob's staff was not discovered until the end of the last century; before that time the invention of the instrument was commonly attributed to Regiomontanus and its

yard long, one half of which was divided into twenty-four parts. There were several crosspieces of lengths varying from four to twenty-four divisions of the rod. The undivided half of the rod was held near the eye when in use (Figure 39). For astronomical

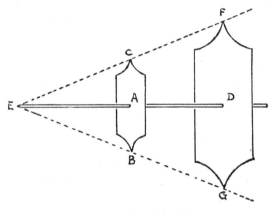

Figure 39. JACOB'S STAFF

work the rod was fastened to an upright and a plumb line hung from the crosspiece when the instrument had to be set up level. There is no mention of any form of sighting eyepiece at the end of the rod. The angle of elevation of a star was determined by calculating its sine.[137] In Figure 39, sin $FED = FD / \sqrt{ED^2 + DF^2}$. Gerson does not discuss the use of the instrument for survey-

development as a nautical instrument to Martin Behaim. (See S. Günther, "Die Erfindung des Baculus geometricus," *Bibliotheca Mathematica*, New Series 4, 1890, No. 3, pp. 73-80.) The two sources which trace the origin of the instrument to Levi ben Gerson are (a) a Muslim astronomical work written between 1328 and 1340 of which there is a Latin translation dating from 1342, *Leo de Balneolis Israhelita de . . . instrumente revelatione secretorum,* Vienna Mss. 5072; (b) Munich Library, Latin Codex, 8089, which is an abstract of the above translation dating from 1610, entitled *Geometricae Conclusiones, Propositiones, et Structura Baculi Jacob, ejusque Usus, ex libro manu scripto.* In Chapter 7, under the title, "De Structura Baculi, quo centrum visus indaget," we read: "Fiat baculus unus cum superficiebus planis, et rectis, in uno capite illius ponatur una tabula quae aequaliter sit cornuta cujus alterutrum cornu experientiae tempore sit in alterutrum oculum collectum, et fiant in hoc tabulae diversarum quantitatum perforatae in medio, superficies rectas habentes, per quae foramina intrare possit baculus ante dictus, et sit altitudo earum super baculum aliquantulum depressior altitudine oculi, et duae earum simul ponantur in baculo uno latere inaequalis, ita quod minor sit propinquior oculo, et ambae super baculum faciant angulos rectos, et sint parallelae. Et linae a centro oculi procedentes tangant utramque extremitatem utriusque tabulae, et terminentur ad Coelum."
[137] von Braunmühl, *op. cit.,* p. 104.

ing. The only other mention of the Jacob's staff within this period is a short treatise on the use of the "baculus geometricus alias baculus Jacob" by Theodorich Ruffi, a Franciscan of Gronenberg.[138] This contains some exercises on heights and distances.

Magnetic Compass

Of all the early surveying instruments, the *magnetic needle* has the most intriguing and elusive history in its initial stages of development. As the surveyor adapted to his own needs the astrolabe of the astronomer, so it seems most likely that he appropriated from the mariner the use of the magnetic needle as a direction-finder. The results of recent research[139] on the origin of the compass may be summarized as follows: first, knowledge of the attractive property of *loadstone* dates from a very early period and seems to have been widespread; secondly, the use of loadstone as a direction-finder seems to have been initiated during the early Middle Ages; thirdly, the theory that different peoples made in-

[138] S. Günther, "Der Jacobstab als Hilfsmittel geographischer Ortsbestimmung," *Geographische Zeitschrift, Jahrgang* 4 (Leipzig, 1898), p. 160. (Munich Library, Latin Codex, 11067.)

[139] The most elaborate work on the history of the compass published in the present century is that of A. Schück, *Der Kompass* (Hamburg, 1915), 2 vols. As to the origin of the compass, he makes the following general statement: "Der Kompass ist ein Findelkind, aber nicht von hoher Abkunst, sondern er dankte sein Dasein und seine erste Ausbildung gewissen Seefahrern und für diese arbeitenden Mechanikern.— Immerhin dürfte daruber manches enthalten sein in alten Handschriften, die an den verschiedensten Orten noch immer gefunden werden." Many magazine articles which deal with particular phases of the subject have appeared, the following being among the more important: R. Hennig, "Die Frühkenntnis der magnetischen Nordweisung," *Beiträge zur Geschichte der Technik und Industrie,* Vol. 21, 1931-1932, pp. 25-42. A. C. Mitchell, "Chapters in the History of Terrestrial Magnetism," *Terrestrial Magnetism and Atmospheric Electricity,* June, 1932, pp. 105-146. This is the most complete documentary summary in English to date. E. O. von Lippmann, "Geschichte der Magnet-nadel bis zur Erfindung des Kompasses (Gegen 1300)," *Quellen und Studien zur Geschichte der Naturwissenschaften und der Medizin,* Vol. 3, 1932, No. 1. H. Winter, "Seit wann ist die Missweisung bekannt?" *Annalen der Hydrographie und Maritimen Meteorologie,* September, 1935, pp. 352-363; "What Is the Present Stage of Research in Regard to the Development and Use of the Compass in Europe?" *Research and Progress,* Vol. 2, 1936, pp. 225-233; "Who Invented the Compass?" *The Mariner's Mirror,* Vol. 23, 1937, pp. 95 ff. Among the more important works on the subject in the last century are: J. Klaproth, *Lettre à M. le Baron Humbolt sur l'invention de la boussole* (Paris, 1834). J. Bertelli, "Studi storici intorno alla bussola nautica," *Memoire della pontificia accademia dei nuovi lincei,* Vol. 9, 1893. J. d'Avezac, "Anciens témoignages historiques relatifs à la boussole," *Bulletin de la societé de géographie de Paris,* 1858; and "Aperçus historiques sur la boussole," *ibid.,* 1860.

dependent discoveries of the directional property of a piece of
magnetized iron having free movement in a horizontal plane has
not as yet been proved untenable; and finally, there is no documentary evidence to show that the magnetic needle or its later
development, the compass, was used as a surveying instrument before the thirteenth century.

The earliest type of "needle" used consisted of a piece of loadstone shaped as a pointed oval; before the end of the thirteenth
century artificially magnetized iron "needles" were in use. We
know from the earliest authentic records that two methods were
developed which allowed for the free horizontal movement of the
needle. These were known as the wet and dry methods. The
former consisted of floating a piece of magnetized iron in a vessel
containing water; straws and pieces of wood were used to support
the iron. The dry method, which we still use, gave free movement
to the needle by pivoting it on the point of a vertical support.
The wet compass is in all probability anterior; it is the type to
which we have the earliest allusion, and its simple mechanism for
free movement strengthens its claim to priority.

Tradition, handed down through the later Middle Ages and the
following centuries, attributed to the Chinese the honor of being
the first users of the magnetic needle and to Marco Polo the introduction of its use into Europe, on his return from his famous
journey in 1260. That the Chinese independently discovered the
directional property of loadstone is entirely possible, but its introduction into Europe by Marco Polo or any other intermediaries between the Orient and the Occident has long since been
repudiated. In the questionable records of early Chinese history
mention is made of the use of south-pointing chariots in a battle
about the year 2600 B.C., but the employment of any magnetic
properties in connection with such chariots is regarded as purely
mythical.[140] The earliest authentic evidence of Chinese knowledge of the directive property of the magnetic needle is to be
found in the encyclopedia of Shon-Kua (1030-1093), who states:
"Fortune tellers rub the point of a needle with the stone of the

[140] This legend is repeated with variations several times in later Chinese chronicles,
even as late as (A.D. 1027. See Sarton, *Introduction to the History of Science,* p. 764.
F. Hirth, *Ancient History of China* (New York, 1911), pp. 129, 135. H. A. Giles, "The
Mariner's Compass," *Adversaria Sinica* (Shanghai, 1918), pp. 107-115, 217-222.

magnet in order to make it properly indicate the south." [141] There
is no genuine record of the use of the magnetic needle as a navigation instrument in China until toward the end of the eleventh
century. We are told that in 1086 "foreigners" who came from
Sumatra to Canton used the magnetic needle when navigating in
bad weather.[142]

The identity of these foreign sailors might throw much light on
the origin of the compass, but unfortunately the chronicler neglected to mention this important item. Were they Muslims or
Vikings or perhaps members of some race of the South Pacific
since lost in oblivion but master navigators in the eleventh century? Since the Muslims had developed sea trade routes in the
Indian Ocean and East Indian Seas by the tenth century, it is
scarcely possible that they would not be designated by some more
specific title than "foreigners" in Canton at the end of the eleventh
century. Again, Muslim superiority in scientific learning at this
period would readily induce us to attribute to them the introduction of the navigational use of the magnetic needle; confirmation
of our belief in this hypothesis, however, is confronted with one
great obstacle, that of the total absence of any scientific discussion
of the magnetic needle in any Muslim writings before the thirteenth century.[143] If the Muslims were the discoverers or even

[141] Hirth, *op. cit.*, p. 132. Sarton, *Introduction to the History of Science*, p. 756.
Mitchell, *op. cit.*, p. 110.

[142] This record is to be found in a work entitled *Ping-chou-Ko-than* written by
Chu-yu in the twelfth century from information given by his father, who had worked
as a merchant at Canton. "In clear weather the captain ascertains the ship's position
at night by looking at the stars, in the day time by looking at the sun; in dark
weather he looks at the south-pointing needle." See Hirth, *op. cit.*, p. 133.

[143] Schück, *op. cit.*, Vol. 2, p. 34, cites the following from Section Four, Chapter
Twenty of *Gāmi 'al Hikājāt*, a collection of Persian anecdotes compiled by al-'Awfī
about 1230, as the earliest allusion to the magnetic needle so far discovered in Muslim
writings: "Once upon a time I went on a sea voyage, suddenly a violent wind arose
from the ambush of obscurity, black clouds that darkened the heavens, the waves
rolled and tossed high, the sea became so agitated that the passengers began to wail.
The master, who was captain, became worried about his direction. Therefore he
brought out a hollow iron in the form of a fish and placed it in a vessel containing
water. It turned about and finally came to rest in the direction of the 'Qibla' [*i.e.,*
toward the South]. From that direction the captain laid out his course. Afterwards
I made inquiries about this phenomenon, and they said that the loadstone possesses
the property, that when it is rubbed hard on iron, so that it leaves a mark on the
iron, that piece of iron will come to rest only in the 'Qibla'. How it happens, God
knows, and no wiseacre can get behind the mystery."

The earliest Muslim description of the wet compass is that of Bailak al-Qabājaqī
(*c.* 1282).

active users of the magnetic needle by the end of the eleventh
century, it is strange that they should have neglected to leave any
documentary evidence; so strange, in fact, that there is grave doubt
about identifying them as the aforementioned "foreigners." Considering the distances to be traveled and the available sea routes,
the presence in Canton in 1086 of Vikings or of their successors
as a sea power in Europe, the Normans, is even more difficult to
believe. In fine, this fragment of information from Chu-yu en-
lightens us no further as to the navigational use of the magnetic
needle than that it was employed by some people other than
Chinese at the end of the eleventh century.

The earliest European distinct references to the magnetic
needle are found in two works of the English monk Alexander
Neckam. In his *De Naturis Rerum* we read:[144]

Mariners at sea, when through cloudy weather which hides the sun during the day, or through the darkness of the night, they lose knowledge
of the quarter of the world to which they are sailing, place a needle over
the magnet, which will revolve in circles until its motion ceasing, it will
point toward the north.

Again in *De Utensilibus* he states:[145]

Whosoever therefore wishes to have a ship fitted out . . . Let him
have a needle placed on a pivot, for the needle will revolve and move
around until the point of the needle points toward the East. In this
way the sailors know on what course they have to steer, when the
North-star is invisible because of unsettled weather, even though it
never goes below [the horizon] because of the smallness of its orbit.

These two passages prove that the dry or pivot magnetic needle
was in use in some European countries before the end of the
twelfth century. The allusion in *De Utensilibus* to the needle

---

[144] Alexander Neckam (1157-1217), Augustinian monk. Lecturer in Paris *c.* 1180-
1185. Abbot of Cirencester 1213. *De Naturis Rerum* was probably written in 1180.
Edited by T. Wright in 1863 (Rolls Series). Lib. 2, Ch. 89: "Nautae etiam mare
legentes, cum beneficium claritatis solis in tempore nubilo non sentiunt, aut etiam
cum caligine nocturnarum tenebrarum mundus obvolvitur, et ignorant in quem
mundi cardinem prora tendat, acum super magnetem ponunt, quae circulariter cir-
cumvolvitur usque dum, ejus motu cessante, cuspis ipsis septentrionalem plagam
respiciat."

[145] *De Utensilibus*, Edited by T. Wright in *A Volume of Vocabularies* (1857), p.
114: "Qui ergo munitam vult habere havem . . . Habeat etiam acum jaculo sup-
positam, rotabitur enim et circumvolvetur acus donec cuspis acus respiciat orientem,
sicque comprehendunt quo tendere debeant nautae cum cinossura latet in aeris
turbatione, quamvis ad occasum numquam tendat, propter circuli brevitatem."

pointing to the east is rather obscure; Chappell [146] points out that it is scarcely an error in transcription, since all manuscript copies contain the same word. He offers the explanation that since the East was the important locality at that period for mariners, perhaps the magnetic needle carried a crossarm to point in this direction.

Shortly after Neckam's account we have the first European description of the wet or floating magnetic needle. This is to be found in the poem "La Bible" of Guyot de Provins (c. 1200). He describes the loadstone as an ugly brownish stone to which iron is attracted and then adds:[147]

After they have caused a needle to touch it, and placed it in a stick, they put it in the water without any more ado and the stick keeps it on the surface. Then it turns its point toward the star with such certainty that no man will ever have any doubt of it, nor will it ever for any reason go false. When the sea is dark and hazy so that they can see neither star nor moon, then they place a light by the needle and have no fear of going wrong. The point goes toward the star and thereby the mariners know the right direction. It is an art which cannot fail.

Although Neckam's is the oldest known European reference to the pivot compass, present-day inquirers feel that other and probably more complete descriptions of the use of the magnetic needle must have preceded it.[148] There is almost unanimity of opinion that in Europe the actual use of the magnetic needle as a direction-finder is at least two centuries older than the date assigned to Neckam's manuscript. The probability of priority of use in

[146] J. Chappell, "The Early History of Magnetism," *Nature,* Vol. 14, 1877, pp. 147-148.

[147] *Histoire littéraire de la France* (Benedictines of St. Maur), Vol. 9, p. 199.

Un art fort qui mentir ne peut	Que jà por rien ne faussera,
Par la vertu de la manette,	Et mariniers nul doutera.
Une pierre laide et brunete,	Quant la mer est obscure et brune
Où li fers volontiers se joint,	Qu'on ne voit estoile ne lune
Ont; si esgardent li droit point,	Donc font à l'aiguille alumer
Puis qu'une aiguille l'ait touchié	Puis n'ont-il garde d'esgarer.
Et en un festu l'ont fichié	Contre l'estoile va la pointe,
En l'ève la mettent sans plus.	Par ce sont li marinier cointe
Et li festu la tient dessus	De la droite voie tenir.
Puis se torne la pointe toute	C'est un art qui ne peut faillir
Contre l'estoile, si sans doute	Moult est l'étoile bèle et clère
	Tiex devroit estre nostre Père.

[148] von Lippmann, *op. cit.,* p. 27. Winter, "What Is the Present Stage of Research in Regard to the Development and Use of the Compass in Europe?"

northern Europe is also receiving much more emphasis in recent times.[149] Schück reminds us of the fact that the Vikings who voyaged to Iceland, Greenland, and North America in the tenth and eleventh centuries had much greater need of the compass, because of the bad weather which they were likely to encounter, than sailors in the Mediterranean; and there is also the consideration that northern instruments for solar and stellar observations were probably inferior to those in use in countries subject to Muslim influences. Although there are references to the loadstone in the Norse sagas[150] under the name of *sejersten* or sailing stone, which would imply the use of the floating compass, the only evidence of its use is negative. The Icelandic historian Ari Frodi Thorgilsson (1067-1144) asserted in his *Landnamabok* that the loadstone was not used by the navigators of the year 868, from which statement it may be presumed to have been in use at the latest by the time the book was written.[151]

As further support for the theory of the north European origin of the compass von Lippmann proposes the fact that the early Italian *wind roses* carried twelve points and later changed to the eight, sixteen, and thirty-two points, whereas the earliest wind roses of northern Europe invariably were eight-pointed. This would tend to show that the eight-point wind rose was carried into the Mediterranean by the Normans, who in turn had received it from the Vikings, when they established a Norman colony in Sicily at the end of the eleventh century. It is well to remember that the origin of the wind rose is entirely independent of, and much older than, the use of the magnetic needle.[152] Besides the

[149] A. Schück, "Gedanken über die Zeit der ersten Benutzung des Kompasses im nördlichen Europa," *Archiv für die Geschichte der Naturwissenschaften und der Technik*, Vol. 3, 1910; "Zur Einführung der Kompass in die nordwest-europäische Nautik," *ibid.*, Vol. 4, 1911.

[150] Winter, "Who Invented the Compass?" p. 100.

[151] The *Landnamabok* (*Book of the Colonization*) states: "Floki, son of Vilgerd, instituted a great sacrifice and consecrated three ravens which should show him the way [to Iceland]; for at that time no men sailing the high seas had loadstones up in the northern lands." The oldest extant gloss of this work dates from 1225. T. Ellwood, *The Book of the Settlement of Iceland* (London, 1908), p. 4.

[152] A. Rehm, "Griechische Windrosen," *Sitzbericht der Königlich Bayerischen Akademie der Wissenschaften, Jahrgang*, 1916, Abt. 3. S. Thompson, "The Rose of the Winds," *Proceedings, British Academy*, Vol. 14, pp. 179-209. A. Schück, "Das Blatt der Kompassrose," *Jahresberichte der geographische Gesellschaft*, Vol. 13, 1890, pp. 20-59.

fact that several writers[153] on the compass in the thirteenth century mention the widespread navigational use of the magnetic needle in northern Europe, there is one other hypothesis, which if corroborated would give clear evidence in favor of the north countries and would also tend to show participation by the landsman, if not the surveyor, in the early development of the compass. Wehner,[154] after some limited observations, proposed in 1905 that it seemed likely that the orientation of churches in northern Europe from the seventh century onward was determined by means of the magnetic needle and that, in accordance with the customs of the period, the method was kept secret among the building guilds. No further evidence seems to have been gathered since for the verification of this remarkable hypothesis.

Although many important persons of the thirteenth century made allusion to the use of the magnetic needle in both the floating and the pivot forms,[155] the first detailed scientific description is that of Petrus Peregrinus de Maricourt. Before giving some of the more important excerpts from the work of Peregrinus, it is well to mention here the tradition which attributed the discovery of the compass to the sailors of Amalfi and particularly to one Flavio Gioja, who, in the words of the poet Panormita, "Primum dedit nautis usum magnetis Amalphis." Even as late as 1600, we find Gilbert[156] repeating this tradition, which must have arisen because of the fact that Amalfi had become, during the eleventh and twelfth centuries, one of the chief shipping centers of the Mediterranean. But there is no local record to substantiate the tradition.[157]

[153] Winter, "Who Invented the Compass?" p. 99. For example, Peregrinus says: "The stone having magnetic properties is commonly found in northern districts, and is carried by seafaring people in all parts of the northern sea, and in particular, Normandy, Picardy and Flanders."

[154] H. Wehner, "Die Kenntnis der magnetischen Missweisung im Mittelalter," *Weltall,* 1905, No. 11. See also von Lippmann, *op. cit.,* p. 13. Winter, "What Is the Present Stage of Research in Regard to the Development and Use of the Compass in Europe?" p. 230.

[155] For details see Schück, *Der Kompass,* Vol. 2, pp. 30 ff. Among these were Cardinal Jacques de Vitry, Albertus Magnus, Hugh de Bercy, Vincent de Beauvais, Heinrich von Krolewiz, Brunetto Latini, Raymond Lullus, and Gerson ben Salomon.

[156] William Gilbert, *De Magnete* (London, 1600), p. 3. "Nevertheless I will not rob the Amalfians of the great honour that the magnetic needle was first by them to a great extent produced in the Mediterranean."

[157] This tradition was propagated chiefly by the historian Flavius Blondus in his

The following excerpts from Peregrinus will show the stage of development reached by the compass in 1269. The first part of the epistle deals with the properties of natural magnets and with the supposed influence of the poles of the heavens upon the poles of the stone. Then follows a description of an improved floating compass (Figure 40):[158]

Let then a round magnet be taken and its poles found as has been described, and let it be filed down between the two poles on the two sides, so that the stone may be like a sphere compressed between the two poles in order that it may occupy a smaller space. Let this stone indeed

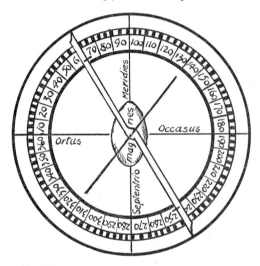

Figure 40. THE FLOATING COMPASS OF PEREGRINUS

thus prepared be shut up in the middle between two capsules in the manner of a mirror; and let the capsules be so joined to one another that they shall not be opened any more and that no water can make its way in. Let the capsules be prepared with cement, suitable for this pur-

Italia Illustrata (c. 1450). In 1511 it was repeated by Baptista Pio in his *Commentary.* Finally in 1540 Gyraldus in his *Libellus de Re Nautica* declared that the directional property had been discovered by a "certain Flavius." This "certain Flavius" later became known as Flavio Gioja and was supposed to have lived about 1300. Even Bertelli repeats the tradition long after the publication by Wright of Neckam's references to the magnetic needle. On the other hand, as early as 1597 William Barlow in his *The Navigator's Supply* calls it a "lame tale."

[158] *Epistola Petri Peregrini de Maricourt ad Sygerum de Foucaucourt Militem de Magnete* (Lucera, 1269. First printed at Augsburg, 1558), English Translation by S. Thompson, Limited Edition (London, 1902). Excerpts taken from this translation by permission of The Chiswick Press.

pose, and let the capsules be of light wood. This being done, place the capsules thus fitted up in a large vessel filled with water, in which the two parts of the world, namely, the South and the North, having been found and known, are marked; and let them be indicated by means of a thread stretched from the Northern part of the vessel to the Southern part. Then set the capsules to float, and let there be a thin strip of wood over them in the position of a diameter. Let this strip of wood be moved over the boxes until it be equidistant from the meridian line previously found and indicated by means of the thread, or is in the same line with it. Which being done, according to the position of this wood so situated or marked, mark the line on the capsules; and it will

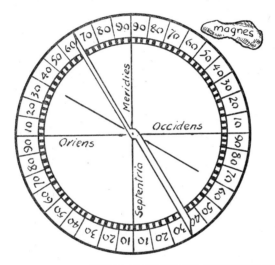

Figure 41. THE PIVOT COMPASS OF PEREGRINUS

be always the meridian line in every region or kingdom. Let this line then be divided through the middle by another line cutting the same at right angles, and that shall be the line of East and West, and so you will have the four quarters actually marked on the boxes, denoting the four parts of the world. Each of these should be divided into 90 parts, so that there may be in all 360 parts in the whole circumference of the boxes. And engrave the parts upon it just as they are wont to be engraved on the back of an astrolabe. There shall be moreover a narrow light bar over the capsules thus engraved like the rule at the back of the astrolabe. In place however of the sights let two spikes be set upright on the ends of the rule. If then you wish to have the Azimuth of the sun by day, place the capsules in water and permit them to move freely until they settle in their proper position. And hold them firmly so with one hand, and with the other move the rule until the shadow of the spike falls along its length, and then the end of the rule on the side of the sun will show the sun's azimuth. If there is a wind let the boxes be covered over with some vessel until they have found their positions. At night, on the other hand, you may do the same with the moon and stars by sight: for you shall move the rule until the tops of the spikes and the moon or the star are in the same line. For the end of the rule on the side of the star or moon will indicate its azimuth as formerly.

He also gives a description of the pivot compass—"another better and more certain instrument" (Figure 41) :[159]

Let a vessel be made of wood or brass or of any solid material, and let it be formed or turned in the fashion of a box, not very deep, and let it be wide enough. And let there be fitted over it a lid of transparent material, such as glass or crystal. And if even the whole vessel is also of a transparent material it will be the better. So let there be arranged in the middle of the vessel itself a slender axis of brass or of silver, fitting at its extremities to the two parts of the box, namely, the upper and the lower. And let there be two holes in the middle of the axis in directions at right angles to one another, and let an iron wire in the fashion of a needle be passed through one of these holes, and through the other let another wire of silver or brass be passed, intersecting the iron one at right angles. Moreover, let the lid be divided first into four parts and afterwards each part into ninety parts as was described in the former instrument, and let it be marked on the same North and South and East and West. And let there be added to it a rule of transparent material with upright spikes at its ends. Then you shall bring near the crystal whichever part of a magnet you wish, over the North, until the needle moves toward it and receives virtue from it. This being done, turn the box round until one end of the needle stands in the line of North on the instrument, on the Northern side of the heavens. Which done, turn the rule toward the sun by day and toward the stars by night, in the manner described above for the other instrument. By means of the instrument you will be able to direct your steps to cities and islands and to any places whatever in the world, and wheresoever you may be on land or at sea, provided the longitudes and latitudes of the places are known to you and certain.

The earliest references we have to the use of the compass in surveying is to be found in the ordinances of the city of Massa relative to the boundary marks in its mines. These mines were being actively worked in the thirteenth century. The exact date of this document is unknown, but it undoubtedly falls within

[159] *Ibid.*

the period under consideration.[160] That ordinary land surveying should have made prior use of the compass seems most likely.

Moreover we decree that all legally sanctioned boundaries already fixed or yet to be fixed between any pits, either by masters (surveyors), or by arbitrators and governors and common friends, chosen by the partisans with the good will and agreement of both parties, ought to be surveyed and marked off by the compass; after they have been laid out and fixed and the directions toward which wind the boundaries bear, according to the instrument, have been recorded, and so that if the said boundaries should be changed, they can be remade and restored to their former position; this compass and the method by which the surveying was carried on ought to be kept by the Camerarios Commune in the archives of the municipality of Massa, to be produced and exposed, whenever and howsoever it will be necessary for the fixing and recording of the aforesaid boundaries and to see toward what point the boundaries were laid out.

Evidences of Medieval Surveying

There is very little evidence to show that there was much in the way of land surveying during this period. This is accounted for by the fact that under the feudal system practically all land was owned by the nobility and the monastic establishments and was only leased annually to the common people. The estates were usually so large that their boundaries could be defined in terms of topographical features; they consisted of the lands of the tenant farmers and the manor demesne proper. The tenants lived in small villages on the estates. Each village had its own "commons," consisting of grass lands on which the cattle of the villagers grazed in common, and wood or forest land which supplied fuel and building material. The arable land was divided into a number of small sections, the right to the cultivation of a certain number of which was granted to each tenant on the basis of a yearly lease. Usually the plots leased to an individual tenant were not contiguous. This arable land of each village was divided into two or three large sections,[161] which were again subdivided into plots of about an acre or half-acre in extent.

[160] "Constitutionum Comunis et Populi Civitatis Massae," Edited by F. Bonaini, *Archivio storico italiano*, Vol. 8, 1845, Appendix 27. Text in Appendix, p. 361.

[161] This depended on whether the two- or three-field system of agriculture was in vogue. For details on these systems, see N. S. Gras, *A History of Agriculture in Europe and America* (New York, 1925), pp. 26 ff.

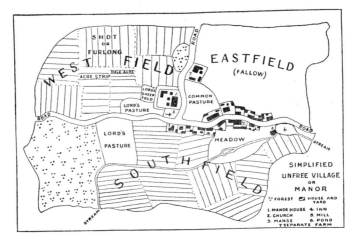

Figure 42. THE OPEN-FIELD SYSTEM OF LAND TENURE. *Reproduced from Gras' A History of Agriculture in Europe and America, by permission of F. S. Crofts and Co., Publishers.*

The form of the manor viewed from the clouds must have looked like an irregular checkerboard with small blocks or strips of land lying side by side or end to end, and somewhere near the center, the cottages of the villagers and the buildings of the lord. Closer inspection of the plan would show the shots (small divisions called furlongs or wrongs, perhaps six to twelve in a field) made up of a dozen or a score of parallel strips.[162]

This is the general picture of land division under the "open-field system" (Figure 42). Since the tenancy of land strips varied from year to year and depended on the caprice of the lord of the manor or his bailiff, there was no need for exact surveys; neither was there any uniformity as to the units of length and area even within the same county.

". . . apart from the general unreliability, estimates frequently included a large measure of chance; rights were sometimes marked by the cast of a hammer; the boundary between the shires of Cambridge and Huntington ran in some of the meres as far as a man might reach with his barge-pole to the shore, the day's journey and the morning's ploughing were other convenient units." [163]

[162] *Ibid.,* p. 89. By permission of F. S. Crofts and Co.

[163] H. C. Darby, "The Agrarian Contribution to Surveying in England," *The Geographical Journal,* Vol. 82, 1933, p. 530. By permission of the Royal Geographical Society. See also F. W. Maitland, *Domesday Book and Beyond* (London, 1897). A. Meitzen, *Siedelung und Agrarwesen* (Berlin, 1895). W. Airy, "The History of Land Measurement in England," *Engineering,* March, 1909, pp. 341 ff.

Where attempts were made at more accurate estimation of areas, we know from the practical geometries of the period that the methods followed were those given by Heron, employing calculations by right triangles, rectangles, and trapezoids. Only one exception to the right-angle method is to be found, and that is the method of similar triangles by simple triangulation. Probably the earliest description of this method is in the manuscript of Dominicus Parisiensis, and is repeated in the *Geometria Culmensis.*[164] This marks the beginning of a new system of calculating areas, which became quite popular in the Renaissance period and from which developed a new series of instruments. The unknown author of the *Geometria Culmensis* describes his method as follows:[165]

Let there be a triangle *ABC,* all of whose sides are known: take three straight rods as big and as long as you desire and let these rods be equally divided into equal parts, as 30, 40, 80, more or less. Join two of these three rods with a nail, in such a manner, that while remaining bound together they will have freedom of movement, the third rod being completely free, so as to be applied at will. Take these three rods, similar in number, size and proportionality to the sides of the proposed triangle *ABC,* and apply the aforesaid rods anglewise in turn, so that a triangle is formed, similar in every way to the triangle *ABC,* in proportion of sides and angles. And since in those two triangles there is a proportion between all corresponding sides, therefore the angles contained by these equal sides are equal, as is clear from Euclid VI.5. Therefore by definition of equal surfaces, implied in the principle of the same sixth, the aforesaid triangles have equal surfaces, and the size of the smaller triangle being known, the size of the greater is known, because it is the same in all respects as has been proved.

Our chief landmarks of surveying in medieval Europe are the Gothic cathedrals; unfortunately, however, we know little of the designers and architects of these monuments to the medieval spirit and still less of their methods of measuring. If the work of De Honnecourt[166] be taken as typical of the surveying methods em-

---

[164] See introduction of Mendthal to the *Geometria Culmensis* for relation between this work and the manuscript of Dominicus Parisiensis.

[165] *Ibid.*, pp. 36-37. Text in Appendix, p. 362.

[166] *Facsimile of the Sketch-book of Vilars de Honecort, an Architect of the Thirteenth Century,* French Edition by M. Lassus and M. Quicherat, English Translation by R. Willis (London, 1859). See also H. Hannloser, *Villard de Honnecourt* (Vienna, 1935).

ployed on such buildings, it would appear that there was little use made of the instruments available at the time. During this period very little was done in the way of building roads, bridges, or canals. Sarton cites as the most remarkable engineering achievement of the period the construction of a thirty-mile canal from Lake Maggiore to Milan, which was used to irrigate the surrounding country.[167]

The building of new canals and the opening up of some of the old Babylonian canals formed the chief engineering feat of the Muslims after the establishment of the 'Abbāsid dynasty.[168] From the Muslim writers we have many references to the process of leveling and the building of canals, bridges, and aqueducts.[169] Canals were built principally for irrigation purposes and were of prime importance in developing highly efficient agricultural communities both in the East and later in Spain. Aqueducts were built to supply large cities, such as Bagdad and Cordova, with water.[170] The fabulous buildings of Bagdad and the remains of Muslim architecture in Spain testify to the attainments of the Muslim architects in the art of measurement.

[167] Sarton, *Introduction to the History of Science*, Vol. 2, p. 408. See also Parsons, *op. cit.*, pp. 367 ff. For descriptions of minor engineering works in England at this time, see A. P. Fleming and H. J. Brocklehurst, *A History of Engineering* (London, 1925), pp. 79, 92.

[168] P. Hitti, *A History of the Arabs* (London, 1937), p. 349.

[169] Wiedemann, *Beitr.* 10, *Sitz. Ber.* 38, 1906, p. 307; *Beitr.* 35, *Sitz. Ber.* 46, 1914, pp. 15-16.

[170] Hitti, *op. cit.*, pp. 301 ff., 527.

IV

ADVANCEMENTS in Europe During the Renaissance

THE two-hundred-and-fifty-year period under consideration in this chapter is undoubtedly the most interesting and the most important in the development of surveying instruments. The reasons why this is such an important period are manifold. It is proposed to point out the more important ramifications of those forces which directed instrument developments along certain lines, before considering the changes wrought by time and necessity on the individual instruments which continued in use and the new ones that appeared owing to the exigencies of the times.

This period has been generally known as the Renaissance. The idea that it was a direct break away from the mode of life of the Middle Ages was popular until recent times. However, modern studies of the medieval period have shown that the so-called "revival of learning" was nothing more than the natural growth and development of the intellectual life of the medieval period.[1] To be sure, two stimuli appeared at the beginning of this period which helped to accelerate the intellectual development; but neither the increase of contact with the ancient Greek thought after the fall of Constantinople (1453) nor the development of printing about the same time could have of themselves been responsible for such an ebullition as was about to take place in all the arts and sciences; primarily the Middle Ages had set the stage.

Besides the impetus given through the dissemination of knowledge by printing; the breakdown of the traditional attitude toward authority, as regards both religious and scientific beliefs, accelerated by the Reformation; the development of the Copernican

---

[1] H. O. Taylor, *The Medieval Mind* (London, 1911), 2 vols.; *Thought and Expression in the Sixteenth Century* (New York, 1920). L. Thorndike, "The Historic Background of Modern Science," *Scientific Monthly*, Vol. 16, 1923, pp. 487-496.

theory; and the general movement toward nationalistic states, there were five movements within this period which were especially powerful in directing the course of development in surveying instruments. These were first, the disintegration of feudalism, which brought about a complete change in agriculture and the relations of the people to the land; second, the reawakening of interest in the science of cartography, due to both the revival of Ptolemy's ideas on geography and the discovery of new lands; third, the development of the initial stages of the science of artillery, which helped the evolution of instruments both directly, by the development of measuring instruments connected with the operation of guns, and indirectly, by the impetus given to the design and construction of fortifications capable of withstanding this new and revolutionizing weapon of warfare; fourth, the development of navigation, which awakened renewed interest in the science of cartography; and finally, the need, created by the astronomical controversies, for more accurate instruments of observation.

These varied developments were being carried on throughout most of Europe within the first century of this period; nevertheless to the peoples of individual countries belongs the credit of having been the pioneers in each movement. The changes in agricultural life are most noticeable first in England, later in the Netherlands, France, Italy, and Germany. Revival of interest in cartography developed first in Germany and spread rapidly to the Netherlands, the Iberian Peninsula, and England. The early history of artillery is primarily Italian, with later developments by Germany, France, and the Netherlands. To the Portuguese belongs the credit of developing the art of navigation, which they passed on in turn to the Spanish, Dutch, and English. The astronomical revolution was, of course, primarily the work of individuals rather than of groups. In the vanguard comes the Pole, Copernicus, followed by the Germans, Regiomontanus, Purbach, and Kepler; but in the development of instruments of observation the laurels go to Tycho Brahe, the Dane, and the Italian, Galileo.

It is obvious that any change brought about with regard to the ownership of land, whereby individual proprietorship became more extensive than previously, would have a marked influence

on the development of surveying instruments. Such a change had
been developing gradually during the fourteenth and fifteenth
centuries and more intensely during the sixteenth century,[2] so
that by 1600 the "manorial system" of the medieval period had
disappeared to a great extent in England, France, and the Netherlands, though in other sections of Europe the change went forward more slowly.[3] In this transformation from the period of
lords and serfs, England assumed the lead. The first important
economic factor which helped to bring about the agrarian revolution was the expansion of the English woolen trade with the
Netherlands. The owners of large tracts of land, sensing the increased profits from such trade, did not hesitate to take over the
lands allotted to the serfs for cultivation and turn them into
pastures for sheep. The amount of tillage being thereby greatly
reduced and the number of serfs required to manage the manorial
demesnes being much less than formerly, the lords pursued a
policy of allowing the serfs liberty of movement. But while such
a policy brought increased wealth to the lords, it resulted also in
widespread unemployment and poverty among the common
people, with the concomitants of unrest and spasmodic uprisings.

The open-field system, which had been established in the early
medieval period, was impracticable when confronted with the
problem of raising sheep in large numbers. The prospective
sheep-raiser had to acquire sufficient strips of land adjacent to each
other and fence off such acquired property in order to keep the
sheep within bounds. Thus arose the process of enclosure. Such
a method of acquiring large tracts of land by eviction of the
partly independent tenants could not have gone on without re-
actions. There were repeated acts of Parliament prohibiting the
turning of tillage into pasturage, but for the most part they proved
ineffective; hence the spontaneous uprisings among the peasants,
which were for the most part ruthlessly suppressed. Devaluation
of the English woolen trade was finally brought about by the wars
with Spain and the Netherlands in the latter half of the sixteenth
century, with the result that many of the large enclosures reverted
to the common people. But now each owner or tenant had rights

[2] R. H. Tawney, *The Agrarian Problem in the Sixteenth Century* (London, 1912).
[3] N. S. Gras, *A History of Agriculture in Europe and America* (New York, 1925).

to tracts of land adjacent to each other, instead of having his land scattered over a large area, as of old.

The establishment of individual ownership brought with it the need for more accurate definition of land boundaries, which had been unnecessary under the medieval open-field system. Hence there were published in England during the sixteenth century a number of treatises on the "art of surveying land." In the earliest of these books we find the duties of the surveyor described as follows:[4]

The name of a Surveyour is a frenche name and is as muche to saye in Englyshe, as an overseer. Than it wolde be known, howe a surveyour shulde oversee or survey a towne or a lordeshyp. As if the citie of London shulde be surveyed, the surveyour maye nat stande at Hygate, nor at Shoters hylle, nor yet at the Blackcheth, nor suche other places, and overlooke the citie on every syde. For if he do, he shall not see the goodly stretes, the fayre buyldnges, nor the great substance of rychesse conteyned in them, for than he may be called a disceyver, and not a surveyour. And in lykewyse if a man shall viewe a close or a pasture, he may not loke over the hedge and go his waye, but he muste other ryde or goo over, and see every parcell thereof, to knowe howe many acres it conteyneth, and howe much thereof was medowe grounde, howe much pasture grounde, howe muche woode grounde, or busshe grounde, heythe, lynge or such other, and what an acre of medowe grounde is worthe. . . . And what manner of cattel it is best for, and howe many cattel it will grasse or fynde by the year. . . . And therefore a surveyour muste be dylygent and laborous and nat slouthefull and retchelesse, for and he be, he is nat worthy to have his fee or wages and may fortune to make an unperfyte boke.

Fitzherbert's treatise was followed a few years later by the more practical book of De Benese, which remained the standard work in English for some forty years. As to his principal instrument, he says:[5]

Meters of Lande, for the moste parte do use to mete land with a pole made of wood, conteynyng in it the length onely of one perch. The whiche is a verye true and a perfyte way of metynge.

In his preface he strikes a note which we find echoing down through this period in English treatises:

[4] Anthony Fitzherbert, *The Boke of Surveyinge* (London, 1523). Quotation taken from the 1539 edition, Chapter 19.
[5] Richard de Benese, *The Boke of Measuring of Lande* (London, 1537).

Bycause in measuringe of Lande, many men somtyme the sellers, sel more measure than ryght, sometyme the byers by lesse measure than ryght be greatly deceived, by y meaters therof, the which be not experte and connynge, both in true measurynge of Lande, and also in true compting and summynge the numbre of acres of the same. Therefore in this lytle booke, ye shall reede certayne rules much necessary for y perfecte knowledge bothe of the measurynge and summynge the numbre of acres of the same.

The importance of surveying at this time may be estimated from the court records, which contain many documents on the buying and selling of land, with details as to the quantity, quality, and boundaries. Such surveys were not always condensed to map form; more frequently they were "elaborate topographical descriptions, furlong by furlong, and strip by strip, of complete villages, extending sometimes in length to 100 pages of Ms." [6] With the increased demand for surveyors, it was but natural that many amateurs entered the field, with the result that the work of the surveyor was not always up to standard. Passages in the prefaces to many of the treatises on surveying clearly bring out this fact and stress the idea that the books were written not only for those about to take up the profession of surveyor but also for farmers and the landowners, so that they might be able to check for themselves the size of their holdings. Thus, Paynell in the introduction to De Benese's book says:[7]

Considering, then, this lyberall Science called Geometry to be in everything much convenient for the use and common profite of all men. A friend and lover of myne, a Chanon of Marton, Syr Richarde Benese, not willing to hyde the treasure that God hath enryched hym withall. But evermore myordinge and labouringe (as the fore sayd Romaynes dyd) to encrease the common wealth, havinge also this saienge of the Phylosopher in memory: The more profytable a thinge is, the more it shulde be common, hee hath, (I saye) compyled this ingenyous and profitable Book, for the common profite and use of every man.

Over a century later we find the same idea expressed by Atwell:[8]

Therefore it behoves every man that hath, or may for himself or friend have occasion to let or hire, buy or sell land or timber, not to go on

---

[6] W. J. Corbett, "Elizabethan Village Surveys," *Transactions of the Royal Historical Society*, 1897, p. 67.

[7] De Benese, *op. cit.*

[8] George Atwell, *The Faithfull Surveyour* (London, 1658).

other mens legs, nor to see with another mans eyes, that have such easie means to attain the skill of it themselves.

That the profession of surveyor was not in high repute among the common people may be seen from the opening statement of the farmer in Norden's dialogue:[9]

I have heard much evil of the profession, and to tell you my conceit plainly I think the same both evill and unprofitable . . . and oftentime you are the cause that men lose their land and sometimes they are abridged of such liberties as they have long used in mannors.

Dee, in his introduction to the first English translation of Euclid, bewails the many errors and great injustices wrought by the would-be surveyors:[10]

till by God's mercy and man's industrie, the Perfect Science of Lines, Plaines and Solides (like a divine Justicier) gave unto every man his owne.

Rathborne deprecates the abuses of the "plaine table" shortly after it had come into use[11]

by the multitude of simple and ignorant persons (using, or rather abusing, that good plaine Instrument called the Plaine Table) who having but once observed a surveyour, by looking over his shoulder, how and in what manner he directs his sights, and draws his lines thereon; they presently apprehend the business, provide them of some cast *Plaine Table,* and within small time after, you shall heare them tell you wonders, and what rare feats they can perform; yea, and will undertake (or I will for them) that for tenne groats a day, and their charges defrayed, they shall be able to undoe any man they deale with; or at leastwise, to doe him such wrong and prejudice, as perhaps he might, with more ease, and lesse losse, have given ten pounds a day to one that would have spoken lesse, and performed more. But what should I say more of them then this, Nonoculi intercaecos oculissimi sunt, and so will I leave the blind, with tumbling the blind in the myre.

In an undated manuscript of Agas the duties of a surveyor are succinctly summarized:[12]

[9] John Norden, *The Surveyor's Dialogue* (London, 1607).

[10] H. Billingsley, *The Elements of Geometrie of the most auncient Philosopher Euclide of Megara . . . With a very Fruitfull Praeface made by M. I. Dee* (London, 1570).

[11] Aaron Rathborne, *The Surveyor* (London, 1616), Preface, Book III.

[12] Ralph Agas, Landsdowne Ms. 165, fol. 95, quoted by H. C. Darby in *The Geographical Journal,* Vol. 82, 1933, p. 531. By permission of The Royal Geographical Society.

No man may arrogate to himselfe the name and title of a perfect and
absolute Serveior of Castles, Manners, Lands and Tenements unlesse he
be able in true forme, measure, quantitie and proportion; to plat the
same in their particulars *ad infinitum* and therefore to retrieve, and
beat out all decaied, concealed, and hidden parcels thereof, fitting the
same to their evidence, how ancient soever; although blemished oblit-
erated and very much worne; besides the quickening and reviving of
Rents, Custumes, Liberties, Privileges, etc. Thereunto belonging; with
perfect knowledge of customarie Tenures and Titles of all sortes: fram-
ing entries accordingly: together with good and commendable penman-
ship as well for the Plat, as Booke, from the same. And for that more
abuse in concealments, incrouchments etc., hath beene offered in these
last 100 years than in the 500 before and that many do now refuse (as
more will hereafter) to pay their rents and duties, otherwise than on
the meeres head, (their lands and tenements first singled out, and set
forth unto them, metis and bundis). I may not terme him so much as a
Surveyor that performeth not these difficulties, and such like incident to
survey.

The movement for proprietorship and enclosure of land was
slower in getting under way on the Continent, but the impetus to
the development of new instruments came from other directions.
Interest in the science of cartography, which was reawakened
in Europe by the rediscovery of Ptolemy's *Geography* and the
multiplication of manuscript copies in the first half of the fifteenth
century,[13] received further impetus from the discoveries of new
lands by the Portuguese and Spaniards. Up to the beginning of
the sixteenth century, European maps consisted chiefly of two
classes: the Portolan charts,[14] used by seamen, and the *carta itineraria*[15] or road maps, which were used chiefly by travelers and
traders in conjunction with the *organum viatorum,* which consisted of a pocket-size instrument combining a compass and sun-

[13] Ptolemy's *Geography* was translated into Latin by Jacob Angelus de Scarparia in
1410. This version was the first to be printed in 1475 at Vincenza. For details on the
various Ptolemy manuscripts, see J. Fischer, *Ptolemaei Geographiae Codex Urbinas
Graecus* (Leipzig, 1932). For a good synopsis of the history of early map-making,
see E. Raisz, *General Cartography* (New York, 1938), Chs. 1, 2.

[14] One of the oldest extant Portolan charts is that of Pietro, Visconte of Genna,
dated 1311, depicting the eastern Mediterranean and Black Sea. See H. Zondervan,
Allgemeine Kartenkunde (Leipzig, 1901), p. 24; and E. L. Stevenson, *Portolan Charts*
(New York, 1911).

[15] The *Rom-Weg* of Erhard Etzlaub, published in Nürnberg, 1492, may be taken as
typical of such maps. See A. Wolkenhauer, "Über die ältesten Reisekarten von
Deutschland aus dem Ende des 15 und dem Anfang des 16 Jahrhunderts," *Deutsche
geographische Blätter,* Vol. 26, 1903, Facs. 3, 4.

dial, the latter being formed by the inside of the compass cover.

Toward the end of the fifteenth century there existed at St. Die, in Lorraine, a small group of intellectuals known as the Gymnasium Vosagenes, whose work was destined to have far-reaching effects on the course of European geographical research. Chief among these, so far as practical surveying and map-making are concerned, was Martin Waldseemüller.[16] Besides his world maps (1507) and Carta Itineraria Europae (1511), his detailed maps of Lorraine and the Upper Rhine published as "Tabulae Chorographie" with the 1513 Strassburg edition of Ptolemy's *Geography*, merit special attention, since they were the first of their kind and show by their accuracy that they were no haphazard compilation but rather the result of a well-worked-out survey.[17] Unfortunately Waldseemüller has left no account of the process by which the details of these maps were compiled, but an important clue to the method employed is given in the 1512 Strassburg edition of the *Margarita Philosophica*,[18] which includes a treatise on architecture and perspective by Waldseemüller. With this treatise, but without any explanation of its use, is inserted a wood cut of an instrument named the *polimetrum*. From the reproduction (Figure 43) it can be seen that here is the earliest European[19] prototype of the modern *theodolite* and *transit,* containing the two essential devices for the simultaneous measurement of horizontal and vertical angles. With such an instrument it was possible to carry out traversing in the modern sense, and we may safely assume that Waldseemüller's method was essentially that described for the first time twenty-one years later by Gemma

[16] For details of the Gymnasium Vosagenes and the world maps of Waldseemüller, which incidentally were the first which gave the name *America* to the newly discovered western land, see *The Cosmographiae Introductio of Martin Waldseemüller (c. 1475–1522)*, United States Catholic Historical Society, Monograph 4, Edited by C. G. Herbermann (New York, 1907).

[17] E. G. R. Taylor, "A Regional Map of the Early Sixteenth Century," *The Geographical Journal,* Vol. 71, 1928, pp. 473 ff.

[18] The *Margarita Philosophica* of Gregor Reisch, a member of the Carthusian Order; first printed in Freiburg, 1503. This is a compendium of theology, philosophy, and science and was the most popular book of its type in the sixteenth century. For details on various editions and additions, see J. Ferguson, "The Margarita Philosophica of Gregorius Reisch—a Bibliography," *The Library,* Series 4, Vol. 10, 1930.

[19] On Muslim prototypes see Figure 44 (p. 110) and L. A. Sédillot, "Mémoire sur les instruments astronomiques des Arabs," *Mémoires présentés par divers savants à l'académie royale des inscrites et belles lettres,* Series 1, Vol. 1, 1844, p. 201.

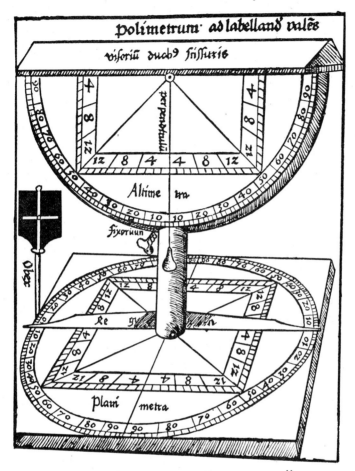

Figure 43. THE POLIMETRUM' OF WALDSEEMÜLLER

Frisius, even though his instrument, the polimetrum, seems to have suffered eclipse by that time.

From the school of St. Die, methods of determining the relative position of important landmarks over a large expanse of territory must have been disseminated in various parts of Europe, because we find that within the first half of the sixteenth century a large literature had accumulated on this subject, written chiefly by men connected with the teaching of mathematics in the various universities. The surprising fact is that in all this literature there is no mention of the polimetrum of Waldseemüller or of any instrument approaching it in design. In Germany the outstanding figures in this movement were Schöner, Werner, Münster, Peter Apian, and his son Philip, whose survey of Bavaria (1553-1563) is regarded as the "topographical masterpiece of the sixteenth century." Peter Apian in his *Cosmographia* (1524) laid the foundation of modern cartography on mathematics and measurement. In

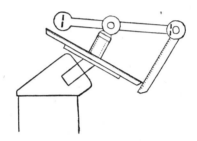

Figure 44. GEBER'S PROTOTYPE OF THE THEODOLITE

Italy a detailed account of the contemporary surveying methods was described by Niccolo Tartaglia in his *Quesiti et Invenzioni* (1546). The instrument he employed was a special type of compass.[20] But the most important work produced on the subject of large surveys was that of Gemma Frisius, who published as an addition to the 1533 Antwerp edition of Apian's *Cosmographia* the first account of the triangulation method. His instrument consisted of a modified astrolabe with inset compass. Thus was the groundwork laid for the accumulation of data necessary for accurate maps, whose publication in quantity began with the work of Mercator and became practically a monopoly of the Netherlands for the next two centuries.[21]

Information on European cartographical methods was brought back to England by such traveling students as Dee[22] and Cuning-

[20] Details on instruments and methods mentioned here are given later.

[21] Mercator (Gerhard Kremer, 1512-1594) published a topographical map of Flanders based on his own surveys in 1540 and a large map of Europe in 1554. He is best known for the projection which he used in his world map in 1569. Of the later Netherlands publications the more important were the *Spiegel der Zeevaart* of Lucas Waghenaer, a collection of marine charts; Hondius' world map, and Blaeu's *Zee-Spiegel*, 1623, containing over one hundred coastal charts.

[22] John Dee (1527-1608). One of the outstanding Englishmen of his time, acquainted with many of the Continental scientists. His wide range of activities may be judged from the extensive catalogue of his library and his own publications. See the appendix to E. G. R. Taylor's *Tudor Geography, 1485–1583* (London, 1930).

ham. Leonard Digges, who became the outstanding English surveyor of this period, had been a fellow student of Dee at Oxford. Whether Digges got his information on Continental surveying methods from Dee, or whether he spent some time himself on the Continent in pursuit of such knowledge, is unknown. Digges published his first book on practical geometry, entitled *Tectonicon*, in 1556, but his important work, *Pantometria,* was published posthumously by his son, Thomas, in 1571. The year of Leonard Digges' death is unknown, and therefore it is impossible to fix the date of the invention of his "instrument topographicall" described in *Pantometria*.[23] In this same book Digges describes another instrument, which he named *theodelitus*. By a strange quirk of fate, the name *theodelitus* was soon transferred to the "instrument topographicall," [24] and so we have the origin of the name of our present instrument (*theodolite*) of which Digges' "instrument topographicall" was a prototype.

As pointed out previously, surveying of estates and farm lands had long been important in England, but it was not until the second half of the sixteenth century that any large-scale surveys for the purposes of map-making were undertaken; by then the groundwork for such projects had been laid by Cuningham, Bourne, and Digges. The first important survey of England and Wales was carried out by Christopher Saxton; he spent about nine years on the task, and his series of county maps was published in 1579. Nothing is known of the instruments and methods employed, the only clue we have that he followed the triangulation method of Frisius being contained in his letter of authorization from Elizabeth for the survey of Wales which he carried out in 1576:[25]

[23] R. T. Gunther in his preface to a reprint of the *First Book of Pantometria*, Old Ashmolean Reprints IV (Oxford, 1927), suggests the date 1550. If this were so, it would probably be included in his *Tectonicon*, 1556. Gunther's claim that Digges' was the first invention of the simplest form of theodolite is untenable in view of the prior existence of Waldseemüller's polimetrum and Rotz's differential quadrant. (See pp. 108, 126).

[24] This may be seen from Rathborne's description of a theodolite. *Op. cit.*, Bk. 3, Ch. 2.

[25] H. G. Fordham, *Some Notable Surveyors and Map-Makers of the 16th, 17th, and 18th Centuries and Their Work* (Cambridge, 1929), p. 5. By permission of the Cambridge University Press. "Christopher Saxton of Dunningley [*c.* 1542–*c.* 1616], His Life and Work," *The Publications of the Thoresby Society*, Vol. 28, 1928, pp. 361–384.

To all Justices of peace mayors and others etc. within the severall
Shieres of Wales that whereas the bearer hereof Christopher Saxton is
appointed by Her Majestie under Her signe and signet to set forth and
describe in cartes particularlie all the shieres in Wales that the said
Justices shall be aiding and assisting unto him to see him conducted
unto any towre highe place castle or hill to view that country and that
he may be accompanied with II or III honest men such as do best know
the country for the better accomplishment of that service and that at
his departure from any towne or place that he hath taken the view of
the said towne do set forth a horseman that can speke both Welshe and
Englishe to safe conduct him to the next market towne.

On the basis of a critical study of Saxton's maps and the above
quotation Manley says:[26]

Suggestions have been made with regard to his procedure, based on considerations of his errors in measurement and of the methods of survey
known at the time and likely to be practised by a man working fairly
quickly. These appear to point to a series of compass traverses as the
basis of the survey over much of the country. . . . working rapidly, he
climbed very few hills; as a rule, only when it appeared to him that he
could thereby save a further traverse into sparsely inhabited country.
He was thus accustomed to put in detail by estimating distance along
bearings from a single point. He was conscientious with regard to
county boundaries and other detail in the cultivated lowlands, but
wherever possible he avoided the trouble of going beyond the limits of
habitation through country which he knew or thought to be unin-
habited, especially if he was thereby led into another county.

The third important impetus to the development of measuring
instruments came from the new science of artillery, whose development, for all practical purposes, was contemporaneous with the
period under consideration.[27] The first to attempt to place the art
of gunnery on a mathematical basis was Tartaglia in his *Nuova
Scienza,* 1537. The propositions laid down by Tartaglia were
those which were reproduced in the main, for more than a century
and a half, in books on this subject,[28] even though in the mean-

[26] G. Manley, "Saxton's Survey of Northern England," *The Geographical Journal,*
Vol. 83, 1934, pp. 308-316. By permission of The Royal Geographical Society.
[27] For a brief résumé of the history of medieval and Renaissance artillery, see *Encyclopaedia Britannica,* Fourteenth Edition, Vol. 2, p. 463. For specific facts on Germany, with very fine illustrations, see E. Schoen, *Geschichte des deutschen Feuerwerkswesens* (Berlin, 1936), Sect. 1.
[28] For example, E. Gentilinus, *Instruttione de bombardieri* (Venice, 1592). W.
Bourne, *The Art of Shooting Great Ordnance* (London, 1587). P. Sardi, *L'Artigleria*

time Galileo[29] had established the true path of a trajectory, neglecting air resistance, as a parabola, and Blondel[30] had written his artillery manual in line with this doctrine.

Figure 45. TARTAGLIA'S GUN QUADRANT

In his introduction, Tartaglia states that the greatest range can be attained when the gun elevation is 45°. For the measurement of the angle of elevation he had a special type of plumb-bob quadrant with a long counterbalancing arm which rested in the bore of the gun (Figure 45). In Book II he lays down the following fundamental propositions:[31]

I. All the trajectories or natural movements of a uniformly heavy body are parallel to each other and to the perpendicular to the horizontal.

II. Every trajectory or violent movement of a body uniformly heavy which takes place outside of the perpendicular to the horizontal is always of necessity partly rectilinear and partly curved, and the curve of the latter is a portion of the circumference of a circle. . . .

(Venice, 1621). N. Nye, *The Art of Gunnery* (London, 1647). J. Buchner, *Theoria et Praxis Artilleriae* (Nürenberg, 1682).

[29] G. Galilei, *Le operazioni del compasso geometrico e militare* (Padua, 1596), pp. 60-80.

[30] F. Blondel, *L'Art de jetter les bombes* (The Hague, 1683).

[31] Nicolo Tartaglia, *Nuova Scienza* (Venice, 1537).

III. All uniformly heavy bodies shot off in a direction other than perpendicular to the horizontal, finish by moving naturally in the direction which is tangent to the curved part of the violent movement. [In Figure 46] the violent movement is *AB*, rectilinear; *BCD* is the arc of a circle;

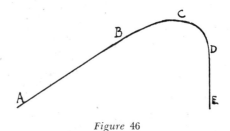

Figure 46

DE is the vertical tangent to the arc of the circle at *D* which represents the natural movement.

IV. When the body uniformly heavy is projected on a horizontal plane the curved part of its trajectory or violent movement is a quadrant of the circumference of the circle from which it is derived.

V. When the trajectory or violent movement of a body uniformly heavy is at an angle with the horizontal, its curved section is greater than the quadrant of a circle and the amount by which it exceeds the quadrant is the greater in proportion to the angle of elevation, but it never becomes a semicircle.

VI. When uniformly heavy bodies, similar and equal, are projected violently into the air by the same force, through all possible angles, that one which is ejected at an angle of 45° with the horizontal goes further than all the others.

By most writers on gunnery, the trajectory, which Tartaglia divided into three sections, is for practical purposes reduced to two by the omission of the circular arc, thus reducing the problem of finding the range, to the solution of a right triangle. Thus Sebastian Münster writes as follows in 1551:[32]

Engineers who handle fire-throwing and rock-throwing machines, even other catapults and similar military engines, must particularly take note of this hypotenuse. For these men do not launch solids vertically or straight at the object, particularly such as fling fire and stones by means of the springs of catapults, moreover bombardiers who attempt to demolish objects situated on heights, take into consideration no side of the right-angled triangle except the hypotenuse. Hence it is necessary to

[32] Sebastian Münster, *Rudimenta Mathematica* (Basel, 1551), pp. 28-31. Text in Appendix, p. 362.

Figure 47. DIAGRAM OF TRAJECTORY BY MÜNSTER

fix quadrants to the engines, that they know their power and force and that they know the exact weight of the rocks, lest being too heavy they fall away from the hypotenuse in transit and not reach their desired destination, from which, falling straight down they either set on fire or hit the object beneath. In this throwing of the bombs we do not mean the end of the path, but we have in mind the maximum force which, at the very peak of its violence, brings about the destruction of the object to be demolished. When therefore anyone tries to launch a fire bomb and vertically to hit a particular mark, he must first of all know the explosive power of the machine, and next, the distance of the spot which he intends to set on fire [Figure 47]. The two distances being known, namely, the base and hypotenuse, the machine is tilted according to the scale of the attached quadrant, so that the pitch-ball may proceed rightly along the hypotenuse and dropping in its course, may fall in its descent upon the destined mark.

One of the most interesting books on this subject is that of Santbech. Figure 48 shows that his method is essentially that of Münster. With reference to this figure, after a long-winded geometrical explanation, he takes the following concrete example:[33]

Assume that the full force of the cannon can fire along *CL,* which is 1000 paces, while the distance *CO* is 600, and altitude *NO* is 100. The first question is whether the power of the cannon can fire the ball so far

[33] Daniel Santbech, *Problematum* (Basel, 1561), p. 223. See also K. P. Williams and R. H. Coon, "Sixteenth Century Gunnery," *The Field Artillery Journal,* Vol. 19, 1929, pp. 128-135, from which the above translation is taken by permission of The United States Field Artillery Association. Text in Appendix, p. 363.

Figure 48. DIAGRAM OF TRAJECTORY BY SANTBECH

as to touch at some point the vertical line *LN*. First square *CL*, which gives 1,000,000, then square *CO,* which gives 360,000. Subtract the latter from the former and there remains 640,000, the square of the vertical. The square root of this is 800 (the number of paces in the vertical line). Since this is greater than 100, there is no doubt of the result. By this demonstration, then, it is established that the ball drops about 700 paces in reaching the point *N*. Now we still have to investigate the angle of elevation of the cannon, a problem to be solved very easily by the table of sines [Santbech finds the elevation to be 53° 8′, which is the correct value of arc sine 0.8000].

The influence of the new methods of warfare brought about by the introduction of artillery may be seen in many of the problems published in the practical geometries of this period. For example, most of the diagrams in Zubler's book,[34] which deals with one of the earliest triangulation instruments, illustrate military situations (see Figure 142) ; while Belli[35] illustrates the solution of all his problems on heights and distances, not only by the use of the geometric square, but also graphically on drumheads used in the capacity of a *plane table* (see Figure 145). The following from

[34] Leonard Zubler, *Novum Instrumentum Geometricum* (Basel, 1607).
[35] Silvio Belli, *Libro del Misurar con la Vista* (Venice, 1566).

De Rojas is typical of the military influence of this period:[36]

Frequently we are in doubt as a result of weakness of sight as to whether distant objects are moving, especially if they are beheld from a great distance and are approaching or receding. This could be seen, Corolus, particularly during your most successful expedition in Tunetus, when you could scarcely perceive on account of remoteness, whether the Moors, dashing all around as was their custom, were in flight or pursuing our men. It will be worth while to learn, by what means, in a state of uncertainty, this can be found out, so that a plan can be at once formed either concerning the pursuing of fleeing foe or concerning the repelling an onset of the enemy. An astrolabe having been hung from a spear or from some other object, so that it may be steadier, turn the alidade towards the enemy. After a short while, the astrolabe and alidade remaining unmoved, observe the same object through the slits of the sights or else along their edges, and we will see at once whether the enemy has approached or withdrawn. If, however (as we said) the alidade remaining unmoved, we sight the enemy time after time, through the slits of the sights, we will conclude that he is neither receding nor advancing, and that he has not changed position.

Although England relied at first on gunners brought from France and the Netherlands, especially during the reign of Henry VIII,[37] it was not long before this new science found its way into the practical geometries. Gunther was of the opinion that the "instrument topographicall" of Digges and also Blagraves's *familiar staff* were invented primarily for the use of gunners and that their use in topography was of secondary importance.[38] Certainly Digges was interested in the science of artillery, as we may gather from the following passage in *Pantometria,* where he points out that he does not agree with the conclusions of Tartaglia:[39]

I have at the last reduced that most irregular course and circute of the Bullet (framed and compounded of violent and naturall motions) within the boundes of numbers and Arithmeticall rules. . . . This surely I will say, that as the ignorant in Geometricall and Arithmeticall proportions, shall never attaine perfection, though hee turmoil in

[36] Jacques de Rojas, *Commentarium in Astrolabium quod Planisphaerium vocant* (Paris, 1550), p. 199. Text in Appendix, p. 363.

[37] J. Headlam, "The Guns, Gunners and Gunnery of the English Renaissance," *The Journal of the Royal Artillery*, Vol. 66, 1939, pp. 469-488.

[38] R. T. Gunther, "The Uranical Astrolabe and Other Inventions of John Blagrave of Reading," *Archaeologia*, Series 2, Vol. 28, 1929, pp. 55-72.

[39] L. Digges, *A Geometrical Practise named Pantometria* (London, 1571), Bk. I, Ch. 30.

power [*sic*] and shot all the dayes of his life: so the Geometer, how excellent so ever he be, learning onely to discourse of reason, without practise (yea and that sundrie wayes made) shall fall into manifolde errors or inextricable Laberinthes. Among many that I have read concerning that matter, I note one Nicholas Tartaglia an Italian, who surely for his singular inventions and perfect knowledge in Geometricall demonstrations, few or none in our time or many ages before may bee compared with him: and yet handling this Argument, he hath erred even in the principall, and as I might terme them the variest trifles: I meane touching the uttermost Randon and circute of the Bullet, which he affirmeth to be made of a Circular and right line.

A stronger denunciation of the errors of Tartaglia followed within a year from the pen of Thomas Digges:[40]

Artillery . . . that Art, hitherto by no nation to any purpose handld. For to passover the apparaunt Errors of Daniel Santbech . . . and grosse errors of many others, that being ignoraunt of the Mathematicals have taken upon them to write of this Arte: Even Tartalea the Italian, albeit he were an excellent Geometer, taking upon him to deliver sundrie Demonstrations in this newe Science, yet for wante of Practise and Experience, hath erred even in the first Principles and so consequentlye in the whole substance of his discourse. This Tartalea averreth the Angle of 45 grades, as meane between the Horizontal and the Vertical mountes or Elevations, to be the Angle of the utmost Randons: an Errour knowen even to the first Practicioners. He affirmeth also the declining Arcke of the Bullet to be a Section Circulare: an Errour likewise, but not so easie to be discerned. And whereas great Fame hatte bene spreade of certaine Tables by him invented, to declare the different Ranges of Bullets from al sorts of Peeces delivered at al Grades of Randon (a matter indeede rare and of great invention) this much I dare truly avowe and approve, that Tartalea upon those his fallible groundes and Erronious Principles, was never possibly able in those matters to deliver anye certaintie. The same among others was indeede by my father long practised, who ioyning continuall experience for many years with Geometrical Demonstrations, sought and at last founde, and did frame an instrument, with certaine Scales of Randons to perform all that by Tartalea his Tables promised.

Despite the protestations of Leonard and Thomas Digges, not much change took place in the art as outlined by Tartaglia. De Cespedes[41] repeats the diagrams of Tartaglia in 1606, and Smith,

[40] T. Digges, *An Arithmeticall Militare Treatise named Stratioticos* (London, 1572), p. 189.
[41] Garcia de Cespedes, *Libro de instrumentos nuevos de geometria* (Madrid, 1606), Ch. 20.

more than one hundred years after Tartaglia, gives the following instructions:[42]

But if the mark be further than the Peece will reach with her metall, then must you elevate the Peece with so many degrees as will reach the same . . . . the most common and special Instrument used among the Professors of the Art of Gunnery: most easie to understand of the unlearnéd, both for bringing their guns levell with any mark, as also to shoot at any degree of the randon. You must have a ruler about two feet long, and of weight to counter-poise the quadrant, fastened to one side of it. This must be put within the concave of ye peece, the quadrant hanging without, and by the plumb-line you shall find how many of these degrees the peece is elevated unto, and the Quadrant being thus placed you may mount the peece to what degree you shall find fit to shortly. If the wind is high you will have very much adoe to make the plummet stand still; if your gun is firing over a wall it is inconvenient to get at, and in field service you cannot use it, the plumb-line is over long before it stand still.

The defects of the quadrant described above (Figure 49) led to the introduction of an instrument known as the *gunner's rule,* which is described by Smith and also by Nye, who, writing a few years later, gives the following recommendations for gunners:[43]

A Gunner ought to be skilful in Arithmetick and Geometry, to the end he may be able through his knowledge in those Arts, to measure heights, depths, breadths and length, and to draw the plot of any piece of ground.

To counteract the offensive advantage of thé new artillery, new types of fortification had to be developed. Here again the lead was taken by Italy with the early designs of Martini of Sienna, San Gallo, and Leonardo da Vinci. Many of the books on surveying mentioned in the course of this chapter carried a special section on fortification design and layout; some of them dealt almost exclusively with this topic. The outstanding change from the medieval castle-fort was the development of the multisided star fort with the bastion as its most important element. The ideas developed in Italy soon spread to other countries; the earliest example of a complete bastion fort is that of Paciotto, built at Antwerp in 1568. France attained to first rank in the art of

---

[42] Headlam, *op. cit.,* p. 486, quoted from Thomas Smith, *The Art of Gunnery* (London, 1641). By permission of the Royal Artillery Institution, Woolwich.
[43] Nathanael Nye, *The Art of Gunnery* (London, 1647), p. 37.

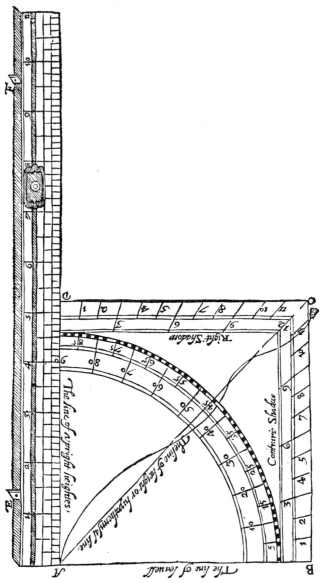

Figure 49. THE GUNNER'S QUADRANT BY THOMAS SMITH. *Reproduced by permission of* The Journal *of the Royal Artillery.*

fortification-building in the latter half of the sixteenth century, chiefly through the work of Vauban. While many of the systems appearing in the practical geometry books were the work of theorists,[44] Vauban had acquired his knowledge in the hard school of experience.[45] It is of interest to note in passing that it was through the solution of problems connected with fortifications that Monge developed the elements of descriptive geometry in the eighteenth century. Besides the demand for surveying instruments in the laying out of such fortifications, we have numerous diagrams in the Renaissance geometries showing instruments being used by besiegers of such forts in order to ascertain heights and distances (Figure 50).

The fourth important influence on instrument development came about from the impetus given to the science and art of navigation in this period of the great discoveries. European navigation, from the thirteenth to the middle of the fifteenth century, had been primarily developed by the Italian city-states, such as Venice and Genoa, and smaller centers of maritime activity such as Amalfi. Its purpose was to provide a means of cheap transportation for the commodities of trade procurable on the North African coast and those from the Indies and Far East which were picked up at the termini of the caravan routes along the eastern Mediterranean and the Black Sea. Large emporiums, stocked with the luxuries of the East, were to be found in these Italian cities and towns whence, by means of coastal sailing vessels, trade was carried on with all important European seaports from Spain to Norway. Two important developments arose from this coastal sailing. One was a gradual improvement in the construction of the marine compass; the second was the pictorial mapping of coastlines on Portolan charts.[46]

Urged on by the economic advantages monopolized by the Italian cities, other maritime peoples had long dreamed of participating in the Eastern trade by developing other routes to the Indies. Foremost among these were the Portuguese, who made

[44] For example, Girolamo Cataneo, *Opera nuova di fortificare* (Brescia, 1564).
[45] He is said to have been chief engineer at some forty sieges. See *Encyclopaedia Britannica*, Fourteenth Edition, Vol. 9, p. 528, article "Fortification and Siegecraft."
[46] G. H. Kimble, "Some Notes on Medieval Cartography," *Scottish Geographical Magazine*, Vol. 49, 1933, pp. 91-98. E. L. Stevenson, *Portolan Charts* (New York, 1911).

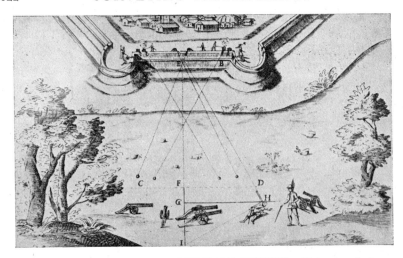

Figure 50. FORTIFICATION SCENE BY BETTINI. *Reproduced from*
Sanford's A Short History of Mathematics, *by permission of the author.*

their first attempts to change their dreams to reality under the
leadership of Henry the Navigator (1395-1460). Before the end
of Henry's reign the Italian Mediterranean trade had received a
severe setback, through the rise to power of the Ottoman Empire,
and more than ever it became imperative to seek new sea routes
to the East. The Portuguese goal was to sail round the African
coast south of the Sahara wastes which they knew through the
Muslims.[47] By 1445 Portuguese ships had reached the neighborhood of the Guinea coast, and before his death, Henry's ships had
traveled south almost to the equator. Henry was not a sailor himself, his claim to the title of "the Navigator" resting rather on the
support which he gave his sailors by providing them with the
best nautical information to be procured at the time.

This he did by establishing at Sagres, in 1416, a school of navigation. To direct the work of this school, Henry induced to come
from Majorca a certain "Mestre Jacomo," known to us only by the
epitomized account of De Barros:[48]

[47] On the map which the Muslim geographer Edrisi constructed for Roger II of
Sicily in 1150, this tract of land is called "Bilad Shana," "the Land of Wealth." Muslim intercourse with this section of Africa was well established through the caravan
routes across the Sahara.
[48] João de Barros, *Decades de Asia,* 1778 Edition (First Edition, Lisbon, 1552),
Decade 1, Bk. 1, Ch. 16.

A man very learned in the art of navigation, and in the construction of charts and instruments, whom it was very desirable to bring to this kingdom to enable Portuguese officers to learn from that master.

Who this Jacomo was is uncertain; the most reliable authorities have identified him with Jafuda Cresques, a cartographer and compass-maker.[49] Neither have we any information as to whether other instruments besides the compass were made use of by the Portuguese during this period, although this is most probable, since the astrolabe, quadrant, and Jacob's staff were long known in the Iberian Peninsula. The first authentic record of an observation on the polestar by means of a quadrant occurs two years after Henry's death. Twenty-six years after Henry's demise his hope of finding a new route to the Indies by rounding the African continent was realized when Bartholomeo Dias rounded the Cape of Good Hope, or as he named it, Cabo Tormentoso, and the goal was finally reached when Vasco da Gama sailed to India and back in 1497.

The excitement caused through Europe by the Portuguese and Spanish discoveries at this time has been graphically depicted by a recent author:[50]

Perhaps only our own generation, which is witnessing the conquest of the air, only we, who little more than thirty years ago were willing to rejoice at the tidings of the flight of an aeroplane which was able to sustain itself in the air for five or ten miles beyond its starting point at the Champ de Mars; who were wildly excited when in 1909, Bleriot flew across the English Channel and then, only eighteen years later, were told of the first flight across the Atlantic and of the successful aerial voyage from England to Australia—only we are perhaps in a position to understand the excitement that ran through Europe when towards the close of the fifteenth century it heard of the triumphs of Portugal.

After Henry's death, interest in navigation was continued under the patronage of Alfonso V (1460-1481), and more intensely under João II (1481-1495), styled by Bensaude[51] "la plus noble

[49] C. R. Markham, "The History of the Gradual Development of the Groundwork of Geographical Science," *The Geographical Journal*, Vol. 46, 1915, p. 173.

[50] S. Zweig, *Conqueror of the Seas—The Story of Magellan*, English Translation by E. and C. Paul (New York, 1938), pp. 18-19. By permission of The Viking Press, Inc.

[51] J. F. Bensaude, *Histoire de la science nautique portugaise, résumé* (Geneva, 1917), p. 39.

figure de l'histoire de découvertes," who founded the famous Junta dos Mathematicos of which the principal members were Diego Ortiz, Jose Vizinto, Rodrigo, and for a time, Martin Behaim. Vizinto was a pupil of the greatest astronomer of Salamanca at this period, Abraham Zacuto, who in 1473 published a perpetual almanac in Hebrew. This, Vizinto translated into Latin,[52] and it was made the basis of calculations carried out by the Junta, since it contained tables of the declination of the sun, by means of which latitude could be calculated from observations of the meridian altitude of the sun. By means of this almanac, one of the problems before the Junta was solved; namely, the determination of latitude in the southern hemisphere.[53] Such tables as Zacuto's and other information useful for mariners were printed in manuals or *regimentos*.

The lack of any copy of such a regimento, the sparse information given by contemporary Portuguese chroniclers, and, above all, the presence of Martin Behaim on the Junta, provided the background for the claim put forward in the last century by German historians that advances in navigation by the Portuguese were due to knowledge of nautical astronomy derived from German sources.[54] This theory was based on a very vague passage from the historian De Barros. Speaking of the Junta dos Mathematicos he says:[55]

In the time of King João II this business was entrusted by him to Master Rodrigo and to Master Joseph, both his physicians, and to one Martin of Boemia, native of these parts, who gloried in having been a disciple of John of Monte Regio, a famous astronomer among the professors of

[52] *Almanach Perpetuum Celestium Motuum cujus Radix est 1473* (Leiria, 1496).
[53] Such was the method followed by Vasco da Gama when he landed at the Bay of Santa Helena, July 4, 1497. Having erected his specially constructed large astrolabe (about five feet in diameter) on a tripod, he found the noon altitude of the sun to be 76°20'. His zenith distance was therefore 13°40'. According to the regimento for November the sun was 26° in Scorpion; this was equivalent to a declination of 19°21' south. Adding this to his zenith distance, he determined his latitude as 33°1' south (true value 32°47' south). See Markham, *op. cit.*, p. 178. By permission of The Royal Geographical Society.
[54] This theory was first proposed by Humboldt (1836). Karl Ritter (1861) proclaimed that Behaim was the inventor of the nautical astrolabe and introduced Regiomontanus' tables of the sun's declination to the Portuguese; finally Breusing (1869) claimed that Behaim acquainted the Portuguese with the use of the *balestille* or Jacob's staff. Later German writers, such as Günther and Steinschneider, have acknowledged the role played by the Portuguese. See Chapter III, note 138.
[55] De Barros, *op. cit.*, Decade I, Bk. 4, Ch. 2.

that science. These found this manner of navigating by altitude of the sun, for which they made their tables of declination[56] as they are now used among mariners, now more accurately than at first, for which those great astrolabes of wood are used.

Farfetched as this theory may seem, in the light of what we know of earlier Muslim and Jewish mathematical accomplishments on the Iberian Peninsula, it remained unrefuted for lack of documentary evidence until the discovery in a Munich library of an old Portuguese regimento. This discovery was the starting point for the brilliant research carried on for many years by the Portuguese Bensaude, as a result of which he has finally established the fact that Portuguese navigation was entirely the result of Portuguese enterprise.[57]

As to the instruments used by the Portuguese mariners under the guidance of the Junta, we have documentary evidence with regard to the astrolabe, quadrant, and compass. In all probability the simplification of the astrolabe was carried out by the Junta. The first recorded use of the astrolabe on a ship is by Diogo d'Azambuja in 1481.[58] The absence of any mention of the Jacob's staff at this time is intriguing. We know that it was first developed on the Iberian Peninsula (see p. 85). Why an instrument which became so popular with mariners in later times could have been altogether ignored by both Portuguese and Spaniards for over a hundred years is a mystery on which no light has yet been shed; it is all the more mysterious since during the same period it had been popularized in Central Europe by Regiomontanus.

With the African route to the Indies monopolized by the Portu-

[56] The independence of Zacuto's tables from Regiomontanus' is pointed out by Markham, *op. cit.*, p. 180. Regiomontanus calculated for an obliquity of 23°30'; whereas Zacuto used 23°33'.

[57] J. F. Bensaude, *L'Astronomie nautique au Portugal à l'époque des grandes découvertes* (Bern, 1912); see also *op. cit.* Besides drawing up his own publications, he has been instrumental in having the Portuguese government publish replicas of the historic documents on which he bases his claims. Among the more important of these are *Regimento do estrolabio e do quadrante* (1509), anonymous. Zacuto, *Almanach Perpetuum Celestium motuum* (1496). Francesco Faleiro, *Tratado del esphera y del arte del marear* (Seville, 1535). An important work which led the way for Bensaude is E. G. Ravenstein, *Martin Behaim, His Life and His Globes* (London, 1908).

[58] Ravenstein, *op. cit.*, p. 16, quoted from Manuel Telles da Silva, *De rebus gestis Joanni II* (Lisbon, 1689), p. 152. See also A. Barbosa, "Instrumente nauticos da Epoca dos Descobrimentos maritimos: sua importancia historica," *O Instituto, Revista Scientifica e Literaria*, Vol. 74, 1927, pp. 470-534.

guese, the other maritime peoples of Europe set about the task of finding a western route. This led to the unexpected discovery of America by Columbus and the circumnavigation of the globe by the survivors of Magellan's expedition (1519-1521). England, the Netherlands, and, to a lesser extent, France, not appreciating the economic value of the newly discovered continent, continued to seek a northeast and a northwest passage to China and the Indies, the result of which was a long period during which instruments of navigation played an important part and ample incentives were offered to bring about improvements in both theory and practice.[59] The question of latitude determination by solar observation had been fairly satisfactorily settled by the Portuguese; but when ships ventured far to sea, the question of longitude became important. Although many methods for its determination were tried, including dead reckoning, observation of lunar eclipses, and variation in declination and inclination of the compass, this period was to have long drawn to a close before the *chronometer* method, suggested as early as 1530 by Gemma Frisius,[60] was made practical by the production of accurate timepieces.[61]

One important instrument, from the historical viewpoint, which developed from attempts to determine longitude from the declination of the compass is the *differential quadrant* of Jean Rotz. Rotz was one of the many French pilots who entered the English service during the reign of Henry VII. After presenting a treatise on nautical science to the King, he was appointed chief hydrographer in 1542. In this treatise[62] he describes his differential quadrant (Figure 51), which was essentially an instrument for determining simultaneously altitude and azimuth angles and

[59] Among the more important voyages of discovery were those of Sebastian Cabot, 1497, to Labrador and Newfoundland; Pedro Cabral, 1500, to Brazil and India; Americus Vespucci, 1497, to Central and South America; Ferdinand Magellan, 1519-1521, in circumnavigation of the globe; João de Castro, 1538-1541, to South America; Hugh Willoughby and Richard Chancelor, 1553, Stephen Burrough, 1556, and William Barents, 1594, seeking the Northeast Passage; and Jacques Cartier, 1534, Martin Frobisher, 1576, John Davis, 1585, Henry Hudson, 1601, and William Baffin, 1615, seeking the Northwest Passage.

[60] Gemma Frisius, *De Principio Astronomicae et Cosmographiae* (Antwerp, 1530).

[61] S. Smiles, *History of the Invention by John Harrison of the Marine Chronometer* (London, undated). See also E. A. Reeves, *Maps and Map-making* (London, 1910), pp. 42 ff.

[62] J. Rotz, *Traicté des differences du compas aymante et de certains pointez notables ducelluy* (Dieppe, 1542), manuscript. See Taylor, *Tudor Geography*, pp. 64-67.

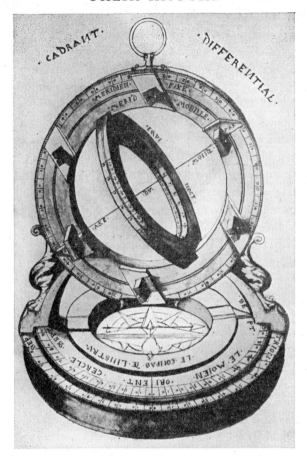

Figure 51. ROTZ'S DIFFERENTIAL QUADRANT. *Reproduced from Taylor's* Tudor Geography, *by permission of Methuen and Co., Publishers.*

must therefore be regarded as the second European prototype of the modern theodolite, though not very much like the latter in appearance and in its prime purpose, which was the accurate determination of the variation of the compass.

Finally, the astronomical revolution climaxed by the publication of the *De Revolutionibus Orbium Coelestium* of Copernicus in 1543 was another source from which the development of surveying instruments gathered impetus. The immediate groundwork for the revolutionizing hypothesis of Copernicus (1473-1543) had been laid in the previous century by Cardinal Nicolaus de

Cusa (1401-1464), Georg Purbach (1423-1461), and Johann Müller (Regiomontanus) (1436-1476). De Cusa's contribution consisted in his being not only an exponent of the heliocentric theory and the diurnal rotation of the earth, but also a reformer of the Alfonsine tables and responsible in part for the education of Purbach, who has been styled "the founder of observational and mathematical astronomy in the West." Purbach, in turn, participated in the education of Regiomontanus, who was to become the most distinguished scientist of his time.

The principal instrument employed by Purbach was the geometric square, which he used in conjunction with a table of natural sines computed at ten-minute intervals.[63] From Schöner's account [64] we know that Regiomontanus made use of the astrolabe, geometric square, and quadrant; but he also gives a description of another instrument—without name—which he says Regiomontanus used to find the apparent diameter of a comet. This instrument happened to be a Jacob's staff, and here we find the first important mention of its use since the time of Levi ben Gerson. From this astronomical use by Regiomontanus, the Jacob's staff soon found employment in surveying in the hands of such men as Apian and Frisius, both of whom were much interested in astronomy, and still later it played an important role as an instrument of navigation.

Although neither Copernicus nor his immediate disciple Georg Rhaeticus[65] (1514-1576) contributed anything directly to instrument development, since they were both chiefly concerned with the mathematical aspects of astronomy, the attempts at refutation and verification of their doctrines, in the hands of Tycho Brahe (1546-1601) and Galileo (1564-1642), led to a wide variation in instruments and finally to the fundamental change brought about by the introduction of *telescopic sights*.

Brahe was essentially an observer of astronomical phenomena and was lucky in securing sufficient royal patronage so that he was

---

[63] *Tractatus Georgii Purbachii super Propositiones Ptolemaei Sinibus et Chordis* (Nürnberg, 1541); and *Quadratum Geometricum* (Nürnberg, 1516-1517).

[64] Johann Schöner, *Scripta clarissimi mathematici M. Johannis Regiomontani, etc.* (Nürnberg, 1544).

[65] Rhaeticus, known as the "great computer." Among his books was a table of natural sines in ten-second intervals to fifteen places of decimals. *Opus Palatinum de Triangulis* (Neustadt an der Haardt, 1596).

able to establish and maintain at Uraniborg for twenty-one years, from 1576 to 1597, the most elaborate observatory established up to that time. Here he had set up a variety of instruments, both large and small, on which he experimented in order to bring about changes conducive to the greater accuracy of his observations. To him we owe the practical development of the use of transversals, or the diagonal scale, for the purpose of reading fractional parts of a main scale.

Whatever doubts may exist as to the original inventor of the telescope,[66] it is fairly certain that Galileo was the first to put it to scientific use. The length of time which elapsed between the first use of the telescope and its adoption for surveying instruments is surprising and is a phenomenon for which it is difficult to offer an explanation. The first use of the telescope in surveying seems to have been in the leveling instrument developed by Picard about 1660; but judging from Bion's work,[67] telescopic instruments were still the exception in the early eighteenth century.

Leveling Instruments

WATER LEVELS   During the greater part of this period, leveling was carried on by means of the astrolabe and the geometric square. Instruments modeled after Heron's dioptra or Vitruvius' chorobates were surprisingly slow in coming into use again. Leonardo da Vinci was the first to describe a level making use of the free surface of a liquid.[68] Da Vinci's instrument is modeled on that of Vitruvius; in fact, he calls it a chorobates. From the rather vague sketch which he made of it, it is impossible to determine the details of construction. It differs essentially from that of Vitruvius in being supported by one upright and seems to carry sights at each end of the horizontal trough. No plumb bobs are indicated, and

[66] On the history of the development of the telescope consult A. Wolf, *A History of Science, Technology and Philosophy in the 16th and 17th Centuries* (New York, 1935), pp. 75-76. See also T. Court and M. von Rohr, "A History of the Development of the Telescope," *Transactions, The Optical Society,* Vol. 30, 1928-1929, pp. 207-260; Vol. 32, 1930-1931, pp. 113-122.

[67] Nicolas Bion, *Traité de la construction et des principeaux usages des instruments de mathématique* (Paris, 1709). English Translation by E. Stone (London, 1724).

[68] Leonardo da Vinci (1452-1519). References here are to the facsimile volumes of his works, *Il Codice atlantico nella biblioteca ambrosiana di Milano,* 1894-1904, fol. 131, Ra.

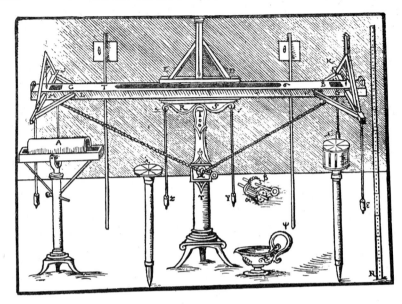

Figure 52. LEVELS AND SURVEYOR'S CROSSES BY WALTER RYFF

the length of the horizontal section is about twenty feet. In the particular instance for which Da Vinci cites the use of this choro-bates ("Se volessi ben livellare un piano di molte miglia"—"If you wish to level a plain miles wide") he says it should be leveled by means of a triangular plumb-bob level, and he seems to neglect altogether the use of the water trough. A far more elaborate in-strument of the same class is described and depicted by Ryff.[69] Figure 52 shows the type of level used by this prominent architect-engineer of the mid-sixteenth century. The most important rec-ords of the leveling instruments of this period are contained in the works of Claramontius and Schott.[70] From these it may be seen that the use of the water level was not much in vogue com-pared with the various types of plumb-bob levels described. Clara-montius describes a simple variety of the chorobates.[71] The level

---

[69] Walter Ryff, *Der furnembsten notwendigsten der gantzen Architectur angehöri-gen mathematischen und mechanischen Kunst* (Nürnberg, 1547).

[70] Scipio Claramontius, *Opuscula varia mathematica* (Bonn, 1653), Part III, pp. 151-277. Casper Schott, S.J., *Pantometrum Kircherianum* (Herbipolensi, 1660), Bk. 9, pp. 271-326.

[71] Claramontius, *op. cit.*, p. 229. "Sit regula *ABCD*, in uniformis canalis modu excauta, atque impleatur aqua, et quiescat, neutra ex parte ad fulchrum *ME* delapsa,

was turnable on a vertical staff, to which it was clamped by means of a screw (Figure 53). He also gives a sketch and description of a more elaborate form with sights and plumb-bob accessories. In reference to the length of the simpler form of instrument, he states:

Esto regula rectangula oblonga pedum nostratuum decem, nempe unius percticae, erit .n. ita viginti pedum circiter Romanorum iuxta praeceptu Vitruvii, nos quidem non tam longo instrumento utimur; attamen fateri oportet quo longius fuerit eo exactius esse, et brevitas ipsius potius commoditati deservit, quam certitudine observationis.

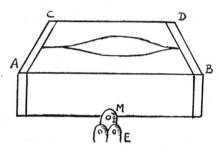

Figure 53. LEVEL BY CLARAMONTIUS

The best water level of the chorobates type was the *trough instrument* of Strumienski.[72] It consisted of a rectangular trough of iron about six feet long supported at its middle by an upright, to which it was held at right angles by means of a board and two screws (Figure 54). Its horizontality was determined by filling the trough with water. Sighting was done through regular sights attached to the narrow sides of the trough.

Another type, which was independent of lack of parallelism between the base of the receptacle and its rim, is described by Schott under the title *vase aquario*.[73] It consisted of a vessel with a large open liquid surface on which floated two congruent wooden blocks in the form of triangular prisms (Figure 55). Since their surfaces extended equally above the level of the water, they could be used as sights. Schott says that such an instrument was in common use in Italy. The blocks were usually weighted so as to pre-

---

versatur vero libra circa centrum, ac clavium *M*, in instrumenti medio positum, sed ad oram inferiorem ut nempe centrum versionis sit infra centrum gravitatis, erit aqua, quae in altera instrumenti medietate est aequalis aquae existenti in altera eiusdem instrumenti parte, etenim sibi dictae aquae partes aequiponderant, non .n. aequiponderent, sed gravior sit aqua ex. gr. *MD*. ergo regula vertetur deorsum ex parte *BD*, ad fulchrum *ME*, ex illis, quae de libra demonstratur, et ponitur manere, et ex neutra parte decidere."

[72] Olbrycht Strumienski, *O sprawie sypaniu wymierzaniu i rybieniu stawow* (Cracow, 1573). See F. Kucharzewski, "Sur quelques niveaux du seizième siècle," *Bibliotheca Mathematica*, Series 3, 1900, Vol. 1, pp. 60-63.

[73] Schott, *op. cit.*, Pl. 24, Fig. 177, p. 276.

vent tilting. The difficulty of procuring blocks of equal size and specific gravity lessened the accuracy of such a device.

For leveling over short distances, a glass vessel filled with water was sometimes used [74] (Figure 56), also two glass vessels of equal height, in which the sighting was done across the rims or across the water surfaces when they were equidistant from the rims[75] (Figure 57). In this latter case it is surprising that the insertion of a connecting tube between the two vessels was omitted, especially since the description of Heron's dioptra must have been known by this time. According to La Hire[76] such a level was finally produced by Riccioli. He gives two sketches, the first of which (Figure 58) closely resembles Heron's dioptra level, while in the second the tube is mounted on a tripod. This type of level, though surprisingly late in adoption, seems to have been in quite common use during the ensuing two centuries,[77] even though in the meantime the *spirit level* had been invented. Thevenot is regarded as the inventor of the spirit level, which he first describes in an anonymous tract published in 1666.[78] Later, in a book on navigation, he again describes the construction and use of his *niveau à bulle d'air*. As to its advantages he says:[79]

Un niveau plus portatif, plus facile à faire et à employer, et plus exact que tous ceux dont on s'est servi jusqu'à cette heure. . . . C'est un instrument où l'air enfermé avec quelque liqueur fait un Niveau, mais qui a ces avantages sur tous ceux dont on s'est servi jusque à cette heure. . . . On le trouve plus justé que les autres, car il n'y-a-point de si petite inclination qu'il ne fasse connoistre.

As to its construction, he says:

On choisit un tuyau de quelque matiere transparente, un canon de verre par example, dont les cotez soient paralleles; d'un diametre qui puisse recevoir le petit doigt, et qui soit environ sept ou huit fois plus

[74] *Ibid.*, Pl. 24, Fig. 173, p. 273. Claramontius, *op. cit.*, p. 201.
[75] Claramontius, *op. cit.*, p. 246.
[76] Philip de La Hire, *L'École des arpenteurs* (Paris, 1689), pp. 146-150. The date of Riccioli's invention is not recorded, but it was probably prior to 1660 even though it is not mentioned by Schott.
[77] Its appearance in many books on surveying justifies this statement; for example: S. F. La Croix, *Nouveau manuel complet d'arpentage* (Paris, 1845). M. Ozanam, *Traité de l'arpentage et du toise* (Paris, 1779).
[78] Melchisedech Thevenot, *Machine nouvelle pour conduire les eaux* (Paris, 1666).
[79] M. Thevenot, *Recueil de voyages* (Paris, 1681), pp. 10-11.

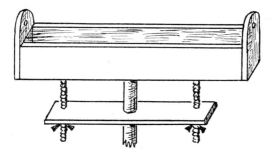

Figure 54. LEVEL BY STRUMIENSKI

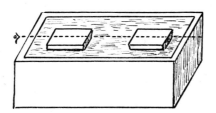

Figure 55. LEVEL BY SCHOTT

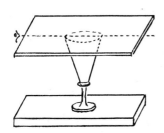

Figure 56. LEVEL BY SCHOTT

Figure 57. LEVEL BY SCHOTT

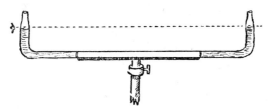

Figure 58. LEVEL BY RICCIOLI

long que large. On le ferme par un bout, et on y met quelque liqueur. L'esprit de vin y est fort propre, parce qu'il ne fait point de sédiment et qu'il ne gele jamais. On laisse du tuyau environ un peu moins de vuide qu'il n'a de diametre; on le bouche apres, ou on le scelle par le feu. Lors qu'on s'en sert et qu'on l'applique sur le plan que l'on veut examiner, l'air qui y est enfermé monte aussi-tost vers la partie du plan la plus élevée, et demeure sans mouvement lorsque le plan est horizontal, et cela toujours avec la mesme justesse, quelque temps qu'il fasse. [Figure 59.]

Information as to this invention must have been spread rapidly, since we find in the 1674 edition of Leybourn:[80]

I have lately seen and used a Water-level contrived by Mr. R. Shotgrave, not above 18 inches long, where the water (or some Spirit to prevent freezing) is inclosed, with a Tube or Telescope underneath the case that holds the trunk, with a Spring and scrues to bring the water to its true Position.

This is quite an advance on his brief mention of water levels in the 1657 edition, which states in Chapter 59, "There is an Instrument called a water-level, for the performance hereof the making whereof is sufficiently known." From the vague diagram accompanying the statement, his water level seems to have been a type of chorobates.

The most complete form of spirit level developed within the period is that of Mallet (Figure 60). The reason why the spirit level was so tardy in coming into common use was the erratic movement of the bubble, since tubes with internal curvature had not yet been developed.[81]

PLUMB-BOB LEVELS   Various forms of plumb-bob levels are to be found in the writings of this period, before the end of which the following improvements over the earlier instruments of the same class were initiated. First, telescopic sights slowly replaced the older forms; second, a graduated arc for measuring angles of slope was introduced; third, suspension forms became more numerous.

[80] William Leybourn, *The Compleat Surveyor* (London, 1653), Third Edition, 1674. Leybourn's first work on surveying, published in 1650 under the pseudonym Oliver Wallinby, was entitled *Planometria, or The Whole Art of Surveying of Land*.
[81] J. C. Sturm, *Nivillirens* (Augsberg, 1715). For changes in liquid levels during the eighteenth century, see A. de Chézy, "Mémoire sur quelques instruments propre à niveler, nommés niveaux," *Mémoires de l'académie des sciences*, Vol. 5, 1768.

Figure 59. THEVENOT'S DIAGRAM FOR LEVEL BUBBLE TUBE

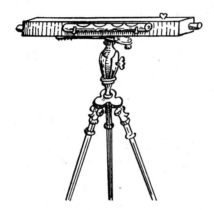

Figure 60. MALLET'S BUBBLE LEVEL

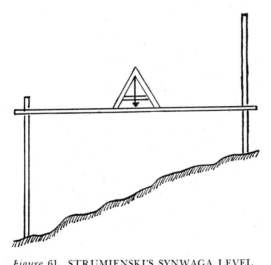

Figure 61. STRUMIENSKI'S SYNWAGA LEVEL

The ordinary isosceles-triangular level, sometimes with a long board attached, seems to have been quite common. Such a combination was called by Strumienski the *synwaga*[82] (Figure 61). From Claramontius and Schott we have descriptions and diagrams of the common forms. Figure 62 shows simple types used for rough work.[83] Figure 63 shows the first improved form of such levels, named by Schott *libella ordinaria*.[84] At about half the height of the triangle, parallel to the ground line, it carried a crosspiece on which was set a pair of sights. As already mentioned, the geometric square was in common use as a level.[85] Another instrument which was adopted for leveling a short while after its inception was the plane table. In general the square plate (Figure 64) was turned on its support into a vertical position, determined by a plumb bob hung along one edge, and sighting was done along the horizontal edge, which was sometimes fitted out with sights.[86] Sometimes two plumb lines were employed to make the plate completely vertical, as by Claramontius (Figure 65). Even more widely used than the two last-mentioned instruments was the quadrant;[87] in contrast with these it was usually used in the hand, except in the case of large-size ones which were mounted on staffs.[88]

The use of a graduated scale on the simplest forms of plumb-bob levels grew, in all probability, out of a device to make quick estimates of small slopes, such as would be used in connection with the conduction of water; it was also used to obtain the angle of elevation of artillery. In some of the isosceles levels the angle divisions were projected onto a horizontal crosspiece, as in Bion's[89] "Du Pied à niveau pour l'artillerie" (Figure 66). Many elaborate

[82] Kucharzewski, *op. cit.*

[83] Similar types may be found in G. Pomodoro, *La Geometria Prattica* (Rome, 1599), Pls. 1, 2. P. Ryff, *Questiones in Euclidis et P. Rami* (Frankfurt a.M., 1600), p. 15. D. Schwenter, *Geometricae practicae novae et auctae, libri IV* (Nürnberg, 1618), Bk. 1, pp. 38-39. And many others.

[84] Schott, *op. cit.*, Pl. 24, Fig. 175, p. 276.

[85] Christopher Clavius, S.J., *Operum Mathematicorum* (Moguntiae, 1611), Tomus Secundus, *Geometria Practica*, p. 103. Tartaglia, *op. cit.*, Bk. 3, p. 24. And many other authors.

[86] Schott, *op. cit.*, Pl. 25, Fig. 198, p. 313. See also Sebastien le Clerc, *Traité de géométrie* (Paris, 1690), pp. 246-248.

[87] See Figures 261 and 263.

[88] Levinus Hulsius, *De Quadrante Geometrico* (Nürnberg, 1594), pp. 41, 46, 50. Claramontius, *op. cit.*, p. 238.

[89] Bion, *op. cit.*, p. 181.

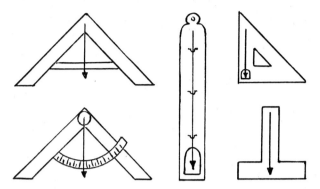

Figure 62. COMMON PLUMB-BOB LEVELS BY SCHOTT

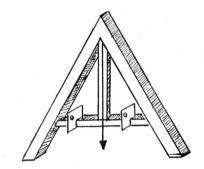

Figure 63. LIBELLA ORDINARIA BY SCHOTT

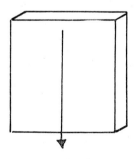

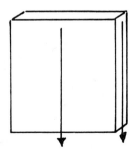

Figure 64. PLANE
TABLE USED AS A
LEVEL BY LE CLERC

Figure 65. PLANE
TABLE USED AS A
LEVEL BY CLARA-
MONTIUS

forms of artillery levels are to be found in the books dealing with this subject. Figures 67 and 68 are typical.[90] Perhaps the most elaborate is that described by Hulsius[91] under the title "De for-

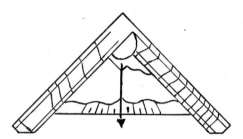

Figure 66. ARTILLERY LEVEL BY BION

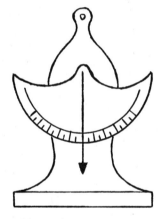

Figure 67. ARTILLERY
LEVEL BY SARDI

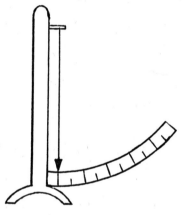

Figure 68. ARTILLERY LEVEL
BY SCHREIBER

manoui Quadrantis Tormentarii" (Figure 69). This contained not only a scale for measuring angles of elevation but also sights and a compass for determining bearings, as well as a sundial; what more could a Renaissance gunner desire!

Semicircular disks with plumb bobs were commonly used in mine-surveying to determine slope. From the descriptions of Agric-

[90] Figures 67 and 68 are respectively from Sardi, *op. cit.*, p. 74; and G. Schreiber, *Buchsenmaister Discurs* (Bresslau, 1656), p. 22.

[91] Levinus Hulsius, *Tractati Instrumentorum Mechanicorum* (Frankfurt a.M., 1603-1615), Tractatus Secundus (1605), Ch. 7, p. 9. Text in Appendix, p. 363.

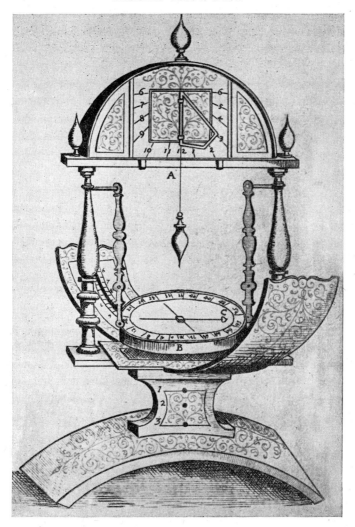

Figure 69. ARTILLERY QUADRANT BY HULSIUS

ola, Bion, and others,[92] we know that such instruments (*clinometers,* Figure 70) were hung from cords stretched along the tunnel. For this purpose suitable hooks for hanging were attached to the diametral edge of the disk. Clavius has left a description of

[92] Georg Agricola, *De Re Metallica* (Basel, 1556), English Translation by **H. C.** Hoover and L. H. Hoover (London, 1912). Benjamin Bramer, *Neuen Instrument zum Grundlegung* (Marburg, 1616). Adrian Metius, *Arithmeticae libri duo et Geometriae libri sex.* (Lugodini, 1626), Part Six. Schott, *op. cit.*, Pl. 25, Fig. 182, p. 282.

a special form of this semicircular plumb-bob level, which, with the aid of a monograph, gave the ratio between the horizontal and vertical projections of any sloping line:[93]

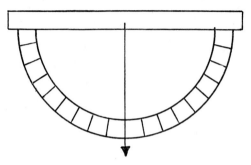

Figure 70. CLINOMETER

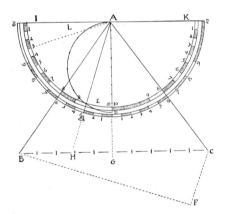

Figure 71. CLINOMETER BY CLAVIUS

Joannes Ferrerius, the Spaniard, a great architect and mathematician, invented a very convenient instrument for leveling, when the given distance is not too great, after this manner. Two rulers AB, AC [Figure 71] of strong and durable wood are joined together, with equal legs whose length is sufficient so that the distance between the extremities B and C contains 10 palms exactly or even more. Then having erected AG perpendicular to BC, a semi-circle of any size whatever IDK is described from A, whose radius AD is divided into as many parts as there are palms in BC. Then, having described on AD an auxiliary semi-circle AED, all the divisions of the straight line AD are transferred from D

[93] Clavius, op. cit., Bk. III, Pr. XLV, 1, 2. Text in Appendix, p. 364.

onto this arc, and then from *A*, straight auxiliary lines are drawn from each point of the semi-circle *AED* and their intersections with the arc *DI* and the other arc *DK* are noted. If then a plumb-line from *A* coincides with the perpendicular, and all the [auxiliary] parts are erased, leaving only the legs *AB, AC* of the instrument together with the arc *IDK*, then an instrument convenient for leveling has been constructed.

BALANCE LEVELS The commonest instrument used in this category was the astrolabe, sighting being done along the alidade when

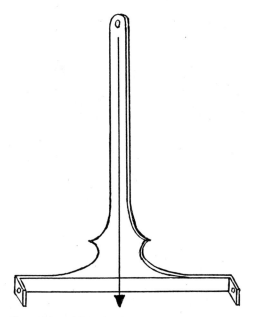

Figure 72. BALANCE LEVEL BY DUBRAVIUS

fastened along the E-W line. Because of its weight, the instrument hung naturally in the vertical plane, so that when the alidade was fixed in the aforesaid position, it established a horizontal line of sight. Many other forms depending on the same principle were developed;[94] probably the most accurate was the dioptra of Dubravius[95] (Figure 72). It consisted of an inverted T-shaped piece of metal with short right-angled jutments which carried the sights. The whole was suspended from a ring and used as a hand

[94] J. Chauvet, *Instruction et usage du cosmomètre* (Paris, 1585), Bk. 8.
[95] Kucharzewski, *op. cit.*, p. 60.

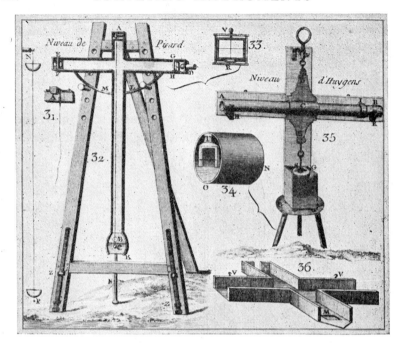

Figure 73. BALANCE LEVELS BY PICARD AND HUYGENS

instrument. Because of the symmetrical distribution of the weight, the line of sight was horizontal. As a check, a plumb bob hung on the vertical section. Dubravius' instrument was about eight inches wide, and thus its accuracy was limited, like that of the astrolabe, because of the smallness of the space between the sights. Similar instruments, though not so elaborate, are described by Alberti, La Hire, and others.[96] The culmination of this line of instruments was reached in the level of Picard [97] (Figure 73). Here the bob and line were enclosed in a wooden box to prevent disturbance due to winds, and a telescopic sight was used.

LEVELING RODS   As in the previous period, so in this there is very little to be found on leveling rods, and in no case is there anything approaching the standard set by Heron. A method of

---

[96] Leone B. Alberti, *Della Architectura* (1553), Italian with English Translation by J. Leoni (London, 1726), Vol. 1, Bk. 10, Ch. 7. Simon Stevin, *Mathematicorum Hypomnematum*, Tomus Secundus, *De Geometriae Praxi* (Leyden, 1605), p. 58.

[97] Jean Picard, *Mesure de la terre* (Paris, 1669).

leveling by night similar to that described by the Muslims (p. 58) is given by Leonardo da Vinci;[98] the only improvement he makes is in the type of lamp used. He employed an oil lamp in which the level of the wick was kept at a constant height despite the consumption of the oil. Leonardo states that the lamp may be placed up to about two hundred yards from the sighting instrument. Schwenter[99] describes a rod used in conjunction with Praetorius' plane table. It consisted of two pieces which slid over each other and were held in place by a vise. The target consisted of a cylindric head on top of the upper rod, the upper half being painted white and the lower black. (See Figure 151.) Pomodoro[100] has a diagram of a rod, divided according to some unit of length, which carries a square target. Leybourn, describing the process of leveling for the conduction of water, says:[101]

Place your Water-level at some convenient distance from the Spring-head, in a right line towards the place to which the water is to be conveyed, as at 30, 40, 60, or 100 yards distant from the Spring-head. Then having in readiness two long straight poles (which you may call your station staves) divided into Feet, Inches and parts of Inches, from the bottom upwards . . . cause your first assistant to move a leaf of paper up and down your station staff, till through the sights you see the very edge thereof, and then by some signe or sound, intimate to him that the paper is then in its true position.

Right-Angle Instruments

Through most of this period, despite the advances made in trigonometry, right-angled surveying was still the prevailing practice. In the case of fields with regular sides, the areas were found by dividing the land into a number of convenient triangles, rectangles, and trapezoids. In a case of an irregular boundary, such as a winding stream, a convenient straight line was laid off and perpendiculars were erected to the stream bank, dividing the area into a number of approximate trapezoids.[102] In this matter of calculating areas there was no improvement on the methods described by Heron. Only toward the end of the sixteenth century

[98] Da Vinci, *op. cit.*, fol. 131 *Ra*.
[99] Schwenter, *op. cit.*, Tractus III, "Mensula Praetoriana," pp. 638-640.
[100] Pomodoro, *op. cit.*, Pl. 31.
[101] Leybourn, *op. cit.*, Ch. 59.
[102] For example, see Clavius, *op. cit.*, Ch. 2, Pr. 42. Pomodoro, *op. cit.*, Pl. 40.

do we find use being made of the trigonometric relations between angles and sides of triangles. Even then they were used only, for the most part, in connection with problems on heights and distances.[103]

SQUARES AND ROPES   Large right-triangular squares such as already mentioned in the *Geometria Culmensis* (p. 59) continued in use. Sometimes they were fitted out with sights and instead of being laid on the ground were held at eye level, as we see from Buteo and others.[104] An interesting application of the square held in the vertical plane is given by Münster and later employed by a number of other authors.[105]

The symmetrical construction of a right angle by means of a stretched rope continued in use, as we see from Schwenter and Bion.[106] Also, the fact that the shortest distance from a point to a line is measured on the perpendicular from that point to the line was used in finding the altitudes of triangular plots by means of a stretched rope.[107] The Pythagorean construction of the right angle naturally continued in use, the common ratio being 3, 4, 5.[108]

Probably the most interesting description of the use of ropes is to be found in Agricola. Referring to Figure 74, in which the surveyor's problem was to find the depth of the shaft and the

[103] The first author to make use of the trigonometric functions in surveying problems was Bartholomew Pitiscus, whose *Trigonometriae* was published in 1600. See pp. 224-232 of that book for height and distance problems. Probably the largest collection of such problems solved by trigonometry is that of Clavius, *op. cit.*, pp. 43-70. Leybourn, *op. cit.*, Bk. 4, Ch. 41, uses the common trigonometrical method employed today to determine whether a survey closes, but the calculation of areas by the "double meridian distance" method was not developed until Thomas Burgh published *A Method To Determine the Areas of Right-Lined Figures Universally* (Dublin, 1724). Burgh was Chief Engineer of the army of occupation in Ireland from 1700 to 1730. In addition to his military duties, his interests extended to architecture, and he both planned and supervised the erection of many fine buildings. The best-known example of his architectural work is the library of Trinity College, Dublin.

[104] Johannes Buteo, *Opera Geometrica* (Lyons, 1554), pp. 110-111. Mario Bettini, *Apiaria Universae Philosophiae Mathematicae* (Bonn, 1645), Progymnasma Prima, Props. 3, 4, 5. Pomodoro, *op. cit.*, Pl. 12.

[105] See p. 277.

[106] Schwenter, *op. cit.*, pp. 305-306. Bion, *op. cit.*, Pl. 11, Fig. 3, p. 101.

[107] Johann Gutmann, *Feldmessung, gewiss, richtig und kurz gestellt* (Heidelberg, 1574), p. 42.

[108] Erasmus Reinhold, *Gründlicher und warer Bericht vom Feldmessen* (Saalfeld, 1574), suggests the use of 20, 21, 29 and the approximation 12, 12, 17. He also favors the substitution of wire for the hemp cord. See *Scientific American*, Vol. 54, 1902, Supplement, p. 22527.

Figure 74. SCENE FROM AGRICOLA'S *DE RE METALLICA*. *Reproduced by permission of* The Mining Magazine, *Publishers.*

length of the tunnel, Agricola gives the following account of the necessary operations:[109]

The surveyor, first of all, if the beams of the shaft-house do not give him the opportunity, sets a pair of forked posts by the sides of the shaft in such a manner that a pole may be laid across them. Next, from the pole he lets down into the shaft a cord with a weight attached to it. Then he stretches a second cord, attached to the upper end of the first cord, right down along the slope of the mountain to the bottom of the mouth of the tunnel, and fixes it to the ground. Next, from the same pole not far

[109] Agricola, *op. cit.*, pp. 130-132. By permission of *The Mining Magazine*.

from the first cord, he lets down a third cord, similarly weighted, so that it may intersect the second cord, which descends obliquely. Then, starting from that point where the third cord cuts the second cord which descends obliquely to the mouth of the tunnel, he measures the second cord upwards to where it reaches the end of the first cord, and makes a note of this first side of the minor triangle. Afterward, starting again from that point where the third cord intersects the second cord, he measures the straight space which lies between that point and the opposite point on the first cord, and in that way forms the minor triangle, and he notes this second side of the minor triangle in the same way as before. Then, if it is necessary, from the angle formed by the first cord and the second side of the minor triangle, he measures upward to the end of the first cord, and also makes a note of this third side of the minor triangle. The third side of the minor triangle, if the shaft is vertical or inclined and is sunk on the same vein in which the tunnel is driven, will necessarily be the same length as the third cord above the point where it intersects the second cord; and so, as often as the first side of the minor triangle is contained in the length of the whole cord which descends obliquely, so many times the length of the second side of the minor triangle indicates the distance between the mouth of the tunnel and the point to which the shaft must be sunk; and similarly, so many times the length of the third side of the minor triangle gives the distance between the mouth of the shaft and the bottom of the tunnel.

Besides the above method of similar triangles, Agricola also refers to another, commonly employed in mining during the Renaissance period:[110]

Some surveyors, although they use three cords, nevertheless ascertain only the length of the tunnel by that method of measuring, and determine the depth of a shaft by another method; that is, by the method by which cords are restretched on a level part of the mountain or in a valley, or in flat fields, and are measured again.

SURVEYOR'S CROSS   Various types of instruments with two sets of fixed sights set at right angles to each other appeared during the early part of this period; they were natural developments from the Roman groma, even though the groma itself does not appear to have been used. They may be divided into two classes according to the nature of the mode of sighting. To one class belong those in which sighting was done through grooves cut into the top

[110] *Ibid.*, p. 137.

surface (Figure 75); to the other those which used sights of the type usually found on the alidade of astrolabes (Figure 76).[111] In shape they were generally either square or circular and made either of wood or of metal. A form more closely resembling the groma is described by Leybourn:[112]

It is only two rulers of wood, in length about 14 inches, crossing one the other in the midst at right angles, and having at each end of both the rulers, back-sights, which serve only to set out right angles in the field itself.

The type which finally evolved from these two classes is described by Bion (Figure 77):[113]

The Surveying-Cross is a Brass Circle of a good Thickness, and 4, 5 or 6 Inches Diameter. It is divided into 4 equal Parts, by two lines cutting one another at right angles in the Center. At the four Ends of these Lines, and in the Middle of the Limb, there are fixed four strong Sights well rivetted in square Holes, and very perpendicularly slit over the aforesaid Lines, having Holes below each slit, for better discovering of distant Objects: the Circle is hollowed to render it more light. Underneath and at the Center of the instrument, there ought to be screwed on a Feril serving to sustain the Cross upon its Staff of 4 or 5 Feet long, according to the Height of the Observer's Eye. This Staff must be furnished with an Iron Point, to go into the Ground the better.

Another form of surveyor's cross which was widely adopted in France in later times consisted of a hollow, regular octagonal prism[114] (Figure 78). Four faces, opposite in pairs and forming a right angle, had each a narrow slit and a wider opening or window. A fine thread was placed vertically in the middle of each window in line with the prolongation of the slit. The slit of one face corresponded with the window of the opposite. The four other faces had each a long vertical slit. With this combination of slit and hair sights it was possible to lay out lines at either 90° or 45°.

[111] For the first class see Pomodoro, *op. cit.*, Pl. 31. Hulsius, *Tractati Instrumentorum Mechanicorum*, Tractatus Primus, p. 102. Describing the second class, Stevin, *op. cit.*, p. 8, says: "In sumo baculo lamina est, plerumque aenea, 8 aut 10 digitos lata, in cujus plano duae rectae ejus latera, et sese in centro ad angulos rectos bisecant, ut crucem facient."
[112] Leybourn, *op. cit.*, Bk. 2, Ch. 8.
[113] Bion, *op. cit.*, Stone Translation, p. 103.
[114] The earliest diagram of this type of cross is to be found in Walter Ryff, *op. cit.* See Figure 52. See also M. Oddi, *Dello squadro* (Milan, 1625).

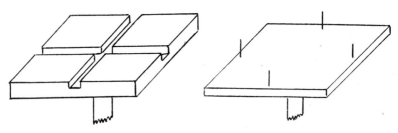

Figure 75. SURVEYOR'S CROSS
BY POMODORO

Figure 76. SURVEYOR'S CROSS
BY STEVIN

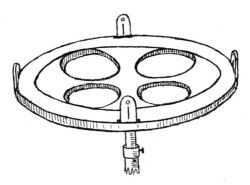

Figure 77. SURVEYOR'S CROSS BY BION

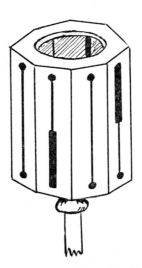

Figure 78. OCTAGONAL SURVEYOR'S CROSS

As long as compass traversing remained in vogue the surveyor's cross was part of the surveyor's equipment, since it was used for offsetting boundary lines which, occupied by walls, fences, or other obstacles, could not be measured directly. Hence we find it described in the surveying books of the nineteenth century.[115]

Staff Combinations

There are occasional references to the Indian circles method of determining the meridian.[116] The use of the various combinations

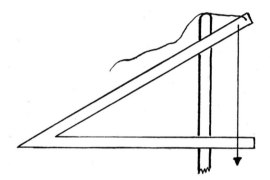

Figure 79. STAFF COMBINATION BY DA VINCI

of horizontal, vertical, and sighting staffs continued throughout this period despite the fact that the instruments which had been developed from them were in common use.[117] Leonardo da Vinci [118] describes a typical combination (Figure 79). It consisted of a sighting rod about five feet long, which could be turned by means of a cord passing through a notch in the top of the vertical staff to the hand of the observer. In order to hold the cord at any desired length, the notch was smeared with wax. The three staffs

---

[115] La Croix, *op. cit.*, Pl. 1, Fig. 12. A. Ewing, *A Synopsis of Practical Mathematics*, Fourth Edition (London, 1799), p. 77. And many others.

[116] Orontius Finaeus, *Protomathesis* (Paris, 1532), fol. 113. We come across the method in some of the instruments developed for the purpose of determining magnetic declination, *e.g.*, the brujula de variacion of Felipe Guillen 1525. (See L. A. Bauer, "The Beginnings of Magnetic Observation," *Terrestrial Magnetism and Atmospheric Electricity*, Vol. 4, 1899, No. 2, pp. 73-86. Translated from the German of G. Hellman). Gilbert, *op. cit.*, Bk. 4, Ch. 12.

[117] Luca Pacioli, *Sūma de Arithmetica, Geometria Proportioni et Proportionalita* (Venice, 1494), Tractatus "Geometria," Ch. 1. Hulsius, *De Quadrante Geometrico*, p. 22. Pomodoro, *op. cit.*, Pls. 43, 44. Belli, *op. cit.*, pp. 50-52.

[118] Da Vinci, *op. cit.*, fol. 131 *Ra*.

were similarly divided and pegs were used for sights. Da Vinci describes its use in finding the height of a mountain. A similar combination but of better construction was the instrument of Errard de Bar-le-Duc[119] (Figure 80) and also that used by Schwen-

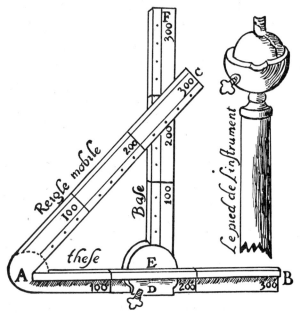

Figure 80. TELEMÊTRE BY ERRARD DE BAR-LE-DUC

ter.[120] Both Foullon and Praetorius made extensive use of staff combinations in connection with plane-table topographical work.[121]

The Astrolabe and Its Derivatives

GEOMETRIC SQUARE   The geometric square was brought into prominence at the beginning of this period through its employment in astronomical observations by Purbach as an angle-reading device. In order to procure readings of greater accuracy than was heretofore available Purbach subdivided the customary one-twelfth

[119] Errard de Bar-le-Duc, *La Géométrie et pratique géneralle d'icelle* (Paris, 1594). Figure 80 is taken from D. Henrion, *Collection ou recueil de divers traictéz mathematiques* (Paris, 1621), p. 18.

[120] Schwenter, *op. cit.,* p. 91.

[121] See Figures 144 and 151.

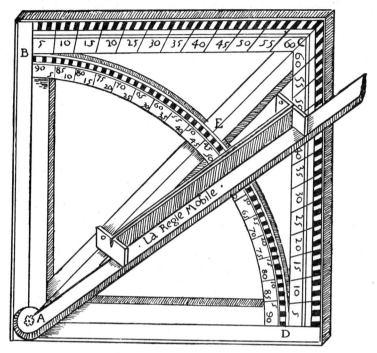

Figure 81. GEOMETRIC SQUARE WITH QUADRANT

division into one hundred parts, thereby making twelve hundred divisions on the side. For this purpose he naturally had to use a larger square, probably about three feet on the side. The method of division is not given by Schöner, to whom we are indebted for the earliest record of the instruments of Regiomontanus and Purbach.[122] It is doubtful whether Purbach used any type of transversal scale to facilitate the reading of small divisions on his geometric square, even though, according to Scultetus, both he and Regiomontanus knew of such scales.[123] Purbach used tables of sines and tangents to compute the value of the observed angles.[124]

[122] Schöner, *op. cit.* See also J. A. Repsold, *Zur Geschichte der astronomischen Messwerkzeuge von Purbach bis Reichenbach, 1450-1830* (Leipzig, 1908), Vol. 1, p. 12.

[123] Bartholomew Scultetus, *Gnomonice de Solariis* (Görlitz, 1572). From this work Repsold quotes the following: ". . . dass Transversalen 'vor zeiten in brauch gehabt von Georgius Purbachius und Joh. Regiomontanus, in welcher ehren und gedechtniss wir denn auch denselben modum allhier beschreiben.' "

[124] Repsold, *op. cit.*, p. 12. On the development of tables of trigonometrical functions by Purbach and others see F. Cajori, *A History of Mathematics* (New York, 1922), pp. 131 ff.

The only important addition made to the original design of the geometric square was the inclusion of a graduated quarter-circle arc for the direct measurement of angles[125] (Figure 81). A few instruments are to be found in which the turning point of the alidade is in the center of the square. Tartaglia[126] describes such a one in connection with measuring angles for artillery. In general, the simple form of the instrument was retained. The most important change that took place was in connection with the types of scales used. At first the common form was in divisions of twelve. Finaeus,[127] who used this instrument extensively, had them made from three to five feet on the side and was therefore able to divide them into 120 parts. One of the most complete works on the geometric square is that of Hulsius. Descriptions of the solutions of numerous problems are given together with very fine illustrations (Figure 82). Describing the instrument, he says:[128]

Tabula praeparetur quadrata ex ligno, vel ex aere, et in angulos rectos latera ipsa dirige, quorum singula uno longa pede erunt. . . . Nos dum facilitati consulimus, ex pede, latera singula constare debere, iudicamus.

This square was to be mounted on a rod about four feet high. Decimal divisions seem to have been introduced by Apian, who extols the advantages to be gained in speed of computation by this system:[129]

Dann es ist gut multiplicirn ein netliche in sich selbst wan du fur ein netliche so vil o nulla fesst als sie vor hin hat so ist sic schon in sich selbst multiplicirt.

Among the later writers we find the decimal division commonly used.[130] A radical departure from the ordinary square is the *squadra mobile* of Fabri[131] (Figure 83). Whatever advantage was to be gained from the use of the 180° arc, it does not seem to have

[125] This type is depicted in many books; for instance, those by Reisch, Pomodoro, and Münster.
[126] Tartaglia, *op. cit.*, pp. 31-32.
[127] Finaeus, *op. cit.*, fol. 64-65. A diagram in Chapter 3 of his *De re et praxi geometrica* (Paris, 1556), shows the observer in kneeling position with the top of the square at eye level.
[128] Hulsius, *De Quadrante Geometrico*, p. 4.
[129] Peter Apian, *Instrument-Buch* (Ingolstadt, 1533), fol. L. 1.
[130] Clavius, *op. cit.*, Bk. 3, pp. 64 ff. Bion, *op. cit.*, Pl. 13, Fig. G, Bk. 4, Ch. 5, pp. 126 ff.
[131] Ottavio Fabri, *L'uso della squadra mobile* (Padua, 1615).

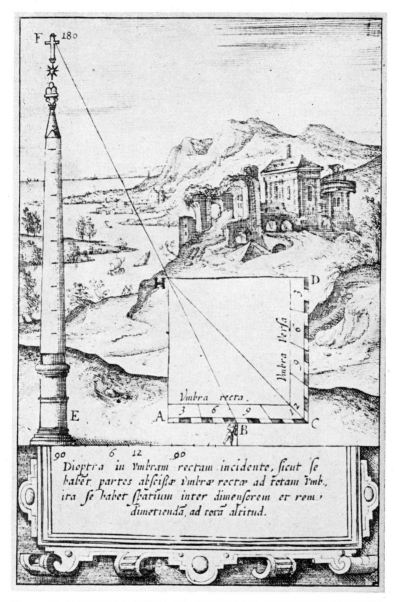

Figure 82. DETERMINATION OF HEIGHT BY GEOMETRIC SQUARE.
From Hulsius' De Quadrante Geometrico.

impressed Fabri's successors, for it stands as a lone sample. Belli[132] uses a solid square on which the sides are divided into thirty parts, from which a network of rectangular coordinates covers the inside space (Figure 84). With the increase in the practice of measuring angles in degrees and the use of the trigonometric functions, the geometric square began to lose its usefulness. On this point Leybourn says, speaking of the square on Digges' "instrument topographicall":[133]

. . . but there are very few of them made now with this square, for the degrees themselves will better supply that want, it being taken only for heights and distances.

Squares with a plumb line instead of the alidade and the sights along one edge were sometimes used in surveying. By Münster and Clavius they are called *quadratum pendulum,* as distinguished from the ordinary type *quadratum stabile.* A special type of square with one side prolonged was used in connection with artillery.[134]

ASTROLABE   Notwithstanding its decline as an astronomical instrument, the astrolabe continued to be an important instrument in surveying and navigation throughout the Renaissance period, and as we shall see later, its variations gradually led to the beginnings of some of our modern instruments. From the large number of books describing specifically the construction and use of the astrolabe, we realize that it was still quite an important instrument in the sixteenth century.[135]

With the introduction of triangulation methods early in the sixteenth century, measurement of obtuse and acute angles became more and more prevalent, and naturally the first instrument to be used for such purposes was the one which had already been so used in astronomy. When adopted for this new function the astrolabe gradually underwent changes in construction to make it more convenient and accurate. The astronomical paraphernalia began

[132] Belli, *op. cit.,* pp. 2 5.
[133] Leybourn, *op. cit.,* Ch. II, p. 43.
[134] Tartaglia, *op. cit.,* Bk. 1, pp. 23-30. Gentilinius, *op. cit.,* p. 49. Smith, *op. cit.* See Figure 49.
[135] Among the more important of these were: J. Stöffler, *Flucidatio Fabricae Ususque Astrolabii* (Tübingen, 1511). Gemma Frisius, *De Astrolabio Catholico* (Antwerp, 1556). Christopher Clavius, S.J., *Astrolabium, Tribus Libris Explicatum* (Rome, 1593).

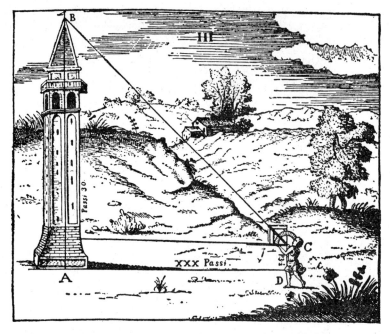

Figure 83. GEOMETRIC SQUARE WITH SEMICIRCULAR ARC BY FABRI. *Reproduced from Smith's* History of Mathematics, *Vol. II, by permission of Ginn and Co., Publishers.*

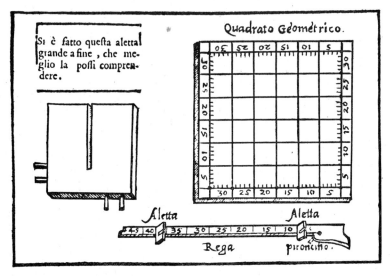

Figure 84. GEOMETRIC SQUARE WITH COORDINATE LINES BY BELLI

Figure 85. ASTROLABE WITH INSET COMPASS IN THRONE BY AR-
SENIUS. *Reproduced from Laussedat's* Recherches sur les instruments,
les méthodes et le dessin topographiques, *by permission of Gauthier-
Villars, Publishers.*

to disappear, the diameter of the plate was enlarged, and with the
increased use of the trigonometric formulas and tables the shadow
square lost its usefulness. Various simplified astrolabes appeared
which were far removed from the Muslim instruments. In general,
the only parts they had in common with their forerunners were
the means of suspension, the alidade, and the divided circular
arc. For triangulation the astrolabe had to be placed in a horizontal position, usually being mounted on a staff.

The first addition to the instrument was the compass, which was
introduced on the edge of the instrument (Figure 85), as in those
constructed by Walter Arsenius, nephew of Gemma Frisius.[136]

[136] Gemma Regnier (1508-1555), was commonly known as Gemma Frisius, from the

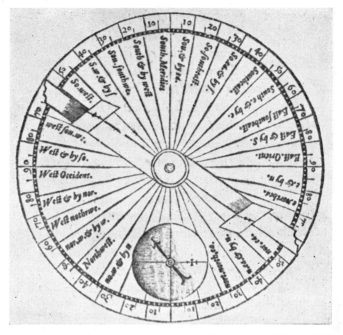

Figure 86. SKETCH OF SURVEYOR'S ASTROLABE WITH INSET
COMPASS BY CUNINGHAM

Later, the compass was placed directly on the "mother," where it replaced the projection plates (Figure 86). In general it may be said that the astrolabe was, from then on, used mainly for astrological purposes;[137] in astronomy it was first replaced by various part-circle instruments, such as quadrants, *octants,* and *sextants,*[138] which in time gave way before the astronomical telescope; its use-

land of his birth. "The most influential of the various Dutch mathematicians of this century." His numerous works on mathematics and instruments are all the more interesting since his real profession was medicine, a professorship of which he held in Louvain University. In 1529 he issued the first Antwerp edition of Apian's *Cosmographia.* The second Antwerp edition in 1533 carried an addition by Frisius himself, entitled *Libellus de locorum describendorum ratione,* which is the earliest known description of triangulation.

[137] Throughout the Renaissance astrology was still a popular vogue, even among the intellectuals, for example, John Dee. Practically all treatises on the astrolabe contained a section on astrology. That beautiful and accurate instruments, of Muslim type, were still being made we see from the 1575 astrolabe of Humphrey Cole, famous London instrument-maker. For photographic reproduction see the *Illustrated London News,* August 14, 1926, pp. 292-294.

[138] Repsold, *op. cit.,* on the instruments of Tycho Brahe.

fulness as a timepiece ceased with the advent of the pendulum and spring clocks.

In his description of triangulation, Frisius speaks of using an *instrumentum planimetrum* instead of the *instrumentum altimetrum* used in determining heights. As far as we can gather from his brief description, this planimetrum consisted of a simplified astrolabe with compass inset, placed horizontally on a vertical staff:[139]

First, on a level staff construct an instrument as follows: let there be a circular plate which is divided into four quadrants, any quadrant at all being again divided in the usual manner into 90 degrees. Then let an alidade with sights, open or solid, be fixed through the center as on the back of an astrolabe. When the instrument has been made, there will also be need of the nautical instrument (which we call the compass) because the whole operation depends on that.

That the astrolabe itself or its modifications were in common use on the Continent in connection with triangulation work may be seen from the fact that even as late as 1598 Gallucci[140] describes the process of mapping with the astrolabe and compass. In another place he speaks of the *specchio geographico,* which consisted of little more than a graduated circular plate with alidade. The same is described by Schwenter.[141] Later still, in 1626, Metius[142] was using the old type of astrolabe with shadow square divided decimally, set up on a staff.

In England, where the surveying of estates became important in the sixteenth century, changes in the astrolabe went on more rapidly than on the Continent. The earliest description of such a modified instrument is that of Cuningham[143] (Figure 86). His instrument is essentially the same as those produced by Arsenius except that the compass is inset excentrically within the circle. Cuningham had studied for some time at Heidelberg, and his

[139] Latin text in Appendix, p. 364.
[140] Giovanni Gallucci, *Della fabrica et uso de diversi stromenti di astronomia et cosmographia* (Venice, 1598), Bk. 4, Ch. 2.
[141] Schwenter, *op. cit.,* p. 345.
[142] Metius, *op. cit.,* pp. 153-154.
[143] William Cuningham, *The Cosmographical Glasse* (London, 1559). On the title page the author is described as a "physician, astrologer and engraver; M.B. Corpus Christi College, Cambridge 1557; M.D. Heidelberg 1559." Cuningham's description of triangulation is given in the Appendix, p. 366.

book gives a clear exposition of the topographical methods then employed on the Continent. Bourne describes with illustration a somewhat similar instrument in his unpublished manuscript[144] of 1559. The theodelitus of Digges, first described in 1571, shows

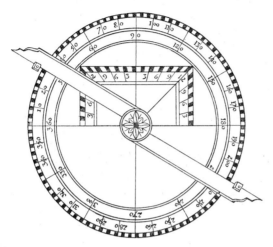

Figure 87. DIGGES' THEODELITUS. *Redrawn from original sketch.*

clearly its relationship to the astrolabe. A compass was used as an auxiliary instrument for purposes of orientation. Digges describes the instrument (Figure 87) as follows:[145]

It is but a circle divided in 360 grades or degrees, or a semi-circle parted in 180 portions, and every one of these divisions in three or rather 6 smaller parts, to it yee may adde the double scale, whose single composition is mentioned. The sides of that scale divided in 12, 60 or 100 partes. The index of that instrument with the sights, etc. are not unlike to that which the square hath; In his backe prepare a vice or scrue to be fastened to the top of some staffe if it be a circle as heere: let your instrument be so large that from the center to the degrees may be a foote in length, more if ye list, so shall you not erre in your practises, the back side must bee plaine and smooth to draw circles and lines upon, as shall be declared.

Probably the most important French derivative of the astrolabe was the *graphomêtre* of Danfrie[146] (Figure 88). In this instru-

[144] E. G. R. Taylor, *Tudor Geography, 1485-1583*, pp. 153-155. William Bourne's manuscript is in the British Museum, Sloane Ms. 3651.
[145] L. Digges, *op. cit.*, Bk. 1, Ch. 27.
[146] Philippe Danfrie, *Déclaration de l'usage du graphomêtre* (Paris, 1597).

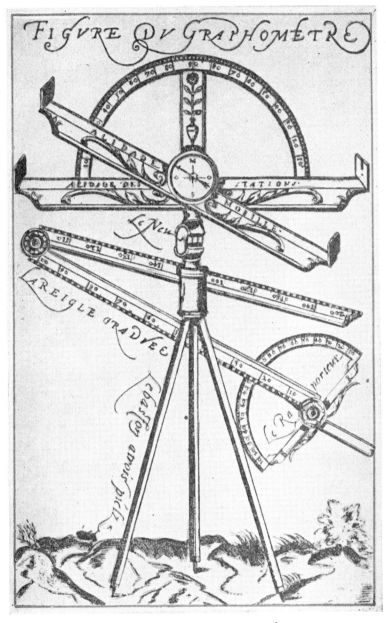

Figure 88. DANFRIE'S GRAPHOMÊTRE

Figure 89. DOU'S HOLLAND CIRCLE. *Reproduced from Laussedat's* Recherches sur les instruments, les méthodes et le dessin topographiques, *by permission of Gauthier-Villars, Publishers.*

ment half the circular arc was removed and an additional station-ary alidade was introduced. The graphomètre was the most gen-erally used surveying instrument in France during the seven-teenth century. Another later and popular derivative of the astrolabe was the *Holland circle* (Figure 89) constructed by Jan Dou.[147] This instrument of pierced metal, in which the compass was centrally inset, carried, besides the sights on the alidade, two stationary pairs of sights fixed at right angles, and could conse-

[147] Jan Dou, *Tractat vant maken ende gebruycken eens nien gheordenneerden mathematischen instruments* (Amsterdam, 1612).

quently be used as a surveyor's cross. The sights consisted of slits in the metal. It carried a ring for suspension, after the manner of the astrolabe. When used horizontally for topographical work, it was mounted on a staff by means of a swivel joint which allowed

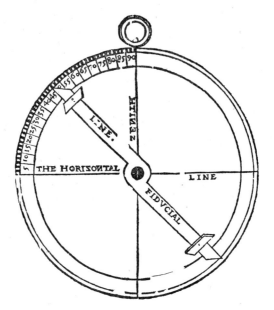

Figure 90. SKETCH OF MARINER'S ASTROLABE BY EDEN

freedom of movement, so that a line of sight between two objects not in the same horizontal plane could be determined by tilting the plane of the instrument.

From another source, and probably earlier, the astrolabe had undergone a process of simplification. At the time of the great geographical discoveries, toward the end of the fifteenth century, we find the astrolabe in constant use on ships to determine latitude by sighting on the polestar or the midday sun.[148] Descriptions of the simplified mariners' astrolabe are to be found in the sea manuals, of which one of the earliest and most important was that of

[148] The earliest record of its marine use is by Diego d'Azambuja in 1481, but it was probably employed much earlier. The Venetian cartographer Mauro wrote in 1457 that Indian (Muslim) pilots used the astrolabe. See A. Baguette, *Die Bedeutung des Astrolabiums* (Bonn, 1909), p. 23. J. Meigs, *The Story of the Seamen* (Philadelphia, 1924), p. 56, mentions a rather vaguely authenticated statement of its use on ships in 1273.

the Portuguese Nuñez.[149] This was followed by the Spanish works of Cortes[150] and Medina.[151] Cortes' work was translated into English by Eden[152] and became the basis for the future study of navigation by English mariners. The first independent work on navigation in English was by Bourne.[153] In all these books are to be found diagrams and descriptions of the simplified sea astrolabe (Figure 90). To be sure, in time it fell behind the Jacob's staff in popularity, but it still remained indispensable for a long while for the measurement of high altitudes. Like other marine instruments it was not replaced until the eighteenth century by the sextant. Fournier,[154] who published an important French work on navigation in 1643, says, "It is impossible to find a better instrument than the astrolabe."

Specimens of the mariner's astrolabe are very rare. Gunther attributes this to the fact that it[155]

lacked the ornamental rete that has given the landsman's astrolabe a high permanent artistic value and when superseded as a navigational instrument, it doubtless passed through the hands of the marine stores to the crucibles of the brass founder.

Gunther lists five known specimens of this astrolabe.[156] Of these the most perfect is the St. Andrews, which bears the inscription

[149] Pedro Nuñez, *Tratado da sphera* (Lisbon, 1537).

[150] Martin Cortes, *Breve compendio de la sphera y de la arte de navegar* (Seville, 1551).

[151] Pedro de Medina, *Arte de navegar* (Vallodolid, 1545).

[152] Richard Eden, *The Arte of Navigation* (London, 1561). Up to the death of Sebastian Cabot in 1557, the science of navigation had remained a close secret among the master pilots of England, who were mostly foreigners. Cabot was succeeded as Chief Pilot of England by Stephen Burrough, who visited Spain and learned at first hand the Spanish methods of training pilots. On his return to England he was instrumental in having Eden translate Cortes' treatise. Its publication was financed by the newly formed Muscovy Company, which was much interested in the possibilities of a Northeast Passage. See E. G. R. Taylor, *Tudor Geography, 1485-1583*.

[153] William Bourne, *A Regiment for the Sea* (London, 1573).

[154] George Fournier, S.J., *Hydrographie, contenant la théorie et la pratique de toutes les parties de la navigation* (Paris, 1643).

[155] R. T. Gunther, "The Mariner's Astrolabe," *The Geographical Journal*, Vol. 72, 1928, pp. 342 ff. By permission of The Royal Geographical Society.

[156] 1. The Valencia, found at Valencia, Ireland, in 1845, now in South Kensington Museum, London. For a description see J. Lecky, "The Valencia Astrolabe," *Kerry Archaeological Magazine*, March, 1913, pp. 74-79. 2. The Vera Cruz, found at Vera Cruz, Mexico; alidade missing; now in Lewis Evans Collection in Oxford. 3. The Champlain, found in St. Lawrence River, 1870; made in Paris, 1603; now in collection of S. V. Hoffman, New York (Figure 91). 4. The Normandy, made in Honnefleur, 1632; now in museum at Caudebec en Caux. 5. The Saint Andrews, described above.

Figure 91. CHAMPLAIN'S ASTROLABE. *Reproduced from Smith's* History
of Mathematics, Vol. II, *by permission of Ginn and Co., Publishers.*

"Elias Allen Fecit 1616." This astrolabe is about sixteen inches
in diameter and about one-half inch in thickness and weighs seven-
teen and one-half pounds. The lower spoke is made more massive
than the others in order to increase the stability. Each quadrant
is divided into 90°, numbered from the horizontal to the vertical,
while the upper left-hand quadrant is subdivided by means of a
transversal scale to read to one-fifth of a degree. In his description
of astrolabes Blundevil states:[157]

But broad Astrolabes though they bee thereby the truer, yet for that
they are subject to the force of the wind, and thereby ever moving and
unstable, are nothing meet to take the Altitude of anything, and espe-

---

[157] Thomas Blundevil, *His Exercises* (London, 1594). Extract from 1638 Edition,
p. 595.

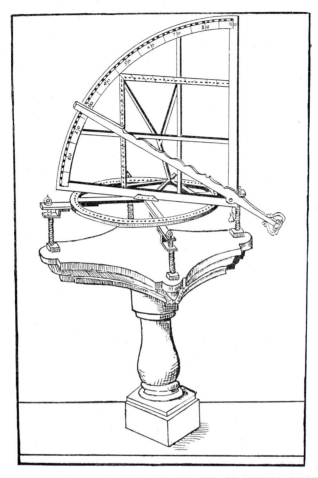

Figure 92. ASTRONOMICAL QUADRANT OF TYCHO BRAHE

cially upon the sea, which thing to avoyd, the Spaniards do commonly make their astrolabes or Rings narrow and weighty, which for the most part are not much above five inches broad and yet do weigh at least four pound.

QUADRANT During the first century of this period the quadrant became the most important astronomical instrument. Following the example of the Muslim astronomer Ulūg Beg (1393-1449), the astronomers of the Renaissance built large quadrants, both the stationary or meridian type and the more serviceable azimuth type which made possible revolution in a vertical plane. Such

instruments were employed by Tycho Brahe[158] (see Figure 92).
Although there exist some European writings[159] on the more
complicated types of quadrants developed by the Muslims, in
general, from the beginning of the sixteenth century, the Europeans simplified the quadrant and used it more and more as a
surveying and nautical instrument. These plumb-bob instruments contained only the graduated arc and the shadow square.
Typical of the period are those described by Apian, Finaeus, and
Münster.[160] Apian describes on one of his quadrants a shadow

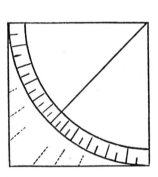   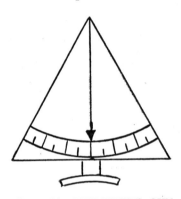

Figure 93. APIAN'S SHADOW   *Figure* 94. SCHREIBER'S GUN
SQUARE   QUADRANT

square in which the divisions are projected onto a quarter-circle,
one half of which contains the "short" shadow and the other half
the "long" shadow (Figure 93). This circular shadow square is
not identical with that used by the Muslims (p. 72).

One of the oldest surveying uses of the quadrant was that of
leveling.[161] Two special forms of plumb-bob quadrant were used
in connection with artillery. One was the ordinary quadrant with
one arm extended and counterbalanced, so that the instrument
could be placed with the arm lying in the barrel of the gun (see
p. 113). The other was made to rest on the upper convex surface

[158] Repsold, *op. cit.*, pp. 21 ff.
[159] Apian, *op. cit.*, fol. A2. Münster, *op. cit.*, pp. 195 ff. Jakob Köbel, *Geometrie von künstlichen Feldmessen* (Frankfurt a.M., 1531), pp. 33 ff. Gallucci, *op. cit.*, fol. 75. Such instruments were used chiefly in connection with astrology.
[160] Apian, *op. cit.*, fols. A3, E3-F3. Finaeus, *Protomathesis*, fols. 66, 69; *De re et praxi geometrica*, p. 6. Münster, *op. cit.*, pp. 35-37. See also G. Cardan, *Opera,* Tomus Quartus (Lyons, 1663), fols. 611-615.
[161] Apian, *op. cit.*, fol. F.

Figure 95. HULSIUS' QUADRANT

of the gun barrel. Figure 94 shows one of this type taken from Schreiber.[162] The purpose of these quadrants was to set the gun barrel in a vertical plane.

Sea quadrants were also of the plumb-bob type. The earliest account of the use of such is by Gomez de Cintra, 1462.[163] Although the astrolabe and quadrant[164] were superseded to a great extent by the Jacob's staff in the determination of the lower latitudes, they were indispensable in the determination of higher latitudes, which were difficult to read on the Jacob's staff scale (see p. 196).

Hand quadrants with alidade were generally rare in surveying; one such *quadrans stabilis* is described by Clavius,[165] while Metius[166] describes a similar one for use at sea. In general the

---

[162] Schreiber, *op. cit.*, p. 32. For others see Bion, *op. cit.*, Bk. 5, Ch. 4. Reference has already been made to the quadrans tormentarius of Hulsius; see p. 139.

[163] De Cintra was the Portuguese discoverer of Sierra Leone in 1465. See Bensaude, *L'Astronomie nautique au Portugal à l'époque des grandes découvertes*, p. 35.

[164] Among others who explain the use of the sea quadrant are: John Davis, *The Seamans Secrets* (London, 1595), fol. M. William Bourne, *Inventions and Devices* (London, 1578), No. 28.

[165] Clavius, *Geometria Practica*, Pr. 1.

[166] Adrian Metius, *Primum Mobile* (Amsterdam, 1633), Bk. 5, Ch. 7.

alidade quadrant was square in shape and differed from the geometric square only by the addition of the arc inside the square; the sides of the square were not usually graduated. Of this type are the *quadratus rectangulus* of Reisch[167] and the gun quadrants of Santbech[168] and Smith.[169] The alidade quadrant, used horizontally on a staff, was frequently employed in topographical work. Although obtuse angles had to be measured by their supplements, and orientation was more difficult than with the astrolabe, still, because it offered an opportunity for clearer graduation, the alidade quadrant held its own against the astrolabe and its other derivatives.[170] The compass formed an integral part of such a quadrant. Of this instrument (Figure 95) Hulsius says:[171]

In altera facie huius instrumenti arcula magnetis est, cuius operculum hic litera *D* notatum est, in quo 32 venti, quorum singuli in 4 minuta divisi, descripti sunt, cuius usus est, in omnibus distantis fluviorum, piscinarum aut lacuum et fossarum mensurandis. In huius usu, planum cum suo foramine *G* supra baculum 4 pedes longum in clavum *H,* ita ut magnes libera moveatur.

It is interesting to note that in both attempts at the measurement of the circumference of the earth carried on in the seventeenth century, the quadrant was the chief instrument employed.[172]

Probably the most interesting item in the history of the quadrant in this period is the fact that it was the principal instrument used as the proving ground for various devices intended to facili-

---

[167] Reisch, *op. cit.,* Bk. 6, Tract 2.

[168] Santbech, *op. cit.,* p. 310 ff.

[169] Smith, *op. cit.*

[170] Clavius, *Geometria Practica,* in expressing his preference for the quadrant in the introduction to Book II says: "Ad harum Dimensiones varii varia adhibent instrumenta, quibusdam enim placet scala altimetra in dorso astrolabi, seu planisphaeri descripta. Aliis radius astronomicus Gemma Frisii, vel radius dictus Latinus, quod a Domino Latino Ursino nobili Romano excogitatus sit: vel baculus Jacob: aliis annulus Astronomicus, vel Holometrum: aliis deinque alia instrumenta arrident. Mihi vero prae caeteris probatur Quadrans Astronomicus in 90 gradus distributus et Quadratum Geometricum tam stabile, tam pendulum."

[171] Hulsius, *De Quadrante Geometrico,* p. 43.

[172] These attempts were the first large-scale triangulation survey carried out by Willebrod Snellius in Holland in 1617, and the corresponding work done later by Picard in 1670 in northern France. Picard's quadrant (Figure 96) was about ten feet in radius and had telescopic sights with cross hairs. See Picard, *op. cit.* Snellius' quadrant was two feet in radius, but by the aid of a transversal scale he was able to read to 1'. See A. J. Porter, "The Earliest Geodetic Triangulation," *Empire Survey Review,* Vol. 1, 1931-1932, pp. 100-109.

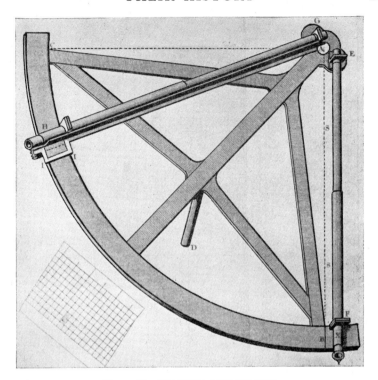

Figure 96. PICARD'S QUADRANT

tate the reading of angle divisions. The first attempt at the solution of this important problem is that of Nuñez. Although his solution refers to readings on a mariner's astrolabe, the statement above with reference to the quadrant still holds true, since he used only the upper left-hand quadrant of the astrolabe. Referring to Figure 97, Nuñez proceeds as follows:[173]

An astrolabe must be made as exact as possible, and it must have a dioptra, that is, a ruler which is as straight as possible and which revolves round the center; and on which sights must be erected as usual; the bigger openings of which must be such that the brightest fixed stars can be seen through them distinctly. For example, let there be a single plane circular surface of this astrolabe, *a, b, c, d,* whose center point is *e,* and divided into quadrants by the diameters *ac* and *bd.* On this, inside the circumference itself, at any distance at all (equal or unequal is immaterial) let there be described, one within the other, quadrants of

---

[173] Pedro Nuñez (also known as Nunes and Nonius), *De Crepusculis* (Lisbon, 1542), Prop. III. Text in Appendix, p. 368.

circles to the number of 44. Let the exterior quadrant, *ab*, be divided into 90 equal parts; the one inside and adjacent to it, into 89 equal parts; the next into 88, the next into 87 and this process is to be carried out, with each in turn, until the least and last of the inner arcs is reached, which will be divided into 46 equal parts. On any quadrant whatsoever each ten divisions are marked by very fine lines projecting slightly from the circumference. For unless the astrolabe were of large • size, if 5 or 10 parts were distinguished by numbers there would be con-

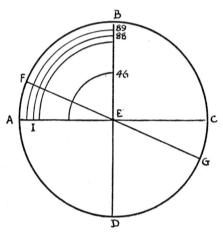

Figure 97

siderable confusion because of the narrowness of the intervals. However, let the number of divisions which each quadrant has be inscribed beside one of its ends near the semi-diameter. If count is made from *a* to *b*, let 90 be written at point *b* in algoristic marks. Below and along the diameter *eb*, the remaining numbers will be arranged in their proper places. Thus, by this means, the number of degrees 90, which each quadrant clearly has, even the inner ones, even though a division into fewer parts be proposed, includes actually each aliquot part which may be indicated by any number whatever less than 90, namely, a half of the whole, 1/3, 1/4, 1/5, 1/6, 1/7, 1/8, 1/9, 1/10, 1/11, 1/12, and the rest in succession up to 1/90 which the exterior quadrant actually has. For by progressing from the lesser divisions to the greater up to the 46th, nobody can deny but that there can be aliquot parts, namely, 1/90, 1/89, 1/88 and so on. And the possibility of its having also other (fractional parts) indicated by those numbers lying between unity and 46, can easily be proved, for he who divides any number into a number, divides it into 1/2, 1/4 and other submultiple numbers which the divisor has; for example, one dividing into 90, divides also into 45, and he who divides into 88 divides also into 44, and so on with the others.

Also the individual numbers from 23 to 45 are subduples of those which are placed in the series of numbers from 46 to 90, unity always omitted; and these also are multiples of the other lesser numbers and so on with the rest, others are related to others in the same way down to unity. Therefore the number of 90 degrees which we know is contained in each quadrant, has as a result of the aforesaid divisions every aliquot part from 1/2 to 1/90. Thus for the structure of the instrument; its use will be extremely simple.

The involved explanation of the use of this system of multiple-divisioned arcs is as difficult to follow as the above explanation of construction. Briefly, it amounts to stating that because of the great number of divisions the edge of the alidade will touch some one among them. Suppose, for example, that it touches the twentieth division on the quadrant divided into sixty-six parts; then the value of the required angle of elevation is found from the following proportion: $20 : 66 :: x : 90$, from which $x = 27° 16' 4''$. In general terms, if m represents the mark on which the alidade falls and q the quadrant on which m lies, then the angle in degrees is given by $90m/q$.

Although the actual use of the *nonius* (for so it came to be known later) is simple, involving besides the reading of the instrument only a simple problem in proportion, yet, because of the difficulty of dividing arcs into so many different parts, it never attained popularity. Tycho Brahe tried it out on some of his quadrant instruments at Uraniborg but was far from satisfied, as may be seen from a letter to his friend Rothmann in 1587:[174]

But when accordingly, I began to determine carefully the height of the stars, by means of the quadrants, and when I discovered by experience that the ordinary graduation, even when extended so far as possible, was not sufficient on the very small instruments, I had recourse to the subtle procedure which Nonius explains in the third proposition of his *De Crepusculis* and I made it still more exact by increasing the number of subdivisions and by calculating the tables by means of which one can know immediately and with precision the height of any point. And since this invention of Nonius, as experience has taught me, did not fulfill his promises, I finally began to wonder if the method by which a straight line is divided into three small parts by means of transverse points, could not be applied just as well to curved lines.

[174] *Tychonis Brahe Dani Epistolarum Astronomicarum libri* (Uraniborg, 1610). Text in Appendix, p. 369.

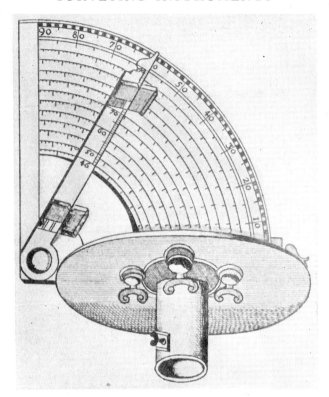

Figure 98. DUDLEY'S QUADRANT WITH NONIUS

A very fine example of the nonius applied to the quadrant is to be found in Dudley's book on navigation[175] (Figure 98), but no explanation of its use is given. Brahe's is the only recorded use of the nonius as described by Nuñez, but important theoretical developments, carried on by Clavius and Curtius,[176] finally led to the development of the *vernier* as we have it today. Curtius was the first to suggest an easier method of graduating the quadrants. He proposed dividing the exterior arc into 90°, then extending the first interior arc to 91°, the second to 92°, and so on, adding one degree to each succeeding arc until the thirty-eighth or last contained 128°. Then each of the arcs was divided into ninety equal

[175] Robert Dudley, *Dell' Arcano del mare* (Florence, 1646).
[176] Johannes Curtius, Chancellor to Rodolph II, was interested in astronomy and mathematics. Description of his method of graduating is given by Clavius, *Operum Mathematicorum*, p. 13.

parts. This allowed for larger divisions, but the method of determining the value of the angle was, in principle, the same as for the nonius.

Clavius describes his modification which simplified the method of division as follows:[177]

Having described with A as center [Figure 99] the quadrant BC, and inside that 39 other quadrants regularly spaced, so as to give the figure a more agreeable aspect; let there be in all 40 quadrants of which the extreme outside one carries as usual 90°, whilst its immediate neighbor is divided into 128 equal parts as follows; first into two parts, and each half again into two, then each of the quarters into two and so on by seven successive and precise operations, which will result in the division of the quadrant into 128 equal parts. After which the other quadrants are prolonged beyond the semi-diameter AB, according to the method spoken of above [referring to the method of Curtius]; first the one which follows the end quadrant BC, that is to say, to the line drawn from A to the 91st degree; that which follows to 92 degrees, the next to 93 and so on to the other degrees in such a way that the 40th quadrant is prolonged to 128°. Each arc so traced is divided into 128 equal parts as had been done on the arc nearest to the farthest edge. When this division is complete, the portion of the arcs which go beyond the semi-diameter AB are erased as superfluous.

Clavius next explains the method to be followed in obtaining the same divisions in the case where the space required for marking the arcs, outside the limits of the quadrant, is missing. As an example of the method of reading the angles he gives the following:[178]

If the edge of the alidade or the string of the plumb-bob falls on division 20 of the 12th quadrant PQ (that is the one, prolonged to 100° and then divided into 128 equal parts) then $20 : 128 :: x : 100$ from which $x = 15° 37' 30''$ exactly.

In order to shorten the work of calculation Clavius made out a table giving the minutes and seconds corresponding to the remainders from 1 to 128 left over after the operation of finding the number of whole degrees, and another table from which it is possible to read immediately the results in degrees, minutes, and seconds.

Still another method for the simplification of the divisions is

[177] Clavius, *op. cit.* Text in Appendix, p. 369.
[178] *Ibid.*

SURVEYING INSTRUMENTS

given by Curtius.[179] In the interior of a quadrant whose outside edge is divided in 90°, Curtius describes fifty-nine concentric quadrants. On the first of these he measures an arc of 61° and divides it into sixty equal parts, each of value 1° 1′, but he keeps only one of these divisions, which he places at the beginning of the graduation, after which the remainder of the quadrant is divided into ordinary degrees. From this it follows that each of the divisions increases by one minute over those of the quadrant exterior to it, the last one containing only 59′. On the next quadrant he takes 62°, divides it into sixty parts, and obtains an initial division of 1° 2″, following which, whole degrees are marked, the last division containing 58′. He continues so until the fifty-ninth quadrant, of which the first division would be 1° 59′ and the last 0° 1′. From this it follows that each division of any quadrant is one minute in advance of the divisions of the quadrant immediately following. The quadrants are numbered from zero to fifty-nine, the zero quadrant being the outside one. After an observation the degrees are read on the zero quadrant and the minutes on that one on which the mark coincides with the plumb line or alidade edge. The advantage of this method was that it made possible direct reading of angles to the nearest minute; but the method of division was as difficult as that which Curtius first prepared.

Another method is given by Clavius[180] for finding small fractions of a degree when the instrument is graduated in degrees only. By means of compasses he takes off carefully the portion of arc between the last degree mark and the edge of the alidade. He steps it off sixty times, starting from 0°, and he counts as minutes the degree value of the mark behind the last point of the compasses. Proceeding in the same way with what is still left over, he gets the number of seconds. Although theoretically correct, this method would prove very difficult and too delicate in practice with the instruments then in use.

Another method advocated by Clavius[181] is to describe, apart from the arc divided into 90°, an arc of the same radius of 61° which he then divides into sixty equal parts. Using this auxiliary

[179] In a letter to Tycho Brahe, 1590. See *Astronomiae Instauratae Mechanica* (Wandesburg, 1598), fol. G.3.
[180] Clavius, *op. cit.*, p. 33. Text in Appendix, p. 370.
[181] *Ibid.*

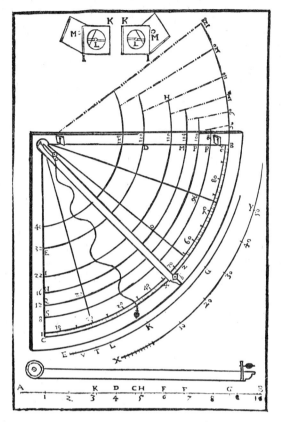

Figure 99. CONSTRUCTION OF NONIUS BY CLAVIUS

scale and a pair of compasses to transfer the readings of the main
scale, he was able to evaluate angles to the nearest minute. Finally,
Clavius[182] applied the same principle to the measuring of straight
lines. Suppose the distance to be measured is the portion DC of a
unit of the ruler AB divided into ten equal parts (Figure 99).
The distance DC is taken on compasses and stepped off ten times
from A to E. The six complete divisions between A and E represent the tenths (at this point the length is four units six tenths
plus FE). To find the hundredths, the space FE is stepped off ten
times in the same way, and supposing the last point of the compasses rests at G, then the length of the line is given by 4.68.

[182] *Ibid.*, pp. 34-35. "Quo pacto reperiatur fractio cuiusque particulae in parte
qualibet lineae rectae in partes aequales divisae." Text in Appendix, p. 370.

From these last two developments by Clavius we see that he had discovered the principle of the vernier. However, it does not seem to have dawned on him to place his auxiliary scale so that it could be slid along the edge of his main scale. It remained for Vernier to make the final simple step in producing that device, indispensable to all refined measurement, which now bears his name. Vernier describes this device in his book, *The New Mathematical Quadrant,* as follows (Figure 100):[183]

The instrument is one foot in radius, it is composed of two parts; the first and principle of which is a circular border raised from the surface on which the fourth part of a circle is divided exactly into ninety equal parts; or better, in terms of the art, into ninety degrees; and again each part into two: so that the half-degrees may be visible. So that the said quadrant contains 180 equal divisions, in order to imagine the entire circle divided ordinarily into 360° or even 720 half-degrees, as all the mathematicians conceive it.

The said border shall be called by the name of the fixed base, because it will be always fixed and stationary for the operations of the instrument: the which quadrant of a circle shall be enclosed and hemmed in by the straight lines, intersecting at the point of center of the said instrument, which lines are named the radii of it.

The division into degrees and half-degrees, mentioned above, are marked on the inner portion of the border of the base and at the edge of it: these divisions are distinguished by numbers every five degrees on the outer part of the said border; commencing the divisions from the radius on the left of the base and continuing to the right.

The second part of the instrument is a plate made in the form and shape of a sector of a circle, the circumference of which contains exactly an angle of 31 half-degrees not marked nor indicated as usual, but rather divided only into 30 equal parts, which circumference is enclosed and hemmed in by two straight lines, meeting at its center, and forming the said angle of 31 half-degrees; that is 15° 30′ as has been said above. So that this second section be applied and adjusted to the first, called the base, and the centers of the two stay together, the end and outermost part of the circle of division, the said second part, must correspond and be contiguous to the end and innermost of the circle of division of the said base.

The divisions of the said second section are distinguished by numbers on every fifth division, commencing to count from the right and going to the left, and each part of thirties, of the said division is, while in operation, equal to a minute of a degree of the circle.

[183] Pierre Vernier, *La Construction, l'usage et les propriétéz du quadrant nouveau de mathématique* (Brussels, 1631). Text in Appendix, p. 371.

The said second part is called the movable sector of the instrument, because it is moved sometimes to the right, sometimes to the left on the base when one wishes to carry out a certain operation. On this said movable sector, the two right lines meet at the center and embrace 31 degrees of the circle, they are called the lines of faith; on each of which are erected two plates pierced and slit in such a way that the visual rays can be exactly recognised and observed: the said lines are thus named because we place faith in the junction which they make on the degrees of the base and because they represent a portion of the visual rays which produce the required angle for the operation.

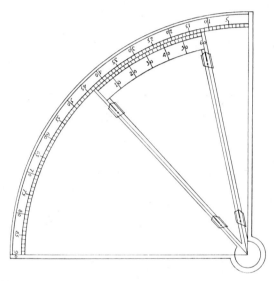

Figure 100. VERNIER'S QUADRANT. *Redrawn from original sketch.*

It will be noticed that this description does not correspond with the accompanying figure. On the diagram the main scale is divided into degrees (not half-degrees), while the sector contains 31°, not 15° 30′, and is represented as divided into sixty equal parts, whereas the description calls for thirty. Nevertheless, it can be easily seen that the vernier of the diagram reads to the nearest minute as well as the vernier described. Vernier gives us no explanation of the differing description and diagram.

Notwithstanding Vernier's adaption of his reading device to the quadrant, it does not seem to have been used to any extent during the seventeenth century. If Bion's catalogue of instruments may be taken as a criterion, the use of the vernier was almost entirely ignored until as late as the end of the seventeenth century.[184]

During the period in which the nonius was in the process of development to its final form in the vernier, another device for the reading of small subdivisions was also being put through similar stages of refinement. This was the method of transversals or diagonal scale. The earliest account of this method is given by

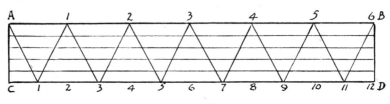

Figure 101

Levi ben Gerson in his description of the Jacob's staff (see p. 85). Here it was used to determine the subdivisions of a straight line. The main unit, such as *ABCD,* on the upper surface of the main staff (Figure 101) was divided as follows: the edge *AB* into six equal parts and the edge *CD* into twelve. Transversals were then drawn. The width of the staff was now divided into five equal parts, and parallels to the edges were drawn. It may easily be seen that the smallest reading on this scale was 1/60 of the main unit. Figure 251 shows the common method of drawing such a scale today. In this case, it is intended to read to the 1/100 part of the main unit. The earliest application of this method to angle measurement is given by Puehler[185] in a description of a quadrant. Figure 102 shows Puehler's application of straight line transver-

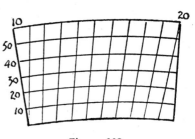

Figure 102

[184] Besides the diagram (Figure 98) given in *Dell' Arcano del mare,* a description of the nonius is given by Benedictus Hedraeus, *Nova et accurata astrolabii geometrici structura* (Leyden, 1643), Ch. 2.

[185] Christopher Puehler, *Eine kurze und gründliche Anlaytung zu dem rechten Verstand der Geometrie* (Dillingen, 1563). Puehler was a pupil of Apian. The lack of any evidence of its use from ben Gerson's exposition in 1342 to Puehler is unexplainable unless we assume that minute readings were not sought after by Purbach, Regiomontanus, and others.

sals. Scultetus is the next important user of this method. He[186] asserts that Purbach and Regiomontanus used this device on their instruments and were able to read angles to the nearest minute. However, Schöner, who has left us the history of their instruments, mentions no system to facilitate the reading of small parts.

Tycho Brahe, who, as we have seen already, was dissatisfied with the results obtainable on the nonius, began to experiment with the diagonal scale. In his account *De Nova Stella Anni 1572* he stated that this method was very satisfactory and that he had become acquainted with it through Hommel.[187] The method of division adopted by Brahe was somewhat different from that of Puehler and Scultetus.

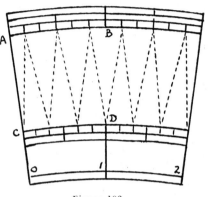

Figure 103

On the outside circumference *AB* (Figure 103) he marked degrees and the smallest convenient fractional parts of a degree. The same divisions were marked on the inner circumference *CD*. The transversal lines were drawn between alternate points. These transversals were divided equally by a number of concentric arcs. Using this method on his large quadrants and sextants, he was able to read angles to 1/6 minute.[188]

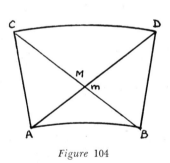

Figure 104

Angle readings determined by means of straight line transversals were slightly in error. Any division such as *AB* (Figure 104)

[186] Scultetus, *op. cit.*, Part 3, Ch. 1.

[187] Johann Hommel (1518-1562), Prof. Mathematics, Leipzig. Scultetus was his pupil.

[188] See Repsold, *op. cit.*, for diagrams of these instruments. Tycho Brahe, *De Cometa anni 1577* (Wandesburg, 1598), p. 461. On Brahe's instruments the intersections of the transversals with the concentric circles are indicated by rows of dots; the actual lines do not appear on the diagrams. Joost Bürgi is supposed to have been the first to introduce the full lines. See R. T. Gunther, *Early Science in Oxford* (Oxford, 1923), Vol. 1, p. 169.

measured on the inner arc is smaller than the corresponding division on the outer arc CD. It follows that the diagonals AB and BC intersect at a point m, which approaches nearer AB as the radius becomes smaller. This point m never coincides with M, the mid-point of transversal BC. Because of this the concentric marks should have been unequally spaced. This fact was known to Brahe, but he says the errors produced were so small that they could be neglected; besides they were minor compared with other errors due to the unrefined construction of the period.

THEODOLITE AND TRANSIT   The modern theodolite and its slight variant the modern American *transit* are essentially instruments by which the horizontal and vertical angles of an objective are simultaneously measured with reference to an assumed zero azimuth direction and an assumed horizontal plane. The transit has, in addition, the property that its telescope can be completely revolved on its horizontal axis, or transited—hence the name. In their earlier forms both the theodolite and the transit were capable of measuring only horizontal angles.[189]   The earliest recorded prototypes of the modern theodolite and transit are to be found in Muslim astronomical works. These instruments usually consisted of a large horizontal ring on which horizontal azimuth angles were measured, and a quadrant erected in the center of the ring, perpendicular to its plane, and capable of being revolved about its vertical axis.[190]   Such instruments were used by Tycho Brahe in the second half of the sixteenth century at his observatory at Uraniborg[191] (Figure 92). However, the earliest example of the application of such instruments in European astronomical work is the *torquetum* of Regiomontanus (Figure 105).

The earliest application of the theodolite principle to surveying instruments in Europe was, as we have shown already (p. 108), the polimetrum of Waldseemüller in 1513. In 1542 appeared the

[189] What is usually recognized as the earliest theodolite was made by Ramsden about 1785 and used by Roy in the first tie-up between the English and French triangulation systems in 1787. The earliest American transit was produced by William J. Young of Philadelphia in 1831. The words *theodolite* and *transit*, as used in this chapter, refer to the later types of these instruments, to which devices for measuring vertical angles had been added.

[190] Sédillot, *op. cit.*, pp. 201 ff.

[191] Repsold, *op. cit.*, pp. 21 ff. Wolf, *op. cit.*, pp. 125 ff.

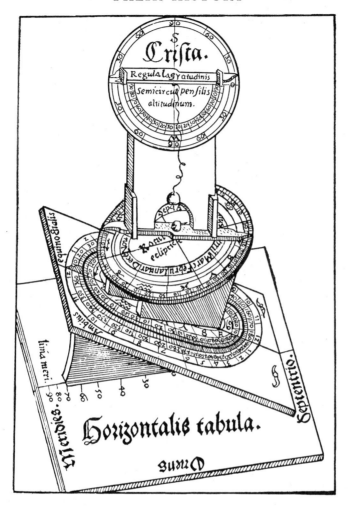

Figure 105. THE TORQUETUM OF REGIOMONTANUS

differential quadrant of Rotz, constructed on the theodolite principle for navigational purposes (p. 126). The polimetrum of
Waldseemüller seems to have been overlooked by subsequent
Continental geographers and surveyors, who apparently were satisfied with the work which could be done by the numerous variations
of the astrolabe in conjunction with the compass, and later by the
graphomêtre and plane table. The instrument which was really
to blaze the way for the present-day transit, though probably in

use some years previously, was first described by Digges in 1571 under the title of an "instrument topographicall." [192]

Having alreadie plainly declared the making of the Quadrant Geo-metricall with his Scale therein contayned, whose use is cheefly for altitudes and profoundities: the composition also of the Square and Planisphere or Circle named Theodelitus for measuring lengthes, breadths and distances. It may seeme superfluous more to write of these matters, yet to finish this treatise, I think it not amisse to shew how you may ioyne these three in one, whereby you shall frame an instru-ment of such perfection, that no manner altitude, latitude, longitude or profunditie can offer it selfe, howsoever it be situate, which you may not both readily and most exactly measure. You shall therefore first prepare some large foure square pullished plate of Latin, wherein you may describe your Geometrical Square, his sides divided into 1200 parts at the lest, with index and sightes as was before shewed: describing also within the same Square the Planisphere or Circle called Theodelitus, then must you uppon an other fine pullished plate, drawe your Quad-rant, or rather a semi-circle divided justly into 180 grades, and within the same a double Scale: every side contayning at the least 120 parts, finally, fixing on the dimetient thereof two sightes perpendicularly reared, and equidistantly persed, so as the line visuall may passe paral-lele to that diameter. You have a double Quadrant Geometricall with a double scale, which you must by the aide of some skilfull Artificer so place over the other plate, wherein your Square Geometricall and The-odelitus was described, that his centre may exactly rest in a Perpendicu-lar line from the centre of the Planisphere or Circle named Theodelitus his Circumference depending downwarde. And the double Quadrant or semicircle must in such sorte be connexed to the Perpendicular erected from the Centre of the Planisphere, and alhidada at the foote thereof, that what way so ever the Diameter with sightes be turned, the Alhidada may alway remayne exactly underneath it, directing bothe to one Verticall Circle or pointe of the Horizon: this Perpendiculare where-unto the semicircles centre is fastened, ought also to be marked with 200 partes equall to the divisions of the scale beginning at the centre, so proceeding downward till you come to the end of those 200 portions: more I need not say of this instrument, considering the construction, if every parte hath beene severally declared sufficiently before, for the placing and conioyning of them behold the Figures. . . . [Figure 106.]

This semicircle ought so to be placed that the centre *B* hang directly over the centre *A,* and that the diameter *DC* with his sightes maye be moved up and downe, and also sidewise whither you list, alwaies carry-ing *GF* about directly under it. You must also prepare a staffe pyked at

[192] L. Digges, *op. cit.,* Ch. 29. "The construction of an Instrument Topographicall serving most commodiously for all manner mensurations."

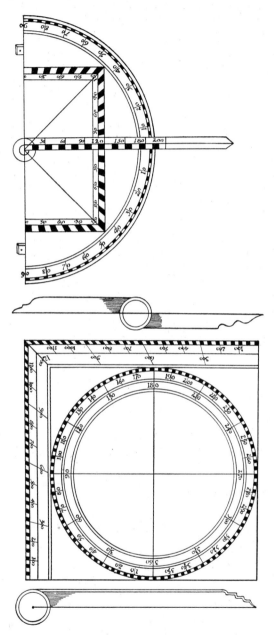

Figure 106. THE "INSTRUMENT TOPOGRAPHICALL" OF DIGGES. *Redrawn from original sketch.*

the end, to pitche on the ground with a flat plate on the top to set this instrument upon. It is also requisite that within Theodelitus you have a needle or flie so rectified, that being brought to his due place, the crosse diameters of the Planisphere may demonstrate the foure principall quarters of the Horizon, East, Weste, North and Southe: And this may you do by drawing a right line making an angle (with that one diameter of youre instrument representing the meridiane) equall to the variation of the compasse in your region: which in England is 11 1/4 grades or neere thereabout, and may be redely observed in all places sundrie wayes . . . . Nowe for y use great heede must you take in pitching of the staffe whereupon the instrument is placed that it stande perpendicularly, whiche by a lyne and plummet ye may trye, also when the instrument is placed thereon, ye shall by a lyne and plummet fixed on the centre of the semicircle discerne whither it be rightly situate: for yf the thread and plummet hanging at libertie fall close by the perpendiculare, then it is well: otherwise ye muste move the staffe to and fro till ye finde it so. This done, it behooveth you also to set this instrument on your staffe, that the needle have his due place, so as the semidimetientes of Theodelitus may directe unto the four cardines or quarters of the Horizon, then whatsoever marke you espye, whose distance, altitude or profunditie you desire, turne the dimetient of the semicircle to and fro, up and downe, till through the sightes thereon fixed you have espied it, alway the circle or Theodelitus remayning immoveable: finally you shall note bothe what degrees the Alhidada cutteth of the circle, and the perpendiculare of the semicircle, and also what partes of the perpendiculare is intercepted with the scale, these numbers thus founde, you shall diversely use as shall thereafter be declared.

From this description we see that the "instrument topographicall" (Figures 106 and 193) was a composite of the principal surveying instruments previously in use. Bearing angles were determined by the position of the alidade on the planisphere or theodelitus inscribed in the horizontal geometric square; for measuring vertical angles a double quadrant, within which was inscribed a double shadow square, was employed; orientation of the instrument by compass is explained by Digges (in Chapter 34).

After Digges' *Pantometria,* several books on surveying appeared in England within the next century.[193] Of these, the works of

[193] Among these were Valentine Leigh, *Surveying of Lands* (London, 1577). Edward Worsop, *Errors of Landemeaters* (London, 1582). Cyprian Lucar, *A Treatise Named Lucarsolace* (London, 1590). John Blagrave, *The Familiar Staff* (London, 1590). John Norden, *The Surveyor's Dialogue* (London, 1607). Arthur Hopton, *The Topographical Glass* (London, 1611). Aaron Rathborne, *The Surveyor* (London, 1616). William Leybourn, *The Compleat Surveyor* (London, 1653). George Atwell, *The Faithfull Surveyour* (London, 1662).

Rathborne and Leybourn were the most important. As to what instruments and methods were in common use, we must base our opinions on the material to be found in these books, since we have

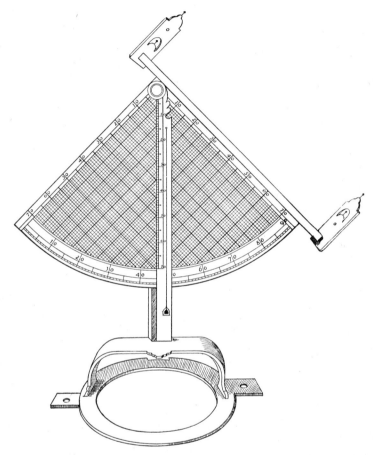

Figure 107. THE PERACTOR OF RATHBORNE. *Redrawn from original sketch.*

very slight information on actual surveys. As Fordham remarks on Saxton's surveys:[194]

As to the method and technical basis of the survey, nothing is apparently known. The system of surveying of the early cartographers merits investigation but the materials for such a study are not abundant.

[194] Fordham, *op. cit.*, p. 4. By permission of The Cambridge University Press.

Something can be gathered from the sketches of surveyors and their instruments and even from diagrams and calculations found here and
there in the foregrounds and ornamental margins of plans and views of
towns of the 16th. and 17th. centuries, and in the margins of maps of
the same period.

Enumerating the principal instruments of his time, Rathborne
states in the preface to his third book:[195]

This Book tendeth chiefly to matter of survey, wherein is first described
and declared the severall Instruments, fit for that purpose (with their
use in practice) as the Theodelite, the Playne Table, and Circumferentor, whereunto I have added an absolute Instrument, which I call the
Peractor, together with the making and use of the Decimal Chayne, used
only by myself.

His evaluation of what he calls the "theodelite" of Digges, after a
brief description[196] which shows that he has in mind the "instrument topographicall," is as follows:[197]

. . . all which together composed, make an excellent Instrument meete
for many purposes, especially for the description of Regions and Countries, or other spacious works . . . not altogether so fitting and com-
modious as the rest before named by reason of the multiplicity of Divisions therein contained, which will be so much the more troublesome
in use and protraction.

To offset the complications which he sees in the "theodelite,"
he proposes a new instrument, the *peractor,* which differs from
Digges' instrument mainly in the substitution of a quadrant with
sine lines for the vertical semicircle, for the purpose of "reducing
Hypothenusall lines to Horizontall." [198]   In his recommendation
of this peractor (Figure 107) we find a note common in most of
the surveying books of this time; namely, the effort to reduce
mathematical calculation to a minimum:[199]

I then ever use this Quadrant here expressed most fitte for the speedy
taking of all manner of altitudes and profundities, and the suddaine
reduction of those lines with Arithemeticall calculation.

[195] Rathborne, *op. cit.*
[196] *Ibid.,* Bk. 3, Ch. 2. Text in Appendix, p. 372. Brief, because "M. Thomas Digges
in his Pantometria hath made large and particular description thereof." It is of
interest to note in this passage the change of the name of Digges' "instrument topographicall" to Theodelite, which later became Theodolite.
[197] *Ibid.*
[198] *Ibid.,* Bk. 3, Ch. 20, gives a problem showing the use of the sine lines.
[199] *Ibid.,* Bk. 3, Ch. 5.

Figure 108. RATHBORNE'S "THEODELITE"

Despite the fact that Rathborne extols the virtues of his peractor above those of the "instrument topographicall" of Digges, we find that on the title page of his book the instrument depicted (Figure 108) is what he describes in the text as Digges' "theodelite," modified from the original by the omission of the geometric

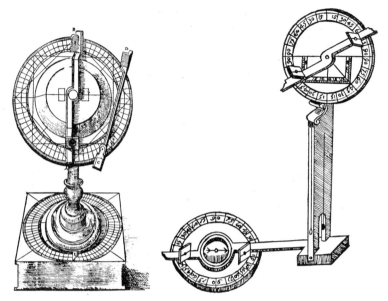

Figure 109 *(left).* THE NEU ERFUNDEN INSTRUMENT OF WALTER RYFF
Figure 110. BARTOLI'S INSTRUMENT FOR TOPOGRAPHICAL MAPPING

square in the horizontal base, while both the circle and the semi-circle with shadow square seem to be made of pierced metal.

Leybourn, remarking on the various instruments in use in his time, says that he will describe those which[200]

are the ground and foundation for all the rest, and are now the only instruments in most esteem amongst Surveyors, and those are chiefly these three, the Theodolite, the Circumferentor and the Plain Table.

His description of the theodolite corresponds essentially with Digges' "instrument topographicall"; an improvement is to be noted here in the subdivision by means of a diagonal scale. The geometric square is omitted, showing the influence of the increase in the number of applications of the trigonometrical functions. Leybourn also had an instrument (unnamed) of his own to publicize, "which will perform the work of the Theodolite or Circumferentor, but especially of the Peractor." So likewise the last important English writer[201] on surveying within the seventeenth century had his own brain child, the *pandoron*, proposed to re-

[200] Leybourn, *op. cit.*, Bk. 2, Ch. 1, p. 41. The *circumferentor* was a surveyor's cross with a compass centrally inset (Figure 135).   [201] Atwell, *op. cit.*, Ch. 16.

Figure 111. HABERMEL'S UNIVERSALINSTRUMENT

place, with advantages to the surveyor, all previous instruments. However, neither the pandoron, Leybourn's instrument, nor the peractor long survived, but in England and on the Continent Digges' "instrument topographicall," then known as the theodolite, was with slight variations the prevailing instrument in this class.

During the same period various attempts were made on the Continent to produce "universal instruments," a title usually applied to instruments by which horizontal and vertical angles could

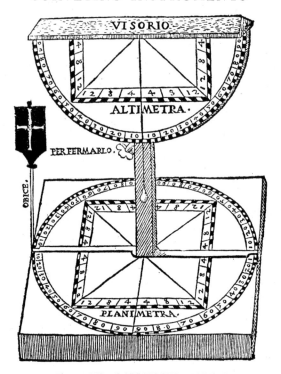

Figure 112. GALLUCCI'S VISORIO

be measured simultaneously. After the polimetrum of Waldseemüller, the next to appear was the *Neu Erfunden Instrument* of
Walter Ryff [202] in 1547 (Figure 109). It differs mainly from the
polimetrum in the employment of a full vertical circle and the
absence of a horizontal geometric square. A compass was used in
an auxiliary role for orientation. In 1564 Bartoli [203] produced an
instrument of radically different design but containing essentially
the same elements (Figure 110). The compass is here an integral
part of the instrument, used in the determination of bearing
angles after the manner described by Tartaglia. Five years after
the publication of Digges' *Pantometria*, Josua Habermel produced his *Universalinstrument*[204] (Figure 111). The general design follows that of the polimetrum, while the compass, as in

[202] Walter Ryff, *op. cit.*, Bk. 3, p. 372.
[203] Cosimo Bartoli, *Del modo di misurare* (Venice, 1564), p. 102.
[204] M. Engelmann, "Die Habermelschen Instrumente in Dresden," *Mitteilung aus
dem sächsische Kunstsammlung*, No. 4, 1913.

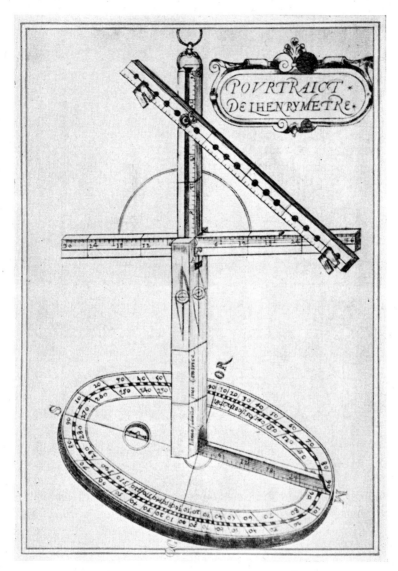

Figure 113. DE SUBERVILLE'S HENRY-MÊTRE

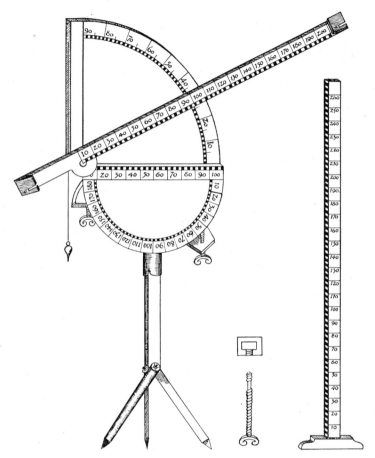

Figure 114. ARDUSER'S INSTRUMENT FOR TOPOGRAPHICAL MAP-
PING. *Redrawn from original sketch.*

Bartoli's instrument, becomes an essential element inserted in the
circular base in anticipation of Rathborne's "theodelite." Habermel's instrument clearly suggests its evolution from the astrolabe.
In 1598 the *polimetrum* was reproduced practically unchanged
by Gallucci [205] under the name of the *visorio* (Figure 112), but
the author neglected to make any mention of Waldseemüller's
previous contribution. An interestingly designed instrument appeared in France in 1598. This was the *Henry-mêtre* of De Suberville (Figure 113). It is quite evident that the design of the in-

[205] Gallucci, *op. cit.*, Bk. 4, Ch. 11.

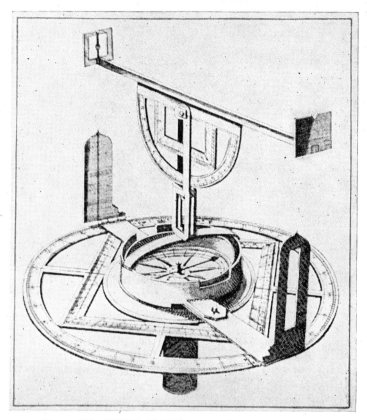

Figure 115. THEODOLITE. *From Blaeu's* Atlas *(1664)*.

strument[206] was inspired by the fundamental rod combinations. Arduser's[207] instrument of 1627 shows an attempt to reduce the size of the horizontal and vertical measuring arcs to a minimum. By comparing this instrument (Figure 114) with that illustrated in Rathborne's book nine years previously, we can see how much more advanced were the makers of English instruments. The first Continental instrument which shows a refinement of construction over the early English theodolite is the one diagrammed in Blaeu's *Atlas*[208] of 1664 (Figure 115). Although the theodolite was used to some extent on the Continent, it never attained the popularity

[206] Henry de Suberville, *L'Henry-mètre, instrument royal et universel* (Paris, 1598).
[207] Johann Arduser, *Geometricae, Theoricae et Practicae* (Zurich, 1627), p. 60
[208] Reeves, *op. cit.*, p. 26.

enjoyed by the plane table and the graphomêtre; while England, the land of its propagation, also took the lead in its later developments.

Jacob's Staff

The Jacob's staff, which seems to have fallen into disuse after the death of its inventor, ben Gerson, in 1344, was brought into prominence again in the early Renaissance by Regiomontanus, who used it for astronomical observations. From the description which has been handed down,[209] this staff of Regiomontanus seems to have been a much simplified form of that of ben Gerson. The main staff was between two and three yards long and graduated into 1,300 equal divisions; it carried only one cross-staff. The instrument was mounted on an upright. As aids to sighting there were three pegs inserted at right angles to the staff, one at the sighting end of the main staff and one at each end of the cross-staff. Half the distance between the two cross-staff sights divided by the distance of the cross-staff from the sighting end gave the tangent of half the measured angle.

From about the third decade of the sixteenth century the Jacob's staff became an important instrument in surveying and navigation and went through an interesting series of evolutions, both in methods of graduation and in modes of construction. Jacob's staffs may be divided into two classes, according to the method of graduation: first, those in which the main staff carried equal divisions and which could be used for angle reading only in conjunction with tables of angle functions; second, those graduated so that angle values could be read directly from the staff. To the first class belong the instruments of ben Gerson, Regiomontanus, and most of those used primarily for surveying. Direct angle reading was of more importance in astronomy and navigation, and this need was supplied by the second class.

The first important development in the refinement of the equal graduation method was the transversal system introduced by ben Gerson. As we have already pointed out (p. 178), this method does not seem to have been employed by the early Renaissance users of the staff, such as Regiomontanus, Werner, and Apian.

[209] Schöner, *op. cit.*

Tycho Brahe's employment of the transversal system on several of his astronomical instruments led the way to the revival of this method. Among the examples of the first class of Jacob's staff, in use during the sixteenth century, we find a great range in accuracy of graduation and construction, from the crude types depicted by Reisch, Köbel, Digges, and Belli (Figure 116) to the transversal

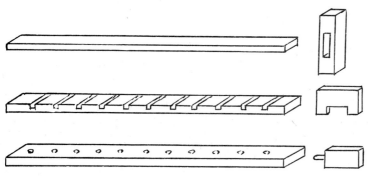

Figure 116. TYPICAL FORMS OF SIMPLE JACOB'S STAFF

division of Brahe. In order to attain a relatively high degree of accuracy without the use of transversals, Werner, Apian, and others used long staffs minutely subdivided. For instance, Werner's staff, about seven feet long, had 2,000 divisions.

In the construction of staffs for direct angle reading Werner took the first important step. His principle of construction may be seen from Figure 117 and the following quotation:[210]

Before approaching the subject itself, I decided deliberately to describe beforehand the structure of the rod or staff. Let a semi-circle be described around *F* as center and let it be denoted by *A, B, C*. And from the point or center *F* let a perpendicular be erected and produced to the circumference, 5, 6, or 7 feet long (for the rod or staff ought to be made according to its length of dense oaken wood of the thickness of a finger), and let it touch the circumference at point *B*, thus the semicircle will be divided into two quadrants, for example *AB* and *BC*. When these have been thus arranged, place one leg of the compasses on *F*, extend the other leg to the width of the plane and with the movable leg make two marks, one towards *A,* naming it *G,* and the other towards *C* where *H* is to be marked. The compasses remaining

[210] This figure and quotation are from Werner's edition of Apian's *Cosmographia* (Ingolstadt, 1524), p. 13. Text in Appendix, p. 372.

unchanged, place the "used" foot on *B,* with the other movable leg describe a light circle to which must be produced tangent lines from both points around *F,* the lines themselves will be equal and parallel to *FB.* Next divide quadrant *AB* and likewise *BC* into 90 parts or degrees, in this manner; first into 3 equal parts and secondly any one part into three, thirdly any of these into 2 and finally into 5. To these [divisions]

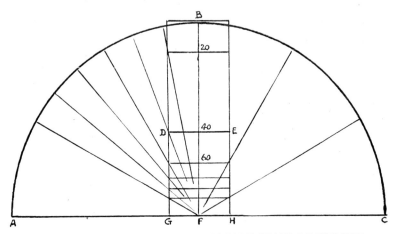

Figure 117. CONSTRUCTION OF JACOB'S STAFF BY WERNER

and to the center apply a ruler and draw light lines through all the divisions and where the produced lines intersect *GD* and *HE* the points are to be noted. When this is done, draw lines from points *G* and *D* to the opposite points on the line *HE.* These transverse lines cut *FB* the semi-diameter. Then construct a rod in length *FB,* having similar divisions as on line *FB.* The numbers of the divisions from *B* toward *F* must be adapted in proportion to the smallness of the division. Then construct a movable plate or pinnacidum in length *GH* or *DE;* construct at its center an opening or slot in which the rod itself can move at right angles and the rod is completed.

Since angles over 90° were rarely if ever measured by the Jacob's staff, graduation did not usually exceed 45°; because of this, for any given cross-staff a part of the main staff equal to half the cross-staff was free of graduations. Besides this graphical method of graduation, Werner also constructed staffs by calculating the positions of the graduation lines, using the tables of Regiomontanus. The common mode of construction later was the graphical.

Apian used the angle graduation with only one crosspiece and

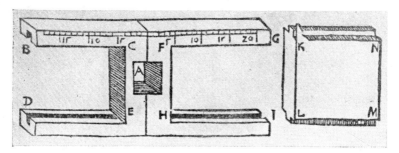

Figure 118. APIAN'S DEVICE FOR VARIABLE CROSSPIECE

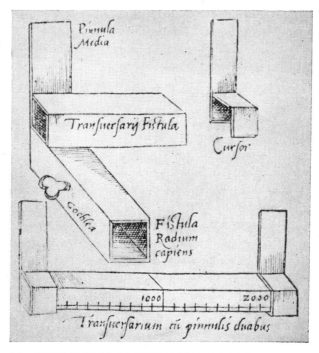

Figure 119. MECHANISM FOR VARIABLE JACOB'S STAFF BY FRISIUS

therefore employed it for a smaller range of angles than did Werner. In his later work he used the equal division method solely, but by that time he had hit upon an ingenious device for the measurement of small angles without lengthening the staff and without using extra crosspieces.[211] His crosspiece consisted of a long frame (Figure 118) in which two small plates could be slid and placed at any desirable distance from the center. Sights were taken on the inner edges of these plates. Variations of Apian's crosspiece were frequent during subsequent years. One of the most important names connected with the history of the instrument is that of Apian's pupil Gemma Frisius, who wrote at length on its applications and carried out some innovations in its mechanism.[212] Figure 119 shows some of the changes made by Frisius. The main staff and the cross-staff were bound together in a compound vise. This allowed for the movement of the cross-staff along the main staff and also at right angles to it, so that an unsymmetrical combination could be set up. At both ends of the cross-staff were small fixed plates, whose inner edges were used as sights, while another plate was set up on the vise when the instrument was used for leveling. Frisius was also responsible for graduating the crosspiece for angle reading. His method of construction is shown in Figure 120, in which the eye was supposed to be at A, whereas in actual use it would be at E. Therefore, in use, the crosspiece was moved until B was at D. The divisions on the main staff were to be used with half the cross-staff. From the figure it can be seen that small angles were measured on the cross-staff, while the main staff carried the larger angles.

Despite the innovations by Frisius, the simple form of cross-staff remained in common use,[213] but the majority of the later writers, such as Finaeus, Ramus, Ryff, and Gallucci, depended to a great extent on the descriptions of the use of the instrument as given by Frisius. Ramus' book [214] is probably the most complete on the applications of the Jacob's staff. The last development of the staff,

[211] Apian, *Instrument-Buch,* fol. N.

[212] Gemma Frisius, *De Radio Astronomico et Geometrico* (Antwerp, 1545).

[213] L. Digges described it at length under the title of "the profitable staffe" in *A Booke named Tectonicon* (London, 1556).

[214] Ramus, *Arithmeticae libri duo, Geometricae septem et viginti* (Basel, 1559). See also W. Ryff, *op. cit.*

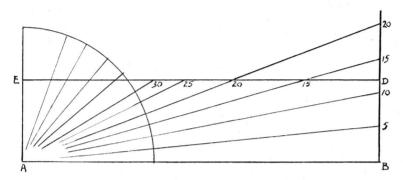

Figure 120. CONSTRUCTION OF JACOB'S STAFF BY FRISIUS

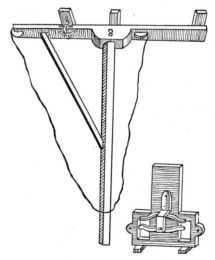

Figure 121. MECHANISM FOR VARIABLE CROSSPIECE BY METIUS

in line with Frisius' idea of movable sights, is to be found in one of Metius' works.[215] From Figure 121 it can be seen that it was possible for the observer to vary the position of the sights by a system of cord and pulleys. This instrument was large and was mounted on a vertical staff.

The history of the Jacob's staff is intimately associated with the marine enterprises of the latter half of the sixteenth century and the early decades of the seventeenth. The *Mohīt* form, used in the East (p. 84), whose origin and antiquity are unknown, does not seem to have been used by Western navigators at any period; at least there is no record of such use. More surprising still is the lack of any recorded use of the Jacob's staff by the Portuguese and Spaniards during the fifteenth and early sixteenth centuries.[216] This is a strange phenomenon in view of the fact that the Iberian Peninsula, which was the hub of the maritime activity during that period, was also the land in which the Jacob's staff was first used.[217] The earliest description of a Jacob's staff for use in navigation is given by De Medina[218] in 1545. His method of construction corresponds with that given by Werner. Nuñez, writing the next year, gives brief mention of this instrument but thinks it too difficult to operate;[219] however, its approval by Cortes,[220] whose work became authoritative on nautical affairs, was probably instrumental in bringing about its wide adoption.

The principal use of the Jacob's staff as a nautical instrument was to "shoot the sun," so as to estimate time, and to observe the altitude of the polestar in order to determine latitude. In the former operation, using the ordinary Jacob's staff, the observer was hampered by the glare of the sun. The first attempt to overcome this inconvenience was made by Bourne. Previously, sighting was done on the upper rim of the sun, the glare being partly

---

[215] Adrian Metius, *Genuino Usu utriusque Globi Tractatus* (Francarae, 1611), p. 108.

[216] A. Schück, "Der Jakobstab," *Jahresbericht der geographischen Gesellschaft*, Vol. 16, 1893, p. 99.

[217] Referring to the part supposed by some to have been played by the Jacob's staff during the discovery period, Bensaude, *L'Astronomie nautique au Portugal à l'époque des grandes découvertes*, p. 37, says, "Il devient de plus en plus évident que le rôle qui lui est attribué pendant la période des grandes découvertes est inadmissible."

[218] De Medina, *op. cit.*, Bk. 5, Ch. 2.

[219] Pedro Nuñez, *De Arte atque Ratione Navigandi* (Coimbra, 1546), Bk. 1, Ch. 6.

[220] Cortes, *op. cit.*, Ch. 9.

blocked by the thickness of the crosspiece, and a correction of fifteen minutes was made. Bourne solved the difficulty by using colored glasses with diaphragms at the ends of the crosspiece.[221]

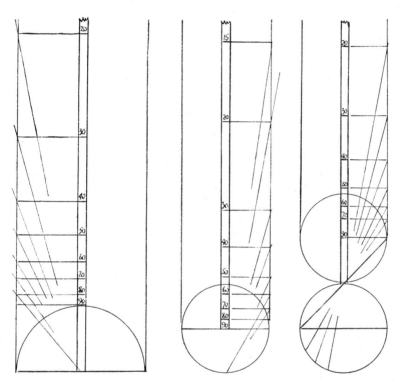

Figures 122, 123, 124. METHODS OF CONSTRUCTING SCALES FOR THE MARINE JACOB'S STAFF BY CORTES, WAGHENAER, AND DE CESPEDES RESPECTIVELY

With respect to methods of graduation, that of Cortes (Figure 122), which was a slight modification of Werner's, remained the standard for many years. Later variations by Waghenaer[222] and De Cespedes[223] are shown in Figures 123 and 124 respectively. The advantage of these methods lies in the fact that spacing for the larger angle graduations is increased. The standard nautical staff of the later sixteenth century carried three crosspieces, with cor-

[221] Bourne, *A Regiment for the Sea.*
[222] Lucas Waghenaer, *Speculum Nauticum* (Amsterdam, 1586).
[223] Garcia de Cespedes, *Regimento de Navegacion* (Madrid, 1606).

responding graduations, and usually had a range of from 6° to 60°.[224]

The most radical change in the Jacob's staff was that developed by Davis in an effort to overcome the inconvenience of the glare of the sun. What has been since known as the *backstaff* or *Davis staff* was originally described by the famous explorer as follows:[225]

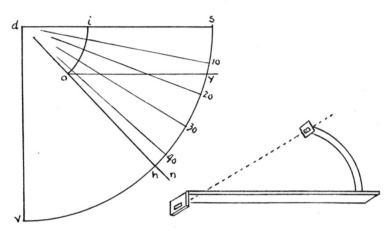

Figure 125. CONSTRUCTION OF DAVIS STAFF

There is a staffe of another projection, which I finde by practise to be an instrument of very great ease and certaintie at the sea, the Sunne not being more than 45 degrees above the Horizon, whose use is contrary to the other before demonstrated, for by this staffe the beame of the Sunne shadowing upon the transversary, doth thereby give the height most preciselye, not regarding how to place the center of the staffe to the eye for the correction of the parallax of the sight, and without looking upon the Sunne, whose demonstration is thus [Figure 125].

Drawe 2 right lines cutting each other at right angles, as doe the lines *d.v.* and *d.s.* upon the angle *d* describe a quarter circle, as is the arke *v.s.* devide that quadrant into 2 equall partes by the line *d.n.* cutting the quadrant in the point *h.* devide the arke *s h* into 45 equall partes or degrees, drawing lines from the center *d* to every of those divisions, Then from the point *i* being the third parte of the line *d.s.* upon the center *d.* describe an arke of a circle, as is the arke *i.o.* which is for the transversary of this staffe, and the line *d.s.* is for the staffe, than

[224] See Blundevil, *op. cit.*, pp. 664 ff. for descriptions of the forms of Jacob's staff in common use in England in the late sixteenth century. See also Edmund Gunter, *Description and Use of the Sector, Crosse-Staffe and Other Instruments* (London, 1624).

[225] Davis, *op. cit.*, fol. L.

from point *o.* where the upper ende of the transversary toucheth the line *d.n.* drawe a parallel to the line *d.s.* as in the lyne *o.y.* and as that line doth cut the lines drawne from the center *d.* so must the staffe *d.s.* be graduated, laying it upon the line *o.y.* putting that parte of the staffe where the point *i.* toucheth, upon the point *o.* and then from the point *i.* lay downe the degrees, as are the intersections upon the line *o. y.* and so is the staffe graduated.

The transversary at the point *i,* must have an artificiall hole made for the staffe to runne in, as other staves have, also there must be a plate of brass with a soccat to be set to the center of the staffe, as is the figure *a* in the midst whereof there must be a slittle, through which the sight must be conveyed to the horizon, and this plate must receive the shadowe of the transversary, and so the staffe is finished.

The use of this staffe is altogether contrary to the other, for the center of this staffe where the brasse plate is fastened, must be turned to that parte of the horizon which is from the sunne, and with your backe toward the Sunne, by the lower edge of the halfe crosse, and through the slitte of the plate you must direct your sight only to the Horizon, and then moving the transversary as occasion requireth, untill the shadowe of your upper edge of the transversary doe fall directly upon the said slittle or long hole, and also at the same instant you see the Horizon through the slittle, and then the transversary sheweth the height desired.

Davis also describes another form of the backstaff, but in less detail:[226]

Finding by practise the eccellencye of the Crosse staffe above all other instruments to satisfie the Seamans expectation, and also knowing that those instruments whose degrees are of largest capacities, are instruments of most certaintie. I have very carefully laboured to search a good and demonstrable meane how a Crosse staffe might be projected, not only to contayne large degrees but also to avoid the uncertaintie of the sight, by disorderlye placing of the staffe to the eye, which demonstration I have found, and have had the instrument in practise, as well as under the Sunne as in our[227] climates: but because it hath a large demonstration with manifolde uses, I heere omit to manifest the same, proposing to write a perticular treatise thereof, notwithstanding his forme and use, by picture I have thought good to expresse.

This staffe is a yard long, having 2 halfe crosses, the one circular, the other straight, the longest not 14 inches, yet this staffe doth contain the whole 90 degrees, the shortest degree being an inch and 3/4 long, wherin the minutes are particularly and very sensibly laid downe, by

[226] *Ibid.,* fol. M.
[227] According to a marginal note this is a printer's error and should be "other."

which staffe not regarding the parallax of your sight, nor looking upon
the Sunne, but onelye upon the Horizon, the Sunnes height is most
precisely knowne, as well and as easily in the Zenith as in any other part
of the Heaven. Then which instrument (in my opinion) the Seaman
shall not finde any so good, and in all Clymates of so great certaintie,
the invention and demonstration whereof, I may boldly challenge to
appertain unto my selfe (as a portion of the talent which God hath
bestowed upon me) I hope without abuse or offence to any.

Writing on this same type of staff Metius says:[228]

Vidi apud Ambonae Gubernatorem Fredericum Houtmann Radium
aptissimum ad observandum altitudinem Solis, quae sit alio et con-
trario modo, cuius schema hic proponitur. Sed quia ad eundem modum, uti licet Quadrante, eius usum paucis proponam.

There were two variations of this second backstaff of Davis, the
first that described by Davis himself, in which the upper vane or
transom was straight (Figure 126a), and the second, which seems
to have been more common, that in which both vanes were arcs
of circles[229] (Figure 126b). In use, the sight on the upper arc or
chord was set at any convenient angle; then, with his back to the
sun, the observer looked through the sight on the lower arc at the
horizon, adjusting the sight until he saw the sun's rays through
the upper sight cutting the horizontal line at the same time. Besides these special types of backstaff, the ordinary Jacob's staff was
also used. Figure 127 shows the method of employment. In this
case the crosspiece was fixed at the eye end of the main staff and a
slider with small projecting sights was moved along the main staff
until, while the observer was sighting along the under edge of the
cross-staff toward the horizon, the shadow of the upper end appeared on the slider.

The next important change was developed by Van Breen,[230]
who used a mirror to reflect the image of the sun (Figure 128).
In this instrument the slider on the main staff carried a mirror
with a rectangular hole at its center, set at right angles to the staff.
The observer sighted through the mirror hole toward the horizon,
while manipulating the slider so that the ray through the upper

[228] Adrian Metius, *Mensura Geographica et Usus Globi Terrestris* (Francarae, 1624),
pp. 20-21.

[229] Samuel Sturmy, *The Mariners Magazine,* Fourth Edition (London, 1700), Ch. 14.

[230] Jost Van Breen, *Stiermanns Gemack ofte eene korte Beschryvinge van de Konst
der Stierlieden* (Graven-Hage, 1662).

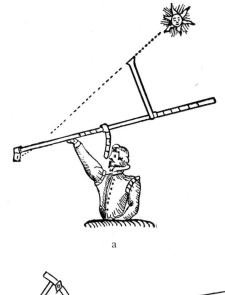

a

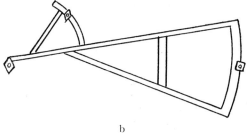

b

Figure 126. **DAVIS STAFF**

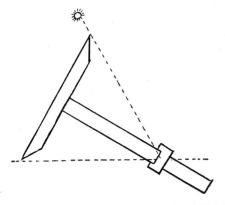

Figure 127. **JACOB'S STAFF USED AS BACKSTAFF**

slit of the cross-staff appeared on the mirror in the same line with the horizon. Colored glass was used in the eyepiece. Here we have the first application of measuring angles by mirror reflection on instruments. The idea was soon developed by Hooke[231] and Flamsteed [232] on the quadrant, but Newton was the first to produce a practical instrument of the quadrant type in his octant (Figure 129). Although the honor of doing this is generally thought to belong to John Hadley, the fact is that Newton in 1700, in a letter to Hadley, the Astronomer Royal, described most minutely an instrument which has certainly the right to be called the first reflecting instrument based on the principle of the sextant.[233]

Compass

The history of the compass during this period may well be considered from two aspects; first, its use as a surveying instrument or as an adjunct to such instruments, and second, the development of ideas with regard to the properties of the magnetic needle which gradually evolved with the expansion of navigation. We have seen in the last chapter that the earliest use of the compass in surveying was in connection with mining (p. 96). In the oldest Renaissance treatise[234] on mining are two diagrams of compasses then in use (Figure 130). Probably the oldest specimen of such compasses is preserved in Neudorfer (Figure 131) :[235]

The 5.5 cm. compass-box fits into the center of a wooden disk 16 cm. in diameter and 2 cm. thick. About it are 3 concentric grooves filled with wax of different colors. Upon the bottom plate of the compass-box is drawn only a meridian line marked at its ends M.R. (Meredies) and S.P. (Septentrio). When in use, the compass and disk were put into the circular cavity of a wooden box and mounted by means of a hole beneath upon a simple staff. . . . The disk was turned until the needle became coincident with the meridian line, then the pointer that revolved about its fiducial edge was brought into the direction of any

[231] Robert Hooke, *Posthumous Works* (London, 1708).
[232] John Flamsteed, *Historia Coelestis Britannica* (London, 1712).
[233] Reeves, *op. cit.*, p. 19.
[234] Anonymous, *Eyn wolgeordent und nutzlich Büchlin wie man Bergwerck suchen und finden soll* (1505).
[235] This instrument is dated 1541. Quotation and diagram from Professor Brathuln given by Dunbar A. Scott in the "Evolution of Mine-Surveying Instruments," *Transactions, American Institute of Mining Engineers*, Vol. 28, 1898, p. 682. By permission of The American Institute of Mining and Metallurgical Engineers.

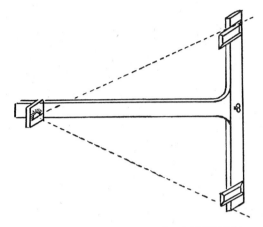

Figure 128. VAN BREEN'S BACKSTAFF

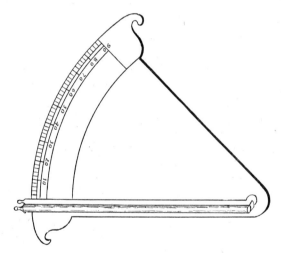

Figure 129. NEWTON'S OCTANT

Figure 130. EARLY RENAISSANCE MINING COMPASS

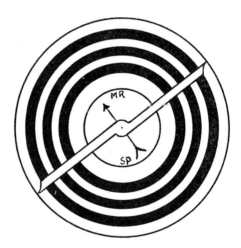

Figure 131. THE NEUDORFER MINING COMPASS. *Redrawn from original by permission of The American Institute of Mining and Metallurgical Engineers.*

course, as nearly as could be judged by the eye, and a mark was made in one of the wax circles to indicate its azimuth with the meridian. . . . The course was then measured and recorded with the characterized mark and the color of the wax circle in which it was made. The survey was then reproduced on the surface commencing usually at the mouth of the shaft, to determine the proximity of the underground workings to the boundary lines.

The most important book on mining and metallurgy of the Renaissance is that of Agricola. It contains a diagram of a compass similar to that described in the paragraph above except that it was

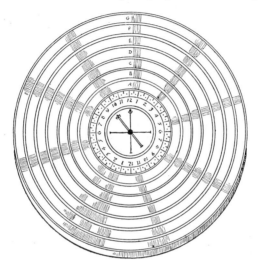

Figure 132. AGRICOLA'S COMPASS. *Redrawn from* De Re Metallica, *by permission of* The Mining Magazine, *Publishers.*

divided into twenty-four divisions and carried seven wax circles (Figure 132). On this method of division Agricola remarks:[236]

Now miners reckon as many points as the sailors do in reckoning up the number of the winds . . . . Any miner who please may therefore call the directions of the veins by the names of the winds.

The wax circles were employed to avoid the use of notebooks. It is clear from the descriptions of Agricola that calculations of lengths and areas by means of similar triangles were not as yet commonly employed by the miners:[237]

[236] Agricola, *op. cit.*, p. 58. By permission of *The Mining Magazine.*
[237] *Ibid.*, p. 142. Hoover's phrase "surveyor's field" is a rather free equivalent of Agricola's "aequatam planiciem."

When the surveyor has carefully observed each separate angle of the tunnel and has measured such parts as he ought to measure, then he lays them out in the same way on the surveyor's field in the open air and again no less carefully observes each separate angle and measures them.

We have already shown how the compass was used as an adjunct to various other surveying instruments from the time of its first

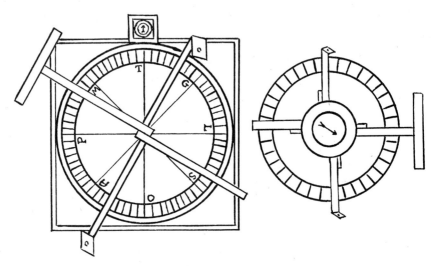

Figures 133 and 134. COMPASS DIAGRAMS BY TARTAGLIA. *Redrawn from originals.*

employment as such by Frisius. Its use as an independent surveying instrument seems to have been first described by Tartaglia, who explains its use in the location of objects by means of bearings and distances. Tartaglia[238] gives diagrams of two types of surveying compasses. Figure 133 shows the small inset compass, following the pattern of Frisius. Tartaglia calls this the common type. Figure 134 shows his "more convenient" type, carrying a large, centrally placed compass with alidade and T-square attached to the collar, which carries a compass card of sixty-four points. As the title of the fifth book points out,[239] this is a discourse on the construction of the topographical compass and an explanation of

[238] Nicolo Tartaglia, *Quesiti et Invenzioni Diversi* (Venice, 1546), Bk. 5.

[239] "Sopra il mettere over tuor rettamente in disegno con il bossolo, li sciti, paesi et similmente le piante delle citta, con il modo di sapere fabricar il detto bossolo, ed in diversi modi, la cui scientia da Ptolemeo è detta Chorografia."

two methods of employment; namely, radial observations and traversing. These methods, described by Tartaglia, are essentially the same as those employed today in compass surveys. The main difference between Tartaglia's second compass and our modern counterpart is the T-square attachment which was parallel to the line of sight. This was to be employed when traversing along a boundary wall, for example in plotting the sides of a fortification, by keeping it tangent to the wall, thereby insuring that the line of sight was parallel to the wall. Another Italian compass instrument, showing the influence of Tartaglia's T-square attachment, was the *squadra zoppa* of Pomodoro.[240] The closest approaches to the modern surveying compass were the Holland circle (Figure 89) and the English circumferentor (Figure 135).

The most interesting portion of the history of the compass at this period is connected with navigation. Although declination marks are to be found on some land compasses made about the middle of the fifteenth century,[241] and allowance for declination was made on the marine compasses before the end of the century,[242] it seems probable that the phenomenon of declination or,

[240] Pomodoro, *op. cit.,* Pl. 40.

[241] A. Wolkenhauer, *Beiträge zur Geschichte der Kartographie und Nautik des 15 bis 17 Jahrhunderts* (Munich, 1904), cites two such sundial compasses on which the declination is marked at about S 10° E. One of these, made in 1451, is preserved at the Museum Ferdinandum, Innsbruck; the other, dated 1456, is in the Bavarian National Museum, Munich. In a note in *Meteorologische Zeitschrift,* August, 1908, G. Hellmann describes a similar marking on a Vienna compass of 1463. Both these authors, after an exhaustive study of existing records, conclude that there is no evidence of scientific observations on variation of magnetic declinations before the end of the fifteenth century and that declination was regarded as an error peculiar to the instrument. Declination marks similar to those on the compasses may also be found on some of the compass roses drawn on early sixteenth century maps such as the *Rom-weg* of Etzlaub and the *Carta Itineraria* of Waldseemüller. The fact that all known fifteenth and early sixteenth century land compasses and "rose" diagrams on maps bear about the same declination tends to disprove a theory sometimes proposed, that the Nürnberg compass-makers of the fifteenth century marked their compasses with the declination of the locality in which the instruments were intended for use. See also G. Hellmann, "Über die Kenntnis der magnetischen Deklination vor Christoph Columbus," *Meteorologische Zeitschrift,* April, 1906, pp. 145-149. L. A. Bauer, "The Earliest Values of the Magnetic Declination," *Terrestrial Magnetism and Atmospheric Electricity,* Vol. 13, 1908, No. 3, pp. 97-104.

[242] Columbus in the diary of his second voyage refers to the variations between the readings of his Genoese and Flemish compasses. For details see N. H. Heathcote, "Christopher Columbus and the Discovery of Magnetic Variation," *Science Progress,* July, 1932, pp. 83-103. Italian compasses of this period made no allowance for declination; Flemish compasses allowed for one point ($11\frac{1}{4}$°) west of north.

Figure 135. THE CIRCUMFERENTOR. *Reproduced from Sanford's* A Short
History of Mathematics, *by permission of the author.*

as it was then called, variation was not recognized as an inherent
property of the magnetic needle prior to the observations of Columbus and other transatlantic pioneers. In view of the fact that
the ordinary mariner's compass of this period carried only thirty-
two points, it is easy to understand why differences in declination
between the important European ports might pass unnoticed and
why variations in the declination were not detected until the
undertaking of the long western voyages. Another factor which
helped to delay the detection of this phenomenom was the manner
in which the mariner's compass was constructed. In contrast with
the ordinary land compass, which was constructed similarly to the
compasses we are accustomed to today, the compass card or rose of
the mariner's compass was attached to the needle and revolved
with it, the needle being hid by the card. The direction of sailing

was indicated by the point of the card which lay beneath a fixed mark on the compass box in line with the bow of the ship. On such compasses, allowance for declination was made by fixing the card on the needle so that the fleur-de-lis of the card was east or west of the north-seeking pole of the needle by the amount of declination predetermined. In this way, when the needle pointed to the magnetic pole, the fleur-de-lis pointed to the geographical pole.

The brief records of Columbus' first detection of variation in declination are worthy of note. In his diary of the first voyage we find the following for September 13, 1492:[243]

This day at night fall, the needles deviated to the North-West, and on the morrow they deviated slightly in the same direction.

For September 17 we have a longer notice:

The pilots took an observation of the north, and found that the needles deviated a good quarter to the north-west, and the mariners were afraid and were dismayed, and did not say why. And the Admiral observed it and bade them repeat the observations of the north at dawn, and they found that the needles were correct; the reason was that the star which they saw moved, and not the needles.

If the phenomenon of variation in declination had been a known fact in Europe before Columbus' voyage there would have been no grounds for the fear expressed in this notice. The fact that such fear was expressed is a strong indication that the Spanish pilots were here dealing with something entirely new and un-expected. It is not surprising that both the Spaniards and the Portuguese, once they had become familiar with the phenomenon, seized upon it as a means of determining longitude. The oldest document[244] in which it is proposed to use magnetic declinations

[243] Martin Fernandez de Navarrete, *Coleccion de los viages y descubrimientos que hicieron por mar los Espanoles desde fines del siglo XV* (Madrid, 1825-1837), 5 vols., Vol. 1, pp. 8-9. "En este dia, al comienzo de la noche, las agujas noruesteaban, y a la manana noruesteaban algun tanto. . . . Tomaron los pilotos el Norte marcandolo, y hallaron que las agujas noruesteaban una gran cuarta, y temian los marineros, y estaban penados y no decian de que. Conociolo el Almirante, mande que tornasen a marcar el Norte en amaneciendo, y hallaron que estaban buenas las agujas; la causa fue que la estrella que parece hace movimiento y no las agujas." Translations from Heathcote, *op cit.* By permission of John Murray, London.

[244] João de Lisboa, *Regimento dos longitudes* (Lisbon, 1514). See Bensaude, *L'Astronomie nautique au Portugal à l'époque des grandes découvertes*, p. 13.

in the determination of longitude dates from 1514; just what attempts were made in the twenty-two years intervening from Columbus' discovery is unknown. The earliest records of scientific

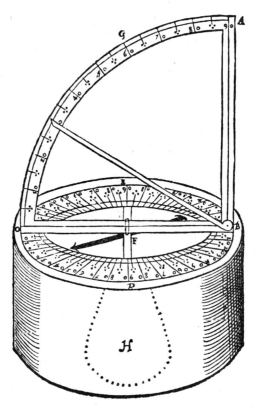

Figure 136. INSTRUMENT FOR DETECTION OF MAGNETIC DECLINATION. *From Stevin's* De Havenvinding.

observations on the variation of magnetic declinations are the determinations made by Felipe Guillen[245] in 1525. Guillen must, then, be regarded as the pioneer of a long line of scientific observers who sought the solution of the longitude problem in the declination of the compass. Guillen's instrument, the *brujula de variacion,* consisted of a combination gnomon and compass. By means of the Indian circles method he determined the meridian

---

[245] Guillen, an apothecary of Seville, left no records of his own. His experimental work was recorded by master pilot Alonzo de Santa-Cruz.

on the gnomon and then found the angles between the needle and
the meridian. The earliest directions in print, giving the manner
of determining the declination, are contained in the navigation
manual of Faleiro.[246] The instrument he proposed for use is
practically the same as Guillen's. In passing it may be stated that
this type of instrument (Figure 136) was most commonly used up
to the end of the sixteenth century,[247] the outstanding exception
being the instrument of Rotz to be described presently. Nuñez[248]
was the first important writer on navigation to uphold the use of
variation in declination as a means of determining longitude.
The most complete set of observations made during the first half
of the sixteenth century was compiled by João de Castro on his
voyages in the years 1538-1541.

The most interesting by-product of the attempts to make use of
the property of declination was the instrument of observation
produced by the French pilot Jean Rotz, who served under Henry
VIII of England. His instrument, the differential quadrant, entirely different from the brujula of Guillen, is of special interest, as
it is the second earliest European instrument embodying the principles of the theodolite. The following description is by E. G. R.
Taylor of the Royal Geographical Society, who has made a study
of Rotz's manuscript. After noting that the sketch (Figure 51) in
the manuscript is faulty, Miss Taylor describes the instrument as
follows:[249]

The horizontal part of the instrument is in 3 concentric sections. The
innermost is the mariner's compass, the needle very delicately poised
and protected by a sheet of glass. This box compass carries an alidade,
the fiducial line corresponding with the N-S line on the compass rose
and extending across the angular graduations on the second section,
the mobile circle. It is into the latter that what Rotz calls the orthog-
onal circle is mortised, so that it can be rotated into any desired position. The outermost base circle is rigid. The vertical portion is also
threefold; the outer and rigid graduated circle embraces a mobile circle
carrying sights. These are joined by a thread representing the axis of
the earth. The mobile circle carries a ring in a third plane which is

---

[246] Faleiro, *op. cit.*, Part II, Ch. 8. See G. Hellmann, *Neudrucke von Schriften und
Karten über Meteorologie und Erdmagnetismus*, No. 10, 1898.
[247] William Gilbert describes the same method in 1600. *De Magnete* (London,
1600), Bk. 4, Ch. 12.
[248] Nuñez, *De Arte Atque Ratione Navigandi*.
[249] Rotz, *op. cit.*, pp. 65-67. By permission of Methuen and Co.

graduated to serve as an equinoctial or universal dial. An important feature not shown in the figure was the levelling device. This consisted of three metal knobs, screwed at equal distances into the rigid base; by twisting these knobs farther in or out the base could be levelled with the help of a plummet. A suspensory ring was provided for use at sea. . . . It is clear from his diagrams that Rotz considered that the needle, wherever it was carried, remained parallel to itself and to a plane drawn through the prime meridian. Hence, if it was taken west, the convergence of the meridians would produce an (apparent) deviation to the west, and similarly, if it were carried to the east, a deviation to the east.

Observation of declination grew mainly out of the hope that the magnetic declination varied over the surface of the earth in such a manner that if lines were drawn through points of equal declination, they would, together with the latitude lines, form a coordinate system by which it would be possible to determine one's position after taking observations for latitude and declination. However, the declination observations of the sixteenth century showed that such a set of lines (isogonics) was irregular. Not only was the hope of proportional declination, which formed the earliest assumption, proved groundless,[250] but the discovery by Gellibrand [251] of a gradual time variation in the declination, showed that such isogonic charts were impracticable. Nevertheless, some such charts were published, the first being that of

[250] Robert Norman, *The Newe Attractive* (London, 1581), Ch. 9. "This variation is adjudged by divers Travellers to be by equal proportion, but herein they are much deceyved; And therefore it appeareth, that notwithstanding their Travell, they have more followed theyr Bookes than Experience in that matter. True it is, that Martin Curtes doth allowe it to bee by proportion, but it is a moste false and erroneous Rule. For there is neither proportion nor uniformity in it, but in some places swift and sudden and in some places slowe." *The Newe Attractive* gives a clear statement of the fundamental laws of attraction and repulsion between magnetic poles. It also contains an account of Norman's independent discovery and measurement of magnetic dip in 1576. This had been previously noted by G. Hartmann of Nürnberg in 1544, but he did not publish any account of it until 1571. See Hellmann, *Neudrucke von Schriften und Karten über Meteorologie und Erdmagnetismus,* No. 10, 1898.

[251] Henry Gellibrand, *A Discours Mathematical on the Variation of the Magneticall Needle* (London, 1635). Speaking of the custom of the period he says (p. 6): "Thus hitherto (according to the Tenets of all our Magneticall Philosophers) we have supposed the variations of all particular places to continue one and the same. So that when a Seaman shall happly returne to a place where formerly he found the same variation, he may hence conclude he is in the same former Longitude. For it is the Assertion of Mr. Dr. Gilberts Variatio unicuiusque Loci constans est, that is to say, the same place doth always retaine the same variation. Neither hath this Asser-tion (for ought I ever heard) been questioned by any man."

Burrus[252] of Lisbon. The most complete record of declinations (without isogonic lines) is in the maps of the *Arcano del Mare*.[253]

A wide variety of hypotheses were put forward during the sixteenth century regarding the position of the "point attractive" or the terrestrial magnetic poles. Norman,[254] summarizing these, says that Cortes held they were "beyond the poles of the worlde, without all the moveable heavens"; others held they were at the geographical poles owing to the presence there of large quantities of loadstone; De Medina believed that variation was accidental, caused by the manner of "placing the wiers on the flie." Norman himself suggests a scientific method for what he prefers to call the "poynt respective" by observing the direction of the needle in various places. Mercator and the Flemish school of cosmographers had already proposed the hypothesis that such a pair of terrestrial poles, at some distance from the geographical poles, were the cause of the magnetic declination. However, Gilbert, who was the greatest experimenter with magnetism during the sixteenth century, dissented from this point of view, and held that the two sets of poles were coincident and that variations in declination were due to local irregularities of land and water distribution.

Despite the varying hypotheses, pilots seem to have used variation in declination to determine location. Bourne in 1573 says:[255]

No Maister or Pilot of a shippe doth keep so simple account of the shippes way, but that he may know what distance he hath into any place, better than he shall know by the varying of the compass; also whether it be or not, that the compass doth keepe any such proportion in the variation, I do refer that unto them that have tried the experience thereof, for I for my part can say nothing in that matter.

Norman sums up the navigational technic of the period thus:[256]

> With joyfull heart to take the height he doth assey,
> His Astrolabie then he setteth by the Sunne,
> Or cross-staffe for the Starrs, called Balles'till:
> And thus with help of them and declination
> How land doth bear of him he knows within a while.

[252] On the work of Fr. C. Burrus, S.J., see Athanasius Kircher, S.J., *Magnes sive de Arte Magnetica* (Rome, 1641), p. 503.

[253] Dudley, *op. cit.*

[254] Norman, *op. cit.*, Ch. 2.

[255] Bourne, *A Regiment for the Sea.*

[256] Robert Norman, *The Safeguard of Saylers, or Great Rutter* (London, 1584).

The following description from Blundevil gives a good picture of the type of marine compass in use during the latter part of the sixteenth century:[257]

The mariners compasse may be very well divided into two essential parts, that is, the Fly and the Wyers, touched with Loadstone, called

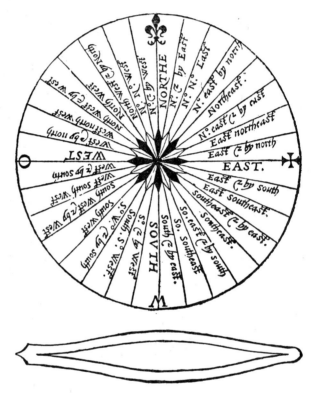

Figure 137. SKETCH OF MARINER'S COMPASS BY BLUNDEVIL. *The top diagram shows the compass card or fly. The lower diagram shows the magnetic needle or wires.*

in Latine Magnes. And first you have to understand, that the Fly is a round white Card traced with 32 lines all passing through the Centre of the Circle, which lines doe signifie the 32 winds in such sort as the figure before set downe doth shew [Figure 137], of which lines that which is marked with the Flower-deluce signifieth the North whose point opposite is the South, and that which is marked with a crosse signifieth the East whose point opposite is the West, and the outermost

[257] Blundevil, *op. cit.*, p. 681.

circle of the said Fly signifieth the Horizon, which circle is divided also into 360 degrees like unto those of the Equinoctiall, so as every space betwixt point and point containeth 11 degrees and 15 minutes, which is the fourth part of a degree. Moreover, the Circle is divided into 24 hours by allowing to every point three quarters of an hour which is 45 minutes, for an hour containeth 60^m, and halfe an hour containeth 30^m, and the quarter 15^m. Moreover, the common Mariners doe divide every point of the Compasse into four quarters to make the more exact account of their Routes or Rombes. But now as touching the other essentiall part of the Mariners Compasse which is the wyars, you shall understand that they are of iron or steele, and made in this form [Figure 137], and being touched at the end with the Loadstone, they are fastened to the back-side of the Flie, either right over the line marked with the Flower-deluce, or else towards the West, for such cause as shall be declared in the next Chapter, for those wyars being thus touched, doe make that part of the Flye that is marked with the Flower-deluce, to stand alwaies towardes the North, and to that end the Flye having at the Centre a latten socket put into a turned bore, in the middest whereof is a sharpe pointed Latten pinne, upon which the Flie turneth about, and that turned bore is covered with glasse, partlie to keepe the Flie cleane but chiefly that the winde should not move it to and fro, And this turned bore is hanged by two rounde narrowe plates of Latten, in another square bore of thinne wainscoat boorde, so as it may alwaies hang levell, howsoever the shippe swayeth or inclineth on eyther side, and though of the Mariners Compasse there be divers uses, as you shall perceive hereafter, yet the chiefest end and use thereof is to shew the North part of the world.

The form of the nautical compass needle remained unchanged during the seventeenth century. Barlowe complains in 1616 that[258]

the Compasse needle, being the most admirable and useful instrument of the whole world, is both amongst ours and other nations for the most part so bungerly and absurdly contrived, as nothing more.

He recommended that the needle be a

true circle, having his axis going out beyond the circle at each end narrow and narrower, unto a reasonable sharpe point, and being pure steele as the circle itself is, having in the middest a convenient receptacle to place the capitell in.

It was not until 1750 that Knight proposed to substitute straight

---

[258] William Barlowe, *Magnetical Advertisements* (London, 1616), p. 66.

steel bars of small breadth, suspended edgewise and hardened throughout.[259]

Triangulation Instruments

Although many of the instruments so far mentioned were used to some extent in triangulation work, the title *triangulation instruments* belongs especially to a new group of instruments which began to appear from about the middle of the sixteenth century. Up to the period of the Renaissance the general method of measuring the distance between two points in a horizontal plane was to consider such a distance as a leg of a right triangle. This method was taken over from the corresponding problem of finding heights or depths in the vertical plane. Although Heron had described another method—that of laying off similar triangles on the ground (see p. 298)—this method seems to have been neglected by the medieval European writers with one exception, the unknown author of the *Geometria Culmensis* (see p. 99).

A triangulation instrument may be defined as that by which it is possible to set up directly, either by means of the members of the instrument itself, or by lines parallel to such members on an auxiliary plane, a triangle or polygon similar to the triangle or polygon being surveyed. Triangulation instruments consisted essentially of three straight-edge members like the *triquetrum* of Ptolemy[260] but used in the horizontal plane. They undoubtedly developed from simple staff combinations. The simplest form consisted of three similarly graduated rods, two of them bound so as to revolve about the ends of the third. Although angle reading is not essential to the use of such an instrument, yet in the earliest description which we have, by Münster, angle reading is provided for. The following is Münster's description of the instrument (Figure 138) and its orientation, together with the observations and calculations necessary:[261]

Construct for yourself an instrument such as you see described here on any table with the movable rulers and add a square compass. The three sides of this *trigonus* have equal divisions. The fixed side is

[259] *Encyclopaedia Britannica,* Fourteenth Edition, Vol. 6, p. 177.

[260] Similar astronomical instruments were used by Copernicus and Brahe. See Repsold, *op. cit.*

[261] Münster, *op. cit.,* pp. 42 ff. Text in Appendix, p. 373.

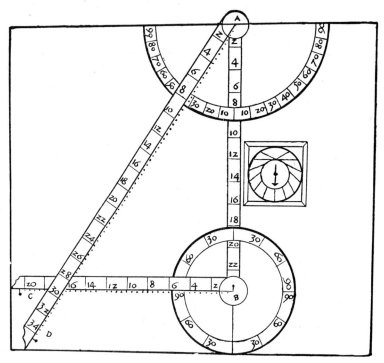

Figure 138. MÜNSTER'S TRIGONUS

limited to 24 divisions, the two movable sides however are not limited
to a definite number of divisions. The rest you can easily describe by
your own effort. The use of this instrument is as follows. You desire to
know how to protect certain things, a camp or a tower under artillery
fire, or how far something is from you, or how great is the width of
some running river, you will work as follows.

Place the instrument on some tree trunk or stone and turn it round,
until through the sights or center points *BA*, you see an object whose
distance from you you wish to find; leaving the instrument in this position, you will look to the right or the left, and you will select some object, to which you can conveniently approach, and which is some paces
distant from you, for example 30 or 40 or even more, for the larger you
make the angle, the more correctly will you work in determining the
distance of the object, the distance which you seek. Then towards that
object, you will turn the ruler *BC*, either right or left, until through the
opening of the sight *B* and the pin erected at *C*, you see the observed
mark. You will note also the intersection of this rod and the circle in
the center of which the ruler *BC* revolves. For in the second position
it will be necessary for the rod to touch the same point of the circle.

Besides you will place a compass above the instrument before you take
the latter from its first position, for example by adapting the south end
of the compass to the line *AB* of the instrument, you will see what hour
or what other point of the divisions between the hours the movable
needle of the compass touches, or if the sun is shining, note what hour
the shadow of the gnomon touches, and preserve carefully that point
of the indicator or the shadow, for you must place the instrument again

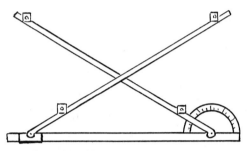

Figure 139. STEVIN'S TRIQUETRUM

in this position at the point observed laterally (where the second station will be) which you can not do without the aid of the compass.
Having finished with this first station, you will cross over to the position observed laterally where the second station will be, and between
them you will count by feet or paces the space included between both
positions, and you will note carefully the number of feet or paces included, for that will be one measured side of the triangle, whence you
will arrive at the knowledge of the two remaining sides by the method
I am about to describe. When you reach the lateral point which you
sighted at the first station and whose distance you have measured, you
will place the instrument on some object raised above the ground, and
having applied the compass, you will fit it in that position which it had
at the first station. This done, you will have no further need of the
compass. You will fit the ruler *BC* in the position it had at the first
station. Then move the ruler *DA* over the ruler *BC* until you see
through its sights the object whose distance from you, you may seek,
and note the divisions made on the ruler *BC* by the ruler *DA,* and likewise, how many divisions are cut on the ruler *DA* by the ruler *BC,* and
you will have a triangle whose three sides are divided by equal graduations. Then you will work by the rule of three as follows. Set down in
the first place the divisions of the ruler *BC,* then the number of feet
or paces which you counted from the first station to the second, in the
third place set down the number of the side *AB* which is always 24,
and multiply the second by the third and divide the product by the
first and you will have the feet or paces from the first station to the ob-

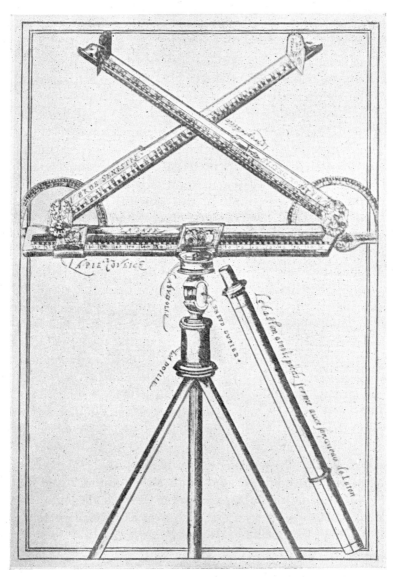

Figure 140. DANFRIE'S TRIGOMÊTRE

ject sighted. And if you also wish to find the distance between the second station and the observed object, set down in the third place the number of divisions of the ruler *DA* which the ruler *BC* cuts off, and work as before.

The same type of instrument is described by Rensberger,[262] while in the triquetrum of Stevin[263] we note an improvement, in that the length of the base line can be varied at will by having one of the movable rulers attached to a socket which slides along the base line. Stevin used only one graduated semicircle (Figure 139). After enumerating the principal surveying instruments in use at his time he states his preference for the triquetrum above all others. A similar instrument of Burgi is described by Bramer.[264] The most finished example of this type of instrument was the *trigomêtre* of Danfrie[265] (Figure 140). Mounted on a tripod, it could be turned into any desired plane by means of an ingenious socket.

Besides the instruments already mentioned, which formed similar triangles by making two sets of angles equal, there were others appearing in the early seventeenth century which depended on the method employed in the *Geometria Culmensis* two hundred years previously; namely, constructing similar triangles by having two sets of sides in proportion and the included angles equal. The earliest of these seems to have been the *novum instrumentum geometricum* of Zubler.[266] From Figure 141 it can be seen that this instrument consisted essentially of a semicircular base *BDC* around the center of which two alidades *AE, AF* revolved; it carried an inset compass for orientation. The third ruler *I* was used to scale off the length of the required side when the lengths of the two known sides had been set off to scale on *AE* and *AF*. From some of Zubler's diagrams (which deal mostly with war scenes) it can be seen that he also used this instrument after the manner described by Münster[267] (Figure 142). Essentially

[262] Nicolas Rensberger, *Geometria* (Augsburg, 1568), fol. 6.

[263] Stevin, *op. cit.*, pp. 47-48.

[264] Benjamin Bramer, *Bericht über Jobst Bürgii geometrische Triangularinstrument* (Cassel, 1648).

[265] Danfrie, *op. cit.*

[266] Zubler, *op. cit.*

[267] In explaining the use of his instrument Zubler says: "Metienti, longitudinem, altitudinem, latitudinem et profunditatem duo semper triangula aequiangula ap-

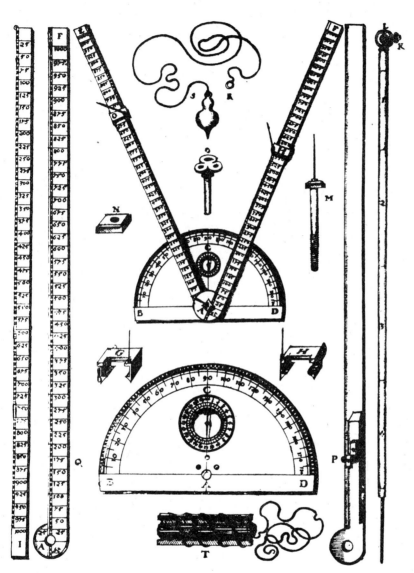

Figure 141. ZUBLER'S NOVUM INSTRUMENTUM GEOMETRICUM

Figure 142. SCENE FROM ZUBLER'S *NOVUM INSTRUMENTUM*
GEOMETRICUM

of the same type, but replacing the graduated semicircle with a
rectangular board bearing angle divisions on three edges and
covered with a network of coordinates parallel to the edges, is the
trigonometria of Bramer[268] (Figure 143). Angles were read to 6'
by means of a transversal scale. The third ruler, used by Zubler,
is replaced here by the network of parallels. Sights were provided
not only on the revolving rulers but also along the long edge on
which lay their center of revolution.

Meanwhile, during the latter half of the sixteenth century
while many variations of the three-sided triangulation instruments
were making their appearance, another type which was destined
to outlast the first and become the most popular triangulation
instrument on the Continent was in the process of development.

parent; unum quidem per lineam notam in area vel campo magnum; alterum vero
in Instrumento parvum vel minutum: Verum proportionale illi, quod videtur in
area vel campo. In quibusdam Instrumentis triangulum ejusmodi conspicitur in-
versum; in hoc vero nostro rectum: ut in Figura capitis sequentis lucide proponitur."
    [268] Benjamin Bramer, *Trigonometria Planorum Mechanica* (Marburg, 1617).

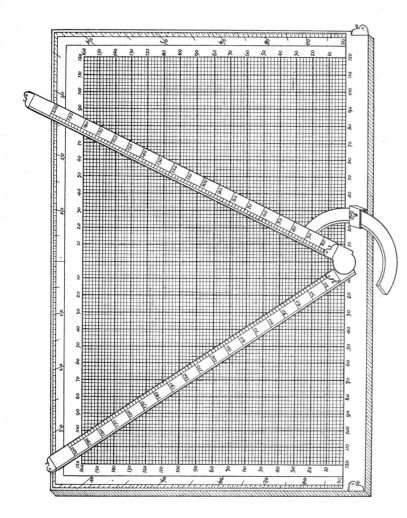

Figure 143. BRAMER'S TRIGONOMETRIA. *Redrawn from original sketch.*

In its final form it was known as the plane table. Its growth may
be traced from the instrument of Münster: first, by the substitution of a solid board or table for the stationary ruler; and secondly,
by the substitution of one free ruler or alidade for the two revolvable ones. The impulse to produce such an instrument grew
out of the desire to avoid mathematical calculations as far as possible by the employment of graphical methods. The earliest description of such an instrument is by Foullon, but his *holomêtre*
is such a complete instrument that it is safe to assume that it must
have been preceded by others of cruder design. Foullon describes
his instrument as follows (Figure 144) :[269]

It contains only six parts, which are the table, the guide, the base,
the two rulers and the foot. The table is that which supports the base
and the two rulers, and it is plane to take measurements exactly. In
the middle of the table there is a compass such as is put on the sun-dials.
The needle is surrounded by signs which represent the winds . . . .
And the compass is used here only for determining direction, in order
that when bringing the *Holomêtre* from one position to another, it
may be possible to place it down as it was before . . . . The guide is a
piece made up of a circle and a small ruler. The circle is divided into
four quadrants and each quadrant into 24 equal parts. I say equal but
I mean on the perpendicular line where they are drawn towards the
center of the said circle, and not otherwise, because, notwithstanding
that the said portions be unequal on the circle nevertheless they are
of equal size above the straight line.[270] And this division will be of use
in ascertaining the measure of all heights and depths. But the little
rulers (otherwise alidades) have at their end sights for looking at the
objects one intends to measure. The alidade is connected at its mid-
point to the guide at the center of the afore-mentioned circle. The
guide is so named because it controls and governs the rulers and the
base, and in order not to fail in placing the guide perpendicularly over
those rulers, it is necessary to hang a little plumb-line through the
center of the said circle, because the plumb-line being over the perpendicular of the guide, it follows that the table is likewise level.
The base is a movable piece which is dovetailed to a groove in the
table . . . . The said groove serves to lengthen or shorten the base, as
much as is needed. Base and groove are graduated in equal divisions.
And this metal is called base because it forms the base of a triangle.
The rulers are two straight rods which are graduated their whole
lengths by equally spaced marks, as are the base and groove. One of

[269] Abel Foullon, *Usaige et description de l'holomêtre* (Paris, 1551). Italian Edition
of S. Ziletti (Venice, 1564), pp. 1 ff. Text in Appendix, p. 374.
[270] The meaning of this last statement is vague and does not agree with the diagram.

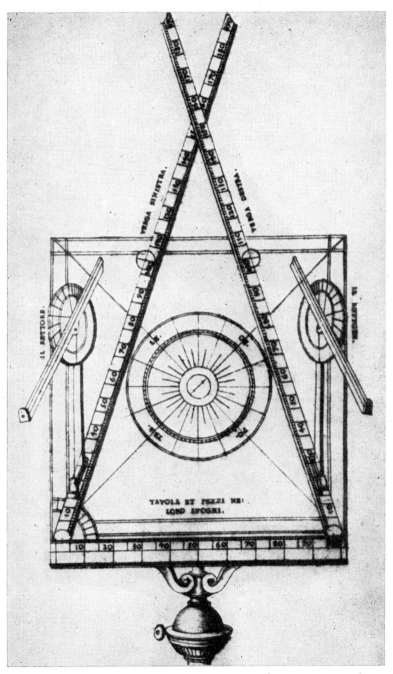

Figure 144. FOULLON'S HOLOMÊTRE

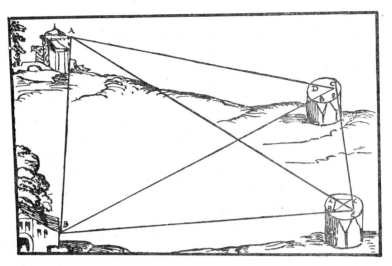

Figure 145. GRAPHICAL SURVEYING ON DRUMHEADS BY BELLI

which (which we call the right ruler) is connected by means of a hinge
with the beginning of the base so that the said right ruler can be closed
and opened like compasses, by means of the said hinge. The other
ruler (which we call the left) is joined in the same way with a small
movable piece. We say movable because it moves under the base by
means of an opening which runs the length of the said groove. And
this movable piece serves to draw near or move further away the left
ruler from the right ruler, as much as there will be need, likewise to
close it and open it with the base, and with the right ruler. And don't
forget that the movable piece is attached to a quadrant divided into 24
parts, which are of the same size as those in the inner circle of the guide.

From this description we see that Foullon's holomêtre was quite
a complicated instrument and adaptable to all kinds of surveying
measurement. The method of orientation and use follows that
outlined by Frisius and Münster. The disadvantage of Foullon's
instrument lay in its complexity; the difficulty of fixing a sheet of
paper to such a table encumbered with rulers and an inset compass was too much for the ordinary surveyor; therefore the trend
was to make the table *plain,* that is as free as possible from encum-
brances. All early English writers speak of it as a *playne* or *plaine*
table;[271] only in later years have we adopted the nomenclature

[271] Rathborne, *op. cit.,* Bk. 3, Ch. 3. "This Instrument for the playnesse and
perspicuitie thereof, and of his easie use in practice receiveth aptly the name and

Figure 146. RATHBORNE'S PLANE TABLE

plane table. Foullon's most important contribution was the direct drawing on the table in the field. Belli's and Lucar's adoption of the graphical method to drumheads (Figure 145) is another example of the trend of the times to rapid and simplified methods.[272] The graphical method was also proposed by Digges.[273] When explaining the use of his theodelitus, he recommends that as soon as the directions of the required lines have been observed, the instrument be inverted and the lines set out to scale on the back of the instrument. Although Rathborne and Leybourn are enthusiastic in their praise of the "playne table," the instrument does not seem to have been adopted for general use in England to the same extent as on the Continent. The plane table described by Rathborne and Leybourn is practically identical with the simple form employed today. Figure 146 shows the table as illustrated by Rathborne. As a warning to those about to use it he says:[274]

appelation of the Playne Table. A most excellent and absolute Instrument for this our purpose in Survey."

[272] Belli, *op. cit.* Lucar, *op. cit.*

[273] L. Digges, *op. cit.*, Ch. 27. ". . . the back side must bee plaine and smoothe to draw circles and lines upon, as shall be declared."

[274] Rathborne, *op. cit.*, Bk. 3., Ch. 3. For Rathborne's description of the "playne table," see Appendix, p. 375.

. . . by reason of this his playnenesse (offering it selfe at first view, in some measure, to the weake understanding of meanest capacities, inciting them thereby to the practise thereof) is more subject to abuse, then all, or any of the rest. For nothwithstanding that these, by the common and ordinary use and practice of the Instrument, may easily attayne to a reasonable truth in Dimension and plotting of regular and even Playnes; yet, if they come to irregular and uneven formes, as Hills and Dales, they are so farre unfitting for the true mensuration thereof, that many using this Instrument, neglect the means and those proper parts of the same Instrument (being the sights, hereafter specified, where they know no use) which is their onely helpe and aide in this kinde.

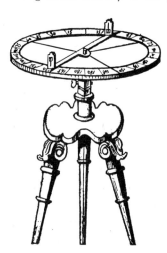

Figure 147. THE PLANCH-ETTE CIRCULAIRE. *Repro-duced from Laussedat's* Recher-ches sur les instruments, les méthodes et le dessin topogra-phiques, *by permission of Gauth-ier-Villars, Publishers.*

When and by whom the single movable alidade was first developed is unknown. In all probability it was a growth from the revolving alidade of Digges' theodelitus. The *planchette circulaire*[275] (Figure 147), which was quite commonly used in France during the seventeenth century, was surely a development from the theodelitus. By placing a paper under the alidade the necessity of reversing the instrument—spoken of by Digges—was avoided. A very simple form of plane table with unattached alidade (Figure 148) was used by Zubler.[276] Probably the most popular treatise on the use of the plane table was that of Le Clerc,[277] from which Figures 149 and 152 are taken, to show various uses of the instrument. Besides the simple type of plane table a few more complicated forms appeared early in the seventeenth century, but they do not seem to have influenced the general form of development. Of these the more important were the *pantometrum* (Figure 150) of Kircher[278] and the *mensula*

[275] Bion, *op. cit.,* Pl. 13. See also Thomas Moette, *L'École des arpenteurs* (Paris, 1692). A. Laussedat, *Recherches sur les instruments, les méthodes et le dessin topo-graphiques* (Paris, 1898), pp. 106 ff.

[276] Leonard Zubler, *Fabrica et Usus Instrumenti Chorographici* (Zurich, 1607).

[277] Le Clerc, *op. cit.*

[278] Kircher's instrument is described by Schott, *op. cit.,* Bk. 1.

Figure 148. ZUBLER'S PLANE TABLE

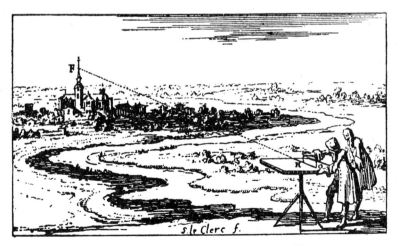

Figure 149. LE CLERC'S PLANE TABLE

Figure 150. KIRCHER'S PANTOMETRUM

(Figure 151) of Praetorius.[279] This latter diagram shows not only the complete table but also its component parts and accessory instruments, such as leveling rod, and chain measure.

[279] (Richter) Jean Praetorius (1537-1616), a Nürnberg mechanic, later professor of mathematics at Wittenberg and Altdorf. A description of his mensula is given by Schwenter, *op. cit.*, Bk. 3. For an English synopsis of Schwenter's description, see J. L. van Ornum, "Topographical Surveys, Their Methods and Value," *Bulletin of the University of Wisconsin*, Engineering Series, Vol. 1, 1896, No. 10, pp. 331-369.

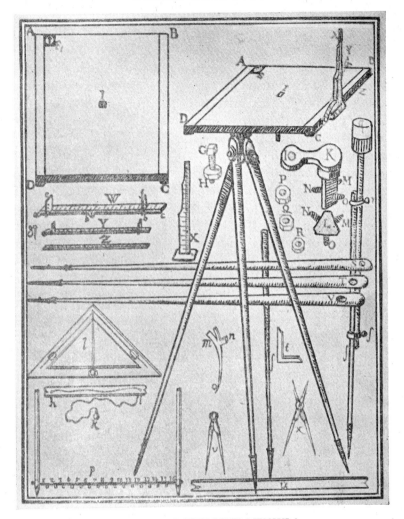

Figure 151. PRAETORIUS' MENSULA

Conclusion

By the end of the seventeenth century all the important items of the modern surveyor's equipment were in use, even though many were still in rather crude form and some were employed by only a few individuals. The work of the ensuing centuries has been chiefly a process of refinement. Besides the items whose development has been traced in the foregoing pages, there are a few others worthy of at least passing mention in order to complete the picture. For the direct measurement of horizontal distances ropes and rods were not superseded by the surveyor's chain until toward the close of the sixteenth century.[280] Although in the description of the solution of one of his surveying problems (see p. 350) Heron of Alexandria uses the word *chain* (ἄλυσις), it is scarcely possible that he had in mind anything resembling the surveyor's chain of later times, since he gives no description of it but has given detailed information on rope measures (see p. 10). The most important chain developed in the English units of measure was that of Gunter,[281] which remained the standard measure of the surveyor, despite its clumsiness, until steel tapes were manufactured for the first time by Chesterman of Sheffield, England, about the middle of the last century.[282] Contemporary with Chesterman's inauguration of the manufacturing of steel tapes were various attempts in New England to produce satisfactory tapes from the hooping required for the crinolines of that period.[283] Cross hairs were introduced on quadrant telescopes about 1640 by the English astronomer Gascoigne, who was killed at the age of twenty-three in the battle of Marston Moor. He is also credited with the introduction of stadia hairs on the micrometer. Measurement of long distances by the stadia method seems to have been first attempted by an Italian surveyor, Geminiano Montanari,[284] in 1674, but stadia measurement was not used to any extent in surveying before the time of Watt (1736-1819). In fact, although Picard and

---

[280] According to F. M. Feldhaus, *Die Technik der Antike und des Mittelalters* (Berlin, 1931), the use of the chain is first mentioned by Conrad von Ulm in his *Geodasia* (Strassburg, 1579).

[281] Gunter, *op. cit.* Gunther, *Early Science in Oxford*, Vol. 1, Part 2, p. 77, quotes the following without mentioning the author: "The Chains now used and in most esteem among Surveyors are Three: as, First, Mr. Rathborn's which had every perch divided into 100 Links: and that of Mr. Gunter's, which had 4 perches or Poles divided into 100 Links; so that each Link of Mr. Gunter's Chain is as long as four of Mr. Rathborn's. And this year [1669] Mr. Wing hath described a Chain of 20 Links in a Perch, for the more ready use in his Art of Surveying." By permission of Mr. A. E. Gunther and Dr. Mavis Gunther.

[282] J. L. Culley, "Steel Tapes," *Journal of the Association of Engineering Societies, Transactions*, Vol. 6, 1887. Chesterman's first patent in 1843 was for cloth tapes reinforced by fine wires. The first American patent for steel tapes was obtained by Eddy and Co., Brooklyn, N. Y., in 1867.

[283] *Engineering News*, December, 1914, p. 1316; February, 1915, p. 405.

[284] W. Jordan, *Handbuch der Vermessungskunde* (Stuttgart, 1904), Second Edition, Vol. 2, p. 673.

Auzout had used this method on the Continent toward the end of the seventeenth century, so little was known about it in England that both Green and Watt claimed to have invented it about 1760. Watt later, as may be seen from his letters,[285] disclaimed priority in favor of the Continental surveyors. There appeared a great variety of scales, the object of which was to shorten computations. Of these the more important were the *proportional compasses* of Galileo and the early *slide rules* of Oughtred and Gunter.[286] There is no need to record here the evidences of surveying during this period, since this topic has already been well treated in several histories of engineering.[287]

[285] J. Muirhead, *The Mechanical Inventions of James Watt* (London, 1855), Vol. 1, Ch. 8.

[286] For a chronological list of developments connected with the early history of the slide rule see Gunther, *Early Science in Oxford*, Vol. 1, Part 2, pp. 61 ff.

[287] W. B. Parsons, *Engineers and Engineering in the Renaissance* (Baltimore, 1939). R. S. Kirby and P. G. Laurson, *The Early Years of Modern Civil Engineering* (New Haven, Conn., 1932). A. P. Fleming and H. J. Brocklehurst, *A History of Engineering* (London, 1935). For an interesting account of early Spanish engineering projects in Mexico, see F. Gomez-Perez, "Mexican Irrigation in the Sixteenth Century," *Civil Engineering*, Vol. 12, 1942, pp. 24-27.

FINDING THE HEIGHT OF A TOWER. *From Hulsius' De Quadrante Geometrico.*

V

DEVELOPMENT of Practical Geometry in the Schools

A FEW years ago, in the course of a very illuminating article on the historical and pedagogical aspects of intuitive geometry, Betz inserted the following searching question and exhortation:[1]

If the Egyptian scribe Ahmes could return for a visit to this earth, and could witness a modern geometry class in action, he would be full of amazement at the spectacle. What has become, in the meantime, of this simple science of "earth measurement"? From direct measurement and sense perception it has advanced step by step, until now it is even more efficient in indirect measurement and in purely mental experiments. But let us not forget that this imposing structure rests firmly, and forever, on the reassuring soil of Mother Earth. Let us return from time to time, with our pupils, to this primeval fountainhead of geometric knowledge and skill.

It is here proposed, first, to answer in brief the hypothetical question of Ahmes by following the trail of events which led to the almost complete abandonment, at least in the English-speaking countries, of the art of measurement as an integral part of the study of elementary geometry and trigonometry; and, secondly, to outline the efforts which have been made by teachers of mathematics, particularly within the past half century, to free themselves from the shackles of Euclid in an effort to present geometric facts by methods and means more suited to the capacities of immature students. It is further proposed, for the consolation of the original Ahmes and the encouragement of all those teachers who believe in practical work as an aid to theoretical for young minds, to outline a series of exercises in outdoor measurement, using the most convenient of the instruments already mentioned.

[1] W. Betz, "The Teaching of Intuitive Geometry. A Study of Its Aims, Development, Content and Method," The National Council of Teachers of Mathematics, *Eighth Yearbook* (New York, 1933), pp. 156-157.

In the foregoing study of the history of the development of surveying instruments, most of the books mentioned, which treat of the construction and use of various instruments, also contain practical exercises exemplifying the uses of theoretical geometry. For this reason, they may all be classed as practical geometries, a title which many of them bore. Beginning with the *Geometria* of Gerbert, they appeared in a steady line of succession until the end of the seventeenth century. In any consideration of the type and amount of geometrical knowledge imparted to students in universities and schools or by private tuition during this period, the contents of such books cannot be overlooked. Unfortunately, detailed courses of study, such as those we have today, have not been handed down from the various centers of education of the Middle Ages and Renaissance, so that it is impossible to determine just how much of a subject, such as geometry, was included in the various curricula.[2] However, we are probably correct in concluding from the frequency of publication of books on the topic that practical geometry, which for the most part meant outdoor exercises in surveying, played an important and probably a predominant role in a great many courses in geometric study.

Since there already exists quite a large body of literature on the history of the teaching of geometry,[3] there is no need to elaborate here on the general topic. However, there is one aspect of the subject, bearing on the pedagogical treatment of geometry in English-speaking countries as compared with the treatment in others, which seems to have been neglected and which is here proposed as an important factor in the development of this differentiation.

[2] For the rather vague information which it has been possible to gather on this topic, see S. Günther, *Geschichte des mathematischen Unterrichts im deutschen Mittelalter bis zum Jahre 1525* (Berlin, 1887); and H. Suter, *Die Mathematik auf den Universitäten des Mittelalters* (Zurich, 1887).

[3] Besides the works mentioned in the two previous notes and the general histories of mathematics by Smith, Sanford, Cajori, Cantor, Kästner, etc., see M. Chasles, *Aperçu historique des méthodes en géométrie* (Paris, 1875). F. W. Kokomoor, "The Teaching of Elementary Geometry in the Seventeenth Century," *Isis*, Vol. 11, 1928, pp. 85-110. A. W. Siddons, "Progress (History of School Mathematics in England)," *The Mathematical Gazette*, Vol. 20, 1936, pp. 7-26. A. W. Stamper, *A History of the Teaching of Elementary Geometry* (New York, 1909). G. Wolff, "The Abstract and the Concrete in the Development of School Geometry," *The Mathematics Teacher*, Vol. 29, 1936, pp. 365-373; "The Development of the Teaching of Geometry in Germany," *The Mathematical Gazette*, Vol. 21, 1937, pp. 82 ff. F. Cajori, *The Teaching and History of Mathematics in the United States* (Washington, D. C., 1890).

Broadly speaking, it may be said that the English-speaking countries during the nineteenth century, within which period government-sponsored systems of education were established in most countries, clung closely to Euclid, with emphasis on the logical to the neglect of the practical; while in other countries, especially France and Germany, the tendency was to present to the students a body of geometric facts which allowed for some development of the practical aspects of the subject.

One factor in the growth of this differentiation can be traced back to the writers of the sixteenth and seventeenth centuries and to the objectives which they seem to have had in mind when writing their books. A cursory examination of a bibliography of such books within these two centuries at once reveals the fact that while all the English publications which may be classified as practical geometries were written by surveyors[4] for the instruction of those interested in acquiring a knowledge of the art of surveying, the Continental writers[5] of the same period were, in the majority of cases, men connected with universities and schools, and their books on practical geometry were but a part of their complete works dealing with various aspects of mathematics and science. Furthermore, their practical geometries were written not only with the purpose of preparing their readers for a particular profession but as a means of simplifying the teaching of geometric facts through practical applications.[6]

[4] For a list of titles of the chief English texts, see Chapter IV, note 193.

[5] For example, Stöffler, Apian, Frisius, Tartaglia, Cardan, Finaeus, Ramus, Clavius, Schott, Schwenter, Metius.

[6] Since the age of clearly stating objectives in prefaces had not yet dawned, it is difficult to pick out definite statements which point to a pedagogical viewpoint. One item is to be found in the introductions to all these books is a discourse, sometimes long-winded, on the practical value of geometry. The following quotations may throw some light on the implied objectives. Finaeus, *De re et praxi geometrica* (Paris, 1556): "There are two factors which are wont to be delightful and useful to all those who devote themselves to any type of learning. The first, a simple introduction to instruction whereby the road to knowledge and a general experience of it are opened up; the second, the general profit derived from the training, a very delightful compensation for the toil involved. Now, as I have already set forth elsewhere the rudiments and principles of the art of Geometry, I now consider it would be worth while were I to set forth in brief in this book the general practice of Geometry." Christopher Clavius, S.J., *Operum Mathematicorum* (Moguntiae, 1611), Tomus Secundus, *Geometrica Practica:* "Since I took up the task of writing on mathematical studies, I have covered, with God's assistance, many parts of them; a treatise on practical geometry is not to be passed over, so that I do not entirely neglect it, even though I merely touched on the subject. . . . And indeed, when I learned by

Another point to be noted from the bibliographies of the sixteenth and seventeenth centuries is the chronological increase in
the number of books whose definite aim was to use the applications of surveying and navigation to illustrate geometric truths,
as compared with the earlier books whose chief aim was the introduction of some new form of instrument. Kokomoor concludes
from his study that [7]

> by the close of the [seventeenth] century a happy combination of theory
> and practice had been reached that came nearer to our present ideals
> and standards than at any other time in the history of geometry. For
> shortly after this the pendulum again began to swing towards the
> ultra-theoretical.

This return to the Euclidean idea, one of the causes for which
was undoubtedly the increase in interest in pure geometry along
with the other and newer phases of mathematics initiated by Fer-
mat, Descartes, and Desargues in the seventeenth century, was
more marked in England than on the Continent. During the
eighteenth century five English geometries appeared closely modeled on the *Elements*,[8] those of Simson and Playfair going
through several editions in the next century. At the same time
only two books comparable to the Continental practical geometries
of the previous century appeared in England,[9] even though books

---

the experience of many years that they are few who are not interested in mathematics with a view to turn to practical use what they have learned, I engaged eagerly
in the toil involved, so that whatever advantages can be derived from mathematics
toward the amelioration of man's life might stand forth, not as mere ostentatious
display, but on their own merits." C. De Chales, *Mundus Mathematicus* (Leyden,
1674), English Translation by Reeve Williams (London, 1685): "Having long since
observed that the greatest part of those that learn Euclid's Elements, are very often
dissatisfied therewith, because they know not the use of Propositions so inconsiderable
in appearance and yet so difficult; I thought it might be to good purpose, not only
to make them as easie as possible, but also to add some Uses after each proposition,
to show how they are applicable to Practice." P. Bourdin, *Le Cours de mathématique*,
Third Edition (Paris, 1661): "Le cours de mathématique, abregé et clairement rep-
resenté par figures, en faveur de ceux qui veulent apprendre les Mathématiques en
peu de temps et sans peine." J. Boulenger, *La Géométrie pratique* (Paris, 1623):
". . . très propre pour ceux, qui sans s'attacher à une profonde Théorie, veulent se
servir utilement des règles de la Géométrie."

[7] Kokomoor, *op. cit.*, p. 415. By permission of the Editor, G. Sarton.

[8] According to T. Heath, *The Thirteen Books of Euclid's Elements* (Cambridge,
1908), Vol. 1, p. 109, these "Euclids" were Scarburgh (1705), Keill (1708), Whiston
(1714), Simson (1756), Playfair (1795).

[9] A. Ewing, *A Synopsis of Practical Mathematics*, Fourth Edition (London, 1799).
C. Hutton, *The Compendious Measurer*, Second Edition (London, 1790).

on surveying and navigation continued to appear.[10] These English surveying books, like their predecessors, had no direct connection with any scheme of mathematical education, which so far as English school geometry was concerned, was completely Euclidean, if, indeed, there was such a subject on the curricula.[11] During the same century, the Continental writers continued to produce, though in diminishing numbers, texts on practical geometry which upheld the tradition of the previous centuries.[12]

In the early colonial days in this country, practical measurement formed part of the geometric information imparted in the schools. To what extent pedagogical reasons, if any, were responsible for this we do not know; a more urgent motive in all probability was the immediate needs of the people. Harriet Shoen, in the course of a plea for greater opportunity for experience with "the spatial reality of the environment" for the children of today, has recently pointed out the need for such knowledge in colonial times:[13]

In the days when the "bounds" of great wilderness tracts were being marked off by deep-cut blazes in the trees along the line, a knowledge of land-surveying was a useful skill, and many a boy learned its elements by following the "boundsgoer" in his work of "running the line." And those who did not actually take part in running the line must

---

[10] The principal English surveying books of this century were: H. Wilson, *Surveying* (London, 1731). R. Gibson, *A Treatise of Practical Surveying* (London, 1767). T. Breaks, *A Complete System of Land-Surveying* (Newcastle-on-Tyne, 1771). J. Hammond, *The Practical Surveyor* (London, 1749).

[11] Siddons, *op. cit.*, speaking of the English Public Schools says: "Mathematics were introduced into the ordinary work at Merchant Taylor's in 1828, . . at St. Paul's in 1842, . . at Westminster in 1828. . . . At Eton before 1836 there appears to have been no mathematical teaching of any kind. At Harrow mathematical teaching seems to have begun really in 1819, and it was first made compulsory in 1837."

[12] Besides new editions of books of the previous century, the important newcomers were: J. C. Sturm, *Mathesis Juvenilis* (Nürnberg, 1699). J. F. Penther, *Praxis Geometriae* (Augsburg, 1732). A. Moitoiret, *Nouveaux élémens de géométrie pratique concernant l'arpentage* (Rouen, 1700). A. C. Clairaut, *Élémens de géométrie* (Paris, 1741). A. G. Kästner, *Anfangsgründe der Arithmetik, Geometrie, eben und sphärischen Trigonometrie* (Göttingen, 1758). S. F. La Croix, *Élémens de géométrie* (Paris, 1794). M. Cagnoli, *Traité de trigonomêtre*, Translation by M. Chompré (Paris, 1786). B. F. de Belidor, *Nouveau cours de mathématique*, Second Edition (Paris, 1757). T. Bugge, *Gründliche und vollständige theoretisch-practische Anleitung zum Feldmessen*, Translated from the Danish of L. H. Jobiesen (Altona, 1798).

[13] H. H. Shoen, *The Making of Maps and Charts*, National Council for the Social Studies, *Ninth Yearbook* (Cambridge, Mass., 1938), p. 83. By permission of the Council.

have attended many a gay springtime "processioning" when neighbors made a festive occasion out of "perambulating the bounds."

Vague land grants and inaccurate surveys made the subject of boundary lines a prime issue in the everyday life of colonial homes, one that caused many arguments and demanded much time and attention.

A perusal of Karpinski's recent work on early American mathematical texts is illuminating for the light it throws on the type of geometrical training imparted in the schools before 1800. As the author remarks:[14]

It is worthy of comment that no Euclidean geometry appears in the 18th. century, although several books on trigonometry, practical geometry and surveying were issued. Euclid appears first, outside the encyclopedias, in 1803, but after that date various English editions of his works enjoyed a wide circulation, extending in all to nearly 100 editions before 1850.

Our information on the colonial educational system is very meager. Latin and Greek formed the core of the curriculum of the Latin Grammar Schools of the first hundred and fifty years, the objectives of which were "predominantly religious and narrowly vocational."[15] On the curricula of the academies and the first public high schools of the late eighteenth and early nineteenth centuries there is more definite information to be had, which leads to the conclusion that surveying went hand in hand with the teaching of geometry and trigonometry. A certificate from Phillips Exeter Academy dated 1799 shows that among the subjects pursued were " . . . arithmetic and practical geometry. . . ."[16] On the program recommended for the Plymouth, Mass., High School in 1826 were ". . . Mensuration, Geometry, Trigonometry and Surveying. . . ."[17] The records of Fryeburg Academy for January 11, 1797, state, "Voted to buy set of mathematical instruments for the Academy"; for April 27, 1803, "Voted also to purchase from the Library Fund mathematical and philosophical instruments, viz., seals and dividers, chain and compass, telescope and thermom-

[14] L. C. Karpinski, *Bibliography of Mathematical Works Printed in America through 1850* (Ann Arbor, Mich., 1940), p. 9. By permission of The University of Michigan Press.

[15] E. D. Grizzell, *Origin and Development of the High School in New England before 1865* (Philadelphia, 1922), p. 10.

[16] *Ibid.,* p. 33.

[17] *Ibid.,* p. 55.

eter." [18] The Massachusetts State Law of 1827 provided that "Every city, town, or district, containing five hundred families, or householders . . . shall also be provided with a master . . . competent to instruct . . . geometry, surveying and algebra." [19] An examination of the various curricula given by Grizzell [20] for high schools within the period, 1820-1870, reveals the fact that while for the first half of this period surveying and navigation are specifically mentioned along with geometry and trigonometry either as part of or auxiliary to the mathematics curricula, in the later years mention of applications becomes less frequent and drops completely out of the picture.

From the foregoing evidence, which is far from being as complete as we might wish to have it, we may, however, rightly conclude that surveying formed an important part of the American mathematical education program during its first two centuries. The predominant reason for this was undoubtedly utilitarian; there is very little evidence that pedagogical reasons played any important part in determining such a mathematical program.

There is another source from which some ideas as to the status of mathematical education in the colonial period may be gathered. This source is the evening school, which was an important cog in the educational machinery of the colonies. These schools were maintained in all the larger towns and cities by private schoolmasters who advertised their "wares" in the local papers. They were intended primarily for young people who had not time to attend the day schools and who wished to acquire such knowledge as they deemed useful to better their position in life. Unfortunately there is little or nothing on record, beyond the advertisements, to give information on these unique schools. With regard to the mathematics taught in these schools, Seybold says:[21]

The most popular of the "practical Branches of the Mathematicks" were surveying and navigation. In fact, the demand for instruction in these "branches" was so great, that they were early elevated to the status

[18] This information has been kindly supplied by Ava H. Chadbourne, Professor of Education, University of Maine.
[19] *Laws of Massachusetts*, 1827, Ch. 143.
[20] Grizzell, *op. cit.*, pp. 301-329.
[21] R. F. Seybold, *The Evening School in Colonial America*, Bureau of Educational Research, University of Illinois, *Bulletin* No. 31, 1925, p. 28. By permission of the Bureau of Educational Research.

of independent subjects. . . . The practical purpose of geometry, and trigonometry is seen in their relation to navigation, and surveying. In the courses of study examined, they were usually allied with these two subjects. In advertisements in 1753, and 1754, John Lewis, of New York City, announced "What is called a New Method of Navigation, is an excellent Method of Trigonometry here particularly applied to Navigation; But it is of great Use in all kinds of measuring and in solving many Arithmetical Questions". James Cosgrove, of Philadelphia, in 1755, taught "geometry, trigonometry, and their application in surveying, navigation, etc.", and Alexander Power, in 1766, "With their Application to Surveying, Navigation, Geography, and Astronomy".

The only further source of evidence on the mathematical curricula is the content of the textbooks in common use.[22] In the preface to Jess we find:[23]

As the Treatises heretofore published on Surveying, are largely deficient in examples, whilst they treat largely on the theory; the design of this publication, is, to supply schools with a system, exemplified with practical illustrations, sufficient to give the learner a competent knowledge of this useful science.

The preface to Flint's text states:[24]

It would be well therefore, for those who do not intend to become practical Surveyors to acquaint themselves with what is here taught; and with this view the following work is very proper to be introduced into Academies and those higher Schools which are designed to fit young men for active business in life.

Day's book, which was "at once everywhere received with eagerness," [25] was, according to the author, "adapted to the method of instruction in American Colleges." In the preface he states:[26]

[22] Among the English surveying texts used in the colonies were: R. Norwood, *Epitome, or The Doctrine of Triangles* (London, 1659). J. Love, *Geodasia, or The Art of Surveying* (London, 1688). Wilson, *op. cit.* Gibson, *op. cit.* For some interesting details on Norwood's text, see E. D. Kingman, "Roger Sherman, Colonial Surveyor," *Civil Engineering*, Vol. 10, 1940, pp. 514-515. Among the more important of the many books on surveying published in the States were: S. Moore, *An Accurate System of Surveying* (Litchfield, Conn., 1796). Z. Jess, *A Compendious System of Practical Surveying* (Wilmington, Del., 1799). A. Flint, *Surveying* (Hartford, Conn., 1804). J. Gummere, *Surveying* (Philadelphia, 1814). J. Day, *Principles of Navigation and Surveying* (New Haven, Conn., 1817).

[23] Jess, *op. cit.*

[24] Flint, *op. cit.*

[25] Cajori, *op. cit.*, p. 64.

[26] Day, *op. cit.*

The principles should indeed be accompanied with such illustrations and examples as will render it easy for the student to make the applications for himself whenever occasion shall require.

Besides those books which dealt directly with surveying, there were also many trigonometry texts, notably those of Abel, Flint, and Day,[27] which gave much attention to practical applications. However, American geometry texts, which began to appear shortly after 1800, followed the Euclidean pattern of the English texts, and, despite the example set by the colonial authors, the traditional European use of practical applications became dormant.[28]

Returning to the European scene, we find that from about the beginning of the nineteenth century pedagogical and psychological ideas began to exercise more and more influence on the methods of teaching geometry. The immediate cause for this was the general reform in education advocated by Pestalozzi and his disciples, Herbert and Frobel. The guiding principle of this reform was that the natural curiosity of children should be stimulated and encouraged. So far as geometry was concerned, this stimulation should be effected by guiding the children to a knowledge of geometric facts by induction, through experiment and measurement. In other words, intuitive or informal geometry should precede demonstrative.[29] In the beginning, this reform concerned itself chiefly with the initial stages of presenting the idea of spatial relationships, but out of it ultimately grew the ideas which have been predominant in educational circles for the past fifty years with regard to the teaching of geometry in general.

In this movement toward a sounder pedagogical method, Germany led the way. Several textbooks appeared advocating not only the motivation of the teaching of fundamental geometric principles through their relationships with reality but also the elucidation of all geometric facts to be met with in the school courses through concrete examples as far as possible, by which the students' powers of abstraction were to be motivated and developed. Naturally,

---

[27] T. Abel, *Subtensial Plain Trigonometry* (Philadelphia, 1761). A. Flint, *Geometry and Trigonometry* (Hartford, Conn., 1806). J. Day, *Trigonometry* (New Haven, Conn., 1815).

[28] For a complete list of early American publications, see Karpinski, *op. cit.*

[29] For a full discussion on this topic, see R. Coleman, *The Development of Informal Geometry* (New York, 1943).

the simplest means of illustrating geometric facts were chosen, and so it is not surprising to find simple exercises in surveying being advocated.[30] In this the nineteenth century teachers were but continuing the Continental tradition of the practical geometries, with this difference, that now the pedagogical reasons for the advocacy of surveying were in prominence. The culmination of this reform in Germany is to be found in the Meran Report[31] of 1905, the drawing up of which is due chiefly to the exertions of the most distinguished mathematical educator in Germany at that time, Felix Klein. The report says, "Geometric instruction should emerge from intuition, perception and practical measurement." [32]

This reform, begun in Germany, soon found echoes in other countries. In France the many editions of some of the earlier practical geometries, such as those of Le Clerc and La Croix, testify to the fact that practical geometry, in the nature of simple surveying, was an integral part of the mathematical program.[33]

[30] Among the more important of these books may be mentioned: J. Neumann, *Neue Beyträge zur praktischen Geometrie* (Munich, 1800). G. S. Ohm, *Grundlinien zu einer zweckmässigen Behandlung der Geometrie* (Erlangen, 1817). W. Harnisch, *Die Raumlehre oder die Messkunst gewöhnlich Geometrie genannt* (Berlin, 1821). A. Diesterweg, *Leitfaden für den ersten Unterricht in der Formen-Grössen und raumlichen Verbindungslehre* (Elberfeld, 1822). G. Grassman, *Raumlehre für Volkschulen* (Berlin, 1824). J. Falke, *Propadeutik der Geometrie, eine Bearbeitung der geometrischen Formenlehre nach einer neuen Methode gegrundet auf praktische Aufgaben aus der Geodäsie* (Leipzig, 1866). M. Kröger, *Leitfaden für den Geometrie-Unterricht im Mittelschulen* (Hamburg, 1889). P. Martin and C. Schmidt, *Raumlehre für Mittelschulen* (Berlin, 1896-1898).

[31] For a summary of the Meran Report, see F. Klein and R. Schimmack, *Vorträge über den mathematischen Unterricht an den höheren Schulen* (Leipzig, 1907), pp. 208-220.

[32] Coleman, *op. cit.*, p. 77.

[33] Artz, an authority on the history of French education, writes as follows on the teaching of mathematics in the seventeenth century: "L'ouvrage type d'introduction aux mathématiques, usité dans les écoles françaises du XVIIᵉ siècle, était un volume de trois cents pages, intitulé: *Institutio totius mathematicae.* Il s'ouvrait sur les quatre règles de l'arithmétique, les fractions et les proportions; la géométrie se divisait alors en deux parties: un ensemble élémentaire et théorique des propositions d'Euclide et une partie plus étendue de géométrie pratique ou appliquée, qui comprenait les méthodes de mesure des distances, des hauteurs, des surfaces planes et des solides. . . . Un autre manuel français typique, était celui du Père J. François, le maître jesuite de Descartes, *L'Arithmétique et la géométrie pratique*, c'est à dire l'art de compter toute sorte de nombres avec la plume et les jetons, et l'art de mesurer toute sorte de lignes, de surfaces et de corps et particulièrement d'arpenter les terres et d'en contre-lever les plans et ensuite de faire des cartes géographiques . . . hydrographiques . . . topographiques." F. B. Artz, "Les débuts de l'éducation technique en France, 1500-1700," *Revue d'histoire moderne*, September-December, 1937, p. 485.

The school geometries and surveying texts of the Brothers of the Christian Schools, who had numerous educational establishments throughout France, bear testimony to the extent practical work was carried on in the secondary schools. The attitude of the French mathematical teachers at the end of the nineteenth century is well summed up in the words of J. Tannery:[34]

Is it creditable that children thirteen or fourteen years old have a natural taste for logical abstraction, for empty ratiocinations, for demonstrations which seem much less evident to them than the things to be demonstrated? Without doubt, they must be trained to reason about realities, or at least to reason about models or images which approximate reality, which are simplifications of what they see, of what they touch. They must be made to experience how, according to Descartes, geometry facilitates all the arts. How shall I make this drawing? How measure this field?

It is interesting to note that in England the initial move for the reform in the methods of teaching geometry was made by men of high standing as mathematicians. The reform advocated by Sylvester, Cayley, and Clifford, as members of the British Association Committee of 1873, seemed for a time to have fallen on deaf ears, but it was really the beginning of a movement against the traditional three-century-old Euclidean grip. The final loosening of the tentacles came after Perry's address before the British Association for the Advancement of Science in 1900. In this country the reform movement was carried forward at the beginning of the present century, chiefly through the exertions of D. E. Smith, J. W. Young and E. H. Moore. The kernel of the new mathematical program is admirably set forth in Moore's address before The American Mathematical Society in 1902.[35]

It must be borne in mind that the improvement of the teaching of geometry was but a part of a movement for the general improvement of mathematical education, and that the advocacy of practical work in simple surveying was also but a part of the recommended improvements.[36] The following extracts show clearly that

[34] Quoted from J. W. Young, "Some Recent French Views on Concrete Methods of Teaching Mathematics," *The School Review*, Vol. 13, 1905, p. 279.
[35] E. H. Moore, *On the Foundations of Mathematics*, The National Council of Teachers of Mathematics, *First Yearbook* (New York, 1926), pp. 32 ff.
[36] The following texts show the new trend in the teaching of geometry at the beginning of the present century: P. Bert, *First Lessons of Experimental Geometry*,

all the important educational committees on the teaching of mathematics in England and the United States during the past half century have advocated the use of outdoor measurements as an aid to the teaching of geometry and trigonometry.

Committee on Secondary School Studies, 1892-1893 [37]

At about the age of ten for the average child, systematic instruction in concrete or experimental geometry should begin, and should occupy about one school hour per week for at least three years. During this period the main facts of plane and solid geometry should be taught, not as an exercise in logical deduction and exact demonstration, but in as concrete and objective a form as possible. This course should include among other things the careful construction of plane figures, both by the unaided eye and by the aid of ruler, compasses and protractor; the indirect measurements of heights and distances by the aid of figures carefully drawn to scale; and elementary mensuration, plane and solid.

The child should learn to estimate by the eye and to measure with some degree of accuracy the lengths of lines, the magnitude of angles, and the areas of simple plane figures; to make accurate plans and maps from his own actual measurements and estimates: and to make models of simple geometrical solids in pasteboard and clay.

Final Report of the National Committee of Fifteen on Geometry Syllabus[38]

Emphasis should be laid also on other work of a concrete nature which involves direct use of geometric facts. Thus the propositions concerning the similarity of triangles should be introduced by means of the drawing of figures to scale. Attention should be called to the cases in which figures have been drawn to scale in the past. The usefulness and the necessity of the operation should be emphasised and such applications as the drawing of house plans, the copying of patterns on a small scale should be given. Finally, after the notions involved are very clear

---

Translated from the French (London, 1886). W. T. Campbell, *Observational Geometry* (New York, 1899). W. D. Eggar, *Practical Exercises in Geometry* (London, 1903). W. Shaw, *First Lessons in Observational Geometry* (London, 1903). N. Edgar, *Elementary and Constructional Geometry* (New York, 1902).

[37] National Education Association, *Report of the Committee of Ten on Secondary School Studies* (New York, 1894), p. 110.

[38] National Education Association, *Final Report of the National Committee of Fifteen on Geometry Syllabus* (Chicago, 1912), pp. 15, 20. By permission of the National Education Association.

indeed, and after actual measurements have been made and reduced to scale, the precise facts regarding similar triangles may be given. This should follow and not precede the work described above. The applications to elementary surveying should be made, if possible, in actual field work.

Any application that adds interest to the study of rigorous geometry is of value. Of special interest are all simple means of effecting individual measurements of distances, such for instance, as the numerous applications of the congruence theories and the theories on similarities of triangles.

International Congress of Mathematicians, Cambridge, England, 1912;[39] Intuition and Experiment in Mathematical Teaching in the Secondary Schools; Report Presented by David Eugene Smith

In the work of measuring and estimating, a more practical form of mensuration seems to be developing, especially in Austria, Germany and Switzerland. England, France and the United States seem to have given the matter less attention, or at least to have secured less definite results. An elementary trigonometry is more commonly found at an early period in the first three countries, thus allowing for outdoor work with simple instruments at an earlier stage.

The educational problem may be stated generally as follows: What simple, inexpensive instruments may advantageously be used to increase the interest in the early stages of mathematics? In particular, what can be done to make the inductive cycle or phase of geometry more real and interesting, without weakening the deductive side? Then what further apparatus can be used to advantage in the later geometry and trigonometry?

Report of the Mathematical Association on the Teaching of Mathematics in Public and Secondary Schools[40]

History thus shows that the mind first forms mathematical ideas by studying practical problems. Ought we not to follow the teaching of history in forming our mathematical syllabus? Ought we not, for example, to lay the foundations of geometry by an easy course of land surveying, in which the pupil learns to measure and calculate the area

[39] Taken from a summary of the report in *L'Énseignement mathématique,* Vol. 14, 1912, pp. 511, 517.
[40] *The Mathematical Gazette,* Vol. II, 1919, p. 412. By permission of The Mathematical Association.

of a field, the height of a tower and so forth. They will thus acquire in a very concrete and pleasing way the idea of perpendicularity, angles, trapezia, etc. Afterwards they will be in a position to appreciate abstract geometry and to reason about the properties of triangles and parallelograms drawn on paper.

The Teaching of Geometry in Schools[41]

The first steps in geometrical work will be largely experimental, and will be connected with arithmetic and geography. Land measurement seems to form an important part of this work, and it is suggested that if circumstances allow, some exercises should be worked out of doors, not, it need hardly be said, forming a continuous course preliminary to all class-room work, but interpolated appropriately. . . .

To locate, say, a buried treasure from the statement that it is equidistant from two trees and 40 yards from a third, needs only a measuring tape and string, and the problem that confronted Poe's hero in "The Gold Bug" required in addition only a plumb line. The plan of a field may be drawn to scale by the use of a plane-table, which can be easily made in the school carpenter's shop.

The Reorganization of Mathematics in Secondary Education[42]

(Material for Grades Seven, Eight and Nine)

Intuitive Geometry:

a) The direct measurements of distances and angles by means of a linear scale and protractor.
b) Indirect measurements by means of drawings to scale; use of square ruled paper.
c) Informal introduction to the idea of similarity.

Numerical Trigonometry:

The introduction of the elementary notions of trigonometry into the earlier course of mathematics has not been as general in the United States as in foreign countries. Among the reasons for an early introduction of this topic are these: Its practical usefulness for many citizens; the insight it gives into the nature of mathematical methods, particularly those concerned with indirect measurement, and into the role that

[41] A Report by The Mathematical Association (London, 1923), pp. 16-17. By permission of The Mathematical Association.

[42] A Report by the National Committee on Mathematical Requirements, Under the Auspices of The Mathematical Association of America, Inc. (1923), pp. 22, 23, 25, 26, 38, 39, 161. By permission of The Mathematical Association of America.

mathematics plays in the life of the world; the fact that it is not difficult and that it offers wide opportunity for concrete and significant application; and the interest it arouses in the pupils. It should be based upon the work in intuitive geometry, with which it has intimate contacts and should be confined to the simplest material needed for the numerical treatment of the problems indicated.

History and Biography:

Teachers are advised to make themselves reasonably acquainted with the leading events in the history of mathematics, and thus to know that mathematics has developed in answer to human needs, intellectual as well as technical. . . . They should use this material incidentally throughout their course for the purpose of adding to the interest of the pupils by means of informal talks on the growth of mathematics and on the lives of the great makers of science.

(Mathematics for Years Ten, Eleven, and Twelve)

Trigonometry:

The use of the transit in connection with the simpler operations of surveying and of the sextant for some of the simpler astronomical observations, such as those involved in finding local time, is of value; but when no transit or sextant is available simple apparatus for measuring angles roughly may and should be improvised. Drawings to scale should form an essential part of the numerical work in trigonometry.

History and Biography:

Historical and biographical material should be used throughout to make the work more interesting and significant.

Additional Electives—Surveying and Navigation:

In practically all of the European countries geometry is studied during the ninth school year. Especial emphasis is put upon the study of proportional lines, congruent and similar figures, areas and volumes. In all of the schools models are extensively used. In Belgium, France, Germany, and Holland, the study of similar figures is supplemented by elementary exercises in surveying.

A Second Report on the Teaching of Geometry in Schools[43]

Stage A (Experimental Geometry):

Playground or Field Work: Outdoor or large-scale work is especially valuable for the interest it arouses. It also answers certain questions

[43] Prepared by The Mathematical Association (London, 1938), pp. 15, 16, 106, 107. By permission of The Mathematical Association.

without direct teaching, *e.g.,* is the size of an angle affected by the lengths of its arms? It is particularly useful to inculcate the idea of a *locus. It imparts a sense of reality, which might otherwise be absent, to the classroom work which is done in connection with it.

For these reasons considerable stress was laid on outdoor work in the 1923 and 1924 Reports. The period that has elapsed since these dates has however considerably shaken the faith of many teachers in the value of this work and various criticisms of it have been made.

In the first place it is clear that outdoor work is much easier in the country than in the town; also that it is much easier for the teacher of a small class than for the teacher of a large class. Further it is difficult not to waste a good deal of time over it.

For these reasons the Committee suggests that most teachers will find it advisable only to use the outdoor work occasionally. Some of the outdoor exercises in geometry may be conveniently set as voluntary exercises to be done in their own time by any boys who are interested. So used they will prove stimulating to some without wasting the time of others.

A few teachers may be favourably placed to make this a large part of their geometry teaching; most teachers will be able to select some exercises which are suitable for their own circumstances. In any case constant reference should be made in the class to large-scale and outdoor applications of geometry.

Contact With Geography: The kindred derivations of geometry and geography suggest that in early times the subjects were regarded as having much in common, more in fact than is now to be found in the elementary course of either subject, through which boys are put at school. We believe that a widening of the overlap would be of real benefit to boys' minds, giving them a better understanding of the world in which they live, making geometry increasingly a practical subject, and supplying an important part of the answer to the question, "Why am I learning this stuff?"

The meanings of latitude, longitude, elevation, depression and the nautical mile should be included in even the most elementary course in Geometry.

. . . In the absence of facilities for finer methods, the position of a point on the ground has often to be fixed on the map by resection, that is, by measuring the angles between the directions of three visible landmarks which are already mapped and proceeding by drawing or calculation. The solution by drawing gives excellent illustrations of the use of the locus-propositions associated with angles in a circle and of the distinction between good and bad intersections.

The Place of Mathematics in Secondary Education,[44] *Report of the Joint Commission of the Mathematical Association of America and the National Council of Teachers of Mathematics*

Essentials of a General Program in Secondary Mathematics.

The Field of Geometric Form and Space Perception.

Fundamental Skills:

f) A use of the technique of indirect measurement in simple field work.

Habits and Appreciations in the Mathematical Classroom:

Historical References:

The history of mathematics should not supersede mathematics; it should supplement its study. It is especially effective in increasing the cultural value of the subject, and a carefully developed account of parts of the history of this old enterprise will give more meaning to both elementary and secondary curricula in mathematics.

Detailed Outline—Informal Geometry:

Basic Skills or Techniques (7, 8):

Determining distances or angles indirectly by using (*a*) the method of scale drawing; (*b*) the method of congruent or similar triangles; (*c*) the Pythagorean relation; (*d*) the tangent ratio.

Trigonometry (7, 8):

   I. Familiarity with such terms as, ratio, proportion, scale, congruent, similar, height, distance, horizontal, vertical.
  II. Drawing a figure to scale on either unruled or squared paper.
 III. (For superior pupils) Making simple outdoor measurements of lines or angles and thus finding required heights or distances.
 IV. (For superior pupils) Using the "shadow method," or a table of tangents to find unknown heights.
  V. (For superior pupils) Making simple surveying instruments.

Trigonometry (9):

  II. Finding heights and distances indirectly by scale drawing; the Pythagorean relation.
 III. Finding heights, or distances, or angles indirectly by using the natural trigonometric functions (sine, cosine, tangent).
 IV. Using a table of natural functions.

[44] The National Council of Teachers of Mathematics, *Fifteenth Yearbook* (New York, 1940), pp. 62, 68, 91, 143, 239. Figures in parentheses refer to proposed grade placement. By permission of the Editor, William David Reeve.

Trigonometry (12th Grade):

Optional topics (e). Instruments used in surveying.

As a matter of significant information that will help form an intelligent outlook on life, slow pupils can appreciate something of the role of mathematics in civilization through the story of numbers and the history of measurement. Use of simple mathematical tools and inspection of more complicated ones contribute to the same end. . . . If the school is equipped with a good mathematical display and the material in it is properly explained, the backward pupil will gain a greater insight into the role of mathematics in civilization than is sometimes suspected.

The Commission believes that it should stress one subject, namely, the history of mathematics. If the study of secondary mathematics is to reveal mathematics as one of the fundamental enterprises of man, which, though rooted in daily need, is an expression of deep impressible and idealistic impulses, then the teaching of it should constantly be associated with its history. One recalls the statement of Glashier: "I am sure that no subject loses more than mathematics by any attempt to dissociate it from its history." The history of mathematics, however, is too often treated by our Universities and Colleges as a stepchild. Though courses in it are provided, the Commission fears that too often they are dry and sterile, and it believes that they will remain so until the subject is properly appreciated and steps are taken to develop more scholars who are ardent in the cultivation of the history of mathematics and enthusiastic in its teaching.

Instruments for surveying, especially a transit, have considerable usefulness in teaching parts of geometry and trigonometry. The interest of many pupils is increased by means of practical problems and an instrument makes it possible for pupils to secure their own data for a variety of exercises. In addition, skill in the use of instruments is valuable. An accurate engineer's transit is not needed unless work in surveying of a high quality is attempted. Very inexpensive transits designed for the use of builders and for farm surveying, as well as special school instruments, are on the market, and they are suitable for demonstration purposes and for the field work that may go with a course in trigonometry.

Mathematics in General Education[45]

A fruitful topic for study in connection with junior high-school mathematics is the subject of old-time surveying instruments. The **A**-shaped

[45] *Report of the Committee on the Functions of Mathematics in General Education for the Commission on Secondary School Curriculum, Progressive Education Associa-*

level used by the Egyptians and others, the carpenter's square, the hypsometer, the cross-staff, the quadrant and the octant, and the plane table may well be studied. The astrolabe is of particular interest, although much of its theory is beyond the students at this level. However, as an instrument for measuring height by indirect methods, it is well within their ability to use. The construction and use of such instruments is a worthwhile manual activity and motivates the study of indirect measurement.

The primary objective of this work is to place before teachers of mathematics the two important factors which are emphasized in the foregoing quotations, so that they may carry on more successfully their important task. First, there is the advocacy of simple surveying as a part of the program for geometry and trigonometry classes; secondly, there is a recommendation to give students some ideas of the history of the development of elementary mathematics and mathematical instruments. It is hoped that the important and interesting historical data placed in the hands of teachers throughout the first four chapters will aid in the carrying out of the second recommendation; in the final chapter our objective is to supply sufficient exercises, based for the most part on historic sources, to enable teachers to carry out a program of simple surveying as an adjunct to the teaching of geometry and simple trigonometry.

In recent years simple surveying, as part of the school mathematical program, has developed much interest among the teachers of this country.[46] This is due to a great extent to the pioneer work carried on by Professor C. N. Shuster, through classes at Teachers College, Columbia University, and State Teachers College, Trenton, N. J. But much work still remains to be done both in the preparation of teachers and in providing suitable instruments. The writer believes that this can be accomplished more readily if the teacher has the proper historical background information and if the older, simpler instruments are used, at least in the early work of the pupils. For this reason it is hoped that the present work will supplement that of Shuster,[47] thereby improving

tion (New York, 1940), pp. 259-260. By permission of The American Education Fellowship.

[46] This may be seen from numerous articles which have appeared in educational magazines.

[47] C. N. Shuster and F. L. Bedford, Field Work in Mathematics (New York, 1935).

the efficiency of this important and well-known teaching vehicle.

When Stark first called attention to the adaptability and educational value of the old instruments,[48] the times were scarcely propitious; surveying had become so identified with the technical and engineering colleges in this country that, except by a few farsighted individuals, even its simpler routines were no longer regarded as suitable and useful for school work. Undoubtedly there are some who will still object for the same reason; there may be even a few college professors among the disgruntled, because some of their students have already been "exposed" to the elements of surveying by mere amateurs before coming under their professional protection—just as there are teachers of senior high school trigonometry who object because their pupils have previously had an opportunity of indulging in the applications of simple numerical trigonometry in the junior high school. With such shortsighted individuals we can only sympathize, hoping that they will, in time, be impressed by the opinions of our best authorities on mathematical education, as expressed through the excerpts in the foregoing reports and elsewhere.

It is important to bear in mind that the type of work advocated here is not just surveying for surveying's sake but consists of simple exercises to motivate and elucidate the geometric and trigonometric curricula. The boy who later goes on to an engineering college will find plenty of new and more complicated work to be done in his surveying course which will be presented from the entirely different viewpoint of a production process governed by economic considerations; while those who terminate their education with high school should have acquired a fund of basic information on important applications of their mathematics, information which will probably be retained long after the intricacies of geometric logic have been forgotten. In practically every geometry text published in the United States within the past fifteen years will be found many of the exercises given in the next chapter; they are inserted as geometric exercises, usually requiring to prove that after such and such operations have been carried out by the surveyor, certain properties can be geometrically es-

---

[48] W. E. Stark, "Measuring Instruments of Long Ago," *School Science and Mathematics*, Vol. 10, 1910, pp. 48 ff., 126 ff.

tablished. The staging of the problem within a surveying or historic background is expected to arouse the interest of the student. Undoubtedly more interest is awakened than if the problem were merely stated in its gaunt geometric outline, but the writer strongly doubts that such hypothetically proposed and solved classroom problems help to make a lasting connection with the real situation.[49] In other words, there is a wide gap between theoretical solutions to practical problems and the actual solutions. This involves not only a difference in technique between classroom work and field work but also a variation in our concepts of geometric entities, such as point, line, and plane.[50] Take the same problems and carry out the actual work, and what a difference in comprehension it means to the student! Here and only here does geometry come to real life.

Of course, the principal reasons why such practice is not more widespread at the present time are the lack of time and the inaccessibility of suitable places for carrying on the work. But even these along with other obstacles can be overcome by the enthusiastic teacher.[51] Even where there is no more ground available than a school play-yard, many exercises on finding inaccessible distances and heights can be carried out with the aid of a little play of the imagination. It is not at all necessary to have the luxury of a wide river in the neighborhood in order to perform the various exercises given under Section 3 of Chapter VI, and other such problems.

A perusal of the excerpts from the various reports already given shows at once the gradual growth of enthusiasm for the increased use of outdoor work, up to and including the 1923 reports. The later reports, although no less strongly sponsoring the same ideas,[52]

[49] He has tested this on freshmen engineers and found the "transfer" to be very slight. If this is the case with prospective engineers, what of the others?

[50] Wolff, *op. cit.*, p. 372.

[51] As an example of what can be done, see E. Sweedler, "The Mathematics Club at Curtis High School," *The Mathematics Teacher*, Vol. 29, 1936, pp. 394-395.

[52] It may be a surprise to many to find such scant attention given to this topic in the 1940 *Report* of the Progressive Education Association, in view of the progressive penchant for "activities." The omission is due not to lack of recognition of the value of this type of work but rather to the general principle, by which the report was governed, of not making definite statements on the content of the mathematics curricula for various classes. See W. Betz, "The Present Situation in Secondary Mathematics," *The Mathematics Teacher*, Vol. 33, 1940, pp. 339-360.

are more cautious in their utterances, no doubt owing to the fact that some teachers overemphasized this type of work, making it the primary objective of their geometric teaching, instead of considering it as it should be; namely, an important but subordinate adjunct, an aid and powerful motivating influence toward the fundamental objective of all mathematical training: quantitative or functional thinking. The wise precautions given in the English report of 1938 should be heeded, for otherwise such outdoor work as that here proposed offers limitless opportunity for wasted effort.

Perhaps there are people who will object to the use of instruments modeled on those of former times, on the ground that such a step is retrogressive. Since we have today instruments of high precision, why put into the hands of a twentieth-century boy or girl the rough-and-ready instruments of three hundred or two thousand years ago? Such an objection is ruled out when we remember that the aim of school surveying is not the attainment of high precision. Considering the manipulative powers of the students and the complexity of the instrument, to put a modern transit into the hands of young students would be sheer waste of time. The necessity of simplifying our modern instruments before putting them into the hands of beginners has long been recognized.[53] But when we simplify our modern instruments, where are we but back to the "measuring instruments of long ago"? In transits we do not produce anything simpler than the polimetrum of Waldseemüller or the "instrument topographicall" of Digges; and if we do not associate our simplifications with these and other early forms, we lose all the historical connections. Likewise, why use an expensive sensitive bubble level, when the old Egyptian triangular plumb-bob level or a simple open-water-tube level suffices to carry on the work with much simpler manipulation? Of the older instruments the only ones in common use are the compass and the simple plane table, but there are many reasons, both pedagogical and economical, why many of the other older types should still find a place in school surveying. For laying out a right angle what gives a clearer view of the operation being

---

[53] See *Mathematics News,* published by Yoder Instruments, East Palestine, Ohio. This company specializes in the manufacture of mathematical instruments for schools.

carried on than the groma or its later development, the surveyor's cross? Why not revive the use of the simplified astrolabe, the geometric square, and the quadrant and associate their use with the history of the development of the trigonometrical functions and with some of the phases of human enterprise outlined in the previous chapters? And above all, why not inform our students of the many simple exercises in surveying that can be solved with no more elaborate apparatus than a few dimensioned straight rods, used either individually or in combination?

Many teachers today are using some of our modern simple instruments, such as the angle mirror and the hypsometer. These instruments may have their own special advantages in certain circumstances, but to use them solely is to neglect a great opportunity of broadening the cultural value of school mathematics. In short, we recommend the use of the old instruments. First, our simplifications naturally lead us back to them; the old instruments were simple in construction, and the complications of the astrolabe and quadrant arose from their connections with astronomy and astrology and have no significance in surveying. Second, the geometric significance of any operation is plainly visible on the instruments themselves; they contain no hidden parts to interfere with the young student's analyzing for himself just exactly what is going on during any given operation. Third, they fulfill the need of ease in manipulation. Lastly, the old instruments are intimately connected with the history of practical measurement, and no course which pretends to give an outline of this history can afford to ignore them.

It may be objected that the use of such instruments leads to only rough estimates of the measurements required. Granted that more accurate work may be done with instruments equipped with telescopes, verniers, and leveling screws, the ease and clarity of operation of the old instruments compensates for this drawback, which, after all, is of minor importance under the circumstances. The objective of such exercises is not primarily the attaining of a high degree of accuracy, which must always be considered relative, but rather the motivation of the learning process through activities properly directed. Besides, the relative accuracy of the old instruments is not to be despised, and if the models put in the hands of students are well constructed,[54] results obtained through their use are quite satisfactory. As a by-product of the question of the relative accuracy of all measurement comes the topic of approximate computations, for the discussion of which these simple surveying exercises are admirably adapted. In the exercises which follow there is no need of measuring angles closer than the nearest degree or accessible straight lines closer than the nearest foot. Does it really matter if the student is in error by one or two feet in finding the height of a fifty-foot flagpole, provided he understands the method he has employed? It does not matter to any extent if the primary objective is kept in mind.

In closing it is well to bring forward an important problem in connection with the relation between the proposed exercises and the ordinary course in demonstrative geometry, even though no attempt will be made here to solve it. Looking through these exercises one is struck by the preponderance of solutions which depend on the proportionality of corresponding sides of similar figures. According to the customary system, such exercises could not be touched until the student was on his way through the "third book." In our informal geometry, the difficulty has long since been overcome.[55] Only recently have the first real attempts been made at the solution of this problem in the demonstrative geometry course. The potency of the properties of similarity has long since been recognized by mathematical educators,[56] but the

[54] It is recommended in some of the previously quoted reports that students be given an opportunity to make their own instruments. As a means of motivation this practice is commendable provided the students are given experience in workshop technique; in this case it may very well be used as a means of correlating the two courses. Where the school does not cater to shop courses not much can be done except in the case of a few individual students who may have taken up manual training as a home hobby. In all cases it is well for the school to have on hand a supply of well-constructed instruments which may at least be used as models for the making of others. For the teacher who wishes to construct or have constructed some of the old instruments not now being manufactured, the diagrams from the old books scattered through this work should offer sufficient data for reconstructions.

[55] This has been accomplished by informal proofs based on measurement, analogies from pictures, maps, etc.

[56] P. Nunn, "Notes on the Place of Similarity in School Geometry," *The Mathematical Gazette*, Vol. 22, 1938, pp. 234-249. H. C. Barber, "Random Notes on Geometry Teaching," *The Mathematics Teacher*, Vol. 30, 1937, pp. 338-339. R. J. Middleton, *The Teaching of Elementary Geometry*, Records of the Education Society, New South Wales, No. 10, 1911. G. D. Birkhoff and R. Beatley, "A New Approach to Elementary Geometry," The National Council of Teachers of Mathematics, *Fifth Yearbook* (New York, 1930).

problem of how put them to use at an earlier stage and still retain a logical system has remained. One solution has been proposed by Birkhoff and Beatley,[57] who establish their system of
geometry on the one-to-one correspondence between the points on
a line and the real numbers. Another solution, still in the experimental stage, which strives at a closer articulation of algebra and
geometry is offered by Mirick.[58] Both of these may seem radical
departures from the familiar Euclid-Legendre organization,
but if we recognize the importance of similarity, they mark the
beginning of a new era in the teaching of geometry. Our oldest
description of a practical geometry problem concerns similar triangles—the traditional account of Thales' finding the height of a
pyramid by the shadow method (see p. 283). This problem can
still retain its historic priority today and serve as an informal introduction to the important topic of similarity fundamental to
many of the ensuing exercises.

[57] G. D. Birkhoff and R. Beatley, *Basic Geometry* (New York, 1941). See review by
R. R. Smith, *The Mathematics Teacher*, Vol. 34, 1941, pp. 373-374. Notwithstanding
the opportunity which the organization of this book affords, problems from surveying
are conspicuous by their absence!

[58] G. R. Mirick, *An Experimental Course in Plane Geometry* (New York, 1941).

VI

APPLICATIONS of Geometry, Trigonometry in Simple Surveying

. . . applications should be used in order to increase interest, to aid understanding, to provide practice in applying knowledge, and to give the students and the community an appreciation of the value of mathematical education.[1]

One simple problem in surveying will teach more geometry than a whole set of textbook problems.[2]

The following exercises are chosen primarily because they are the basic problems to be found in most of the old practical geometries and are considered suitable material for elementary exercises in surveying designed to motivate the course in school geometry. As a secondary consideration, they are of historic interest. A few exercises which belong to a later period are introduced because of their appropriateness to the primary objective. The methods given here are, in most cases, but skeleton outlines; in a few cases, where it was thought the importance of the method or the problem warrant it, direct quotations are given from the old authors. Unfortunately it is found impossible to quote descriptions of all the methods, since they are usually quite verbose and would require too much space. Any teacher interested in the old descriptions can easily find them through the references given after each method. These references are likewise incomplete. Although we would like to supply diagrams from the old books with each problem, it has not been possible to do so. However, several are inserted. It is hoped that these will be of interest in themselves apart altogether from geometric considerations. The other dia-

---

[1] E. G. Olds, "The Use of Applications for Instructional Purposes," *The Mathematics Teacher*, Vol. 34, 1941, p. 83.

[2] E. R. Breslich, "The Nature and Place of Objectives in Teaching Geometry," *The Mathematics Teacher*, Vol. 31, 1938, p. 311.

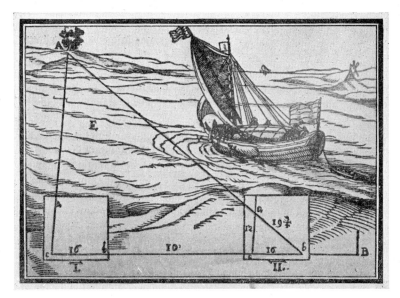

Figure 152. PLANE-TABLE METHOD OF MEASURING THE DISTANCE OF AN INACCESSIBLE POINT. *From Le Clerc's* Traité de géométrie.

grams used are mere outlines, designed to show only the geometric relationships. In all such diagrams the size of the instruments is necessarily exaggerated, relative to the surroundings, in order to show the geometric relations. If this is not borne in mind, a false impression of distances may be gained. Very few directions are given for the manipulation of the instruments, since the instruments considered have been chosen because of the relative ease with which they can be manipulated, and, as Love said in his preface, relative to such directions: "[It] is like teaching the art of fencing by book."[3] The only way to become proficient in the handling of instruments is by practice; for this reason the teacher who intends introducing to students such exercises as are proposed here should work through them in private outside of school hours until he is satisfied with his manipulative powers. To acquire a complete background knowledge of both the theory and practice of elementary surveying with both modern and simplified instruments, attendance at a course, such as several teachers colleges offer at present, is recommended. The information given in the

[3] J. Love, *Geodasia, or The Art of Surveying* (London, 1688).

following pages is not intended in any way as a substitute for lack of practical experience on the part of the teacher.[4]

An important point to bear in mind is that these exercises are adaptable to varying degrees of motivation, depending on the ingenuity of the teacher and the available working space. Thus, exercises on the laying out of lines at right angles to each other take on increased interest if applied to the laying out of a football field, baseball diamond, center lines of street intersections, etc. Many exercises can be combined in the solution of loci problems, as suggested in the English Report of 1938. In the same way, many exercises may be combined in a project such as the planning of an outdoor recreational center; this might embrace the gathering of data for a map of a prescribed area, planning the location of various fields and houses with regard to proper orientation and accessibility, and the staking out of these in the field.

It is often pointed out that applications should follow after deductive geometric proofs have been given; in fact, most of our textbooks are so arranged that this is taken for granted as the ordinary procedure. In this we still suffer from the Euclidean tradition, which belittled the power of intuition. But we are realizing more and more the value of intuition in the development of mathematics.[5] Why not, then, give it ample room in our teaching program? Is it not pedagogically more correct to present the surveying problem first, elicit from the students methods by which the problem may be carried out, and then show that such methods are or are not geometrically correct, perform the required

---

[4] On the need and usefulness of such courses, see P. D. Edwards, "What Specialized Knowledge Should the Teacher Training Program Provide in the Field of Geometry?" *The Mathematics Teacher*, Vol. 34, 1941, p. 116.

[5] "There seems to be great danger in the prevailing overemphasis on deduction—postulational character of mathematics. True, the element of constructive invention, of directing and motivating intuition, is apt to elude a simple philosophical formulation; but it remains the core of any mathematical achievement, even in the most abstract fields. If the crystallized deductive form is the goal, intuition and construction are at least the driving forces. A serious threat to the very life of science is implied in the assertion that mathematics is nothing but a system of conclusions drawn from definitions and postulates that must be consistent but otherwise may be created by the free will of the mathematician. If this description were accurate, mathematics could not attract any intelligent person. It would be a game with definitions, rules, and syllogisms, without motive or goal." R. Courant and H. Robbins, *What Is Mathematics?* (New York, 1941), p. xvii. By permission of the Oxford University Press.

field work, check results if possible, and finally study the geometric proof in detail? Falke, one of the early German reformers of the teaching of geometry, favored such a procedure. In the preface to his book he recommends that the student be encouraged to regard himself as a discoverer and be allowed to carry out his own methods. Only when these have failed should he be forced to follow a prescribed method. Falke then goes on to state:[6]

In treating the subject in this way the writer has seen the gift of invention flash up in the dullest student. And during school-practice of several years, he hardly came across a situation where he had to force a theory. If, however, it has been done occasionally, then the problem not only became clear by the actual doing of it, but was fully comprehended without much exertion.

It is sometimes proposed that the type of work recommended here is admirably suitable for slow students but more or less a waste of time for bright ones. This is due to a misapprehension of one of the basic advantages of such work. True, the bright student may be able to appreciate and assimilate his work in geometry and trigonometry without the aid of such practical applications, but there is no doubt that even for him, practical exercises are of value both to elucidate and to impress the fact that the mathematics being studied may be used with advantage in the solution of many everyday problems. Besides, one of the benefits of mathematical training lies in the power to transfer abstract mathematical knowledge to concrete applications, and this cannot be acquired without actual participation in such work. For the slow student there is no doubt about the benefits which accrue from such exercises; in fact, for many of them it is the only kind of mathematical training which will leave any lasting impression. The fact that they are capable of assimilating but very little of the logical structure of geometry should not deter teachers from seeing to it that the slow group is given a thorough course in the type of work here outlined. For such students "learning by doing," the acquiring of facts by empirical processes, is the only logical way of solving our present mathematical education dilemma.

[6] J. Falke, *Propadeutik der Geometrie, eine Bearbeitung der geometrischen Formenlehre nach einer neuen Methode gegrundet auf praktische Aufgaben aus der Geodäsie* (Leipzig, 1866).

PROBLEMS CLASSIFIED BY MAIN GEOMETRIC FACTS

Main Geometric Fact	Section and Problem or Method*
1. Similar right triangles	II, Case A, 1, 2, 3, 4, 5, 6, 8, 9, 11 *a*; Case D. III, Case A, 1, 3, 4, 5; Case B, 2, 4. IV, Case A, 1, 2, 3, 4, 6, 8; Case B. V, 1, 2, 3, 4, 5. VII, 3
2. Similar oblique triangles	II, Case A, 11 *b*; Case B; Case C III, Case A, 9, 11, 12. IV, Case A, 5. VI, 1, 2, 3, 5, 6. VII, 2, 3, 5
3. Congruent right triangles	III, Case A, 2, 8; Case B, 1. VII, 4
4. Similar right triangles (inverted)	II, Case A, 7, 10
5. Similar polygons	VIII, *1, 2, 3, 4, 5, 6*
6. Congruent triangles	S.A.S.: VI, 3; VII, 4. S.S.S.: VIII, *4*, 4
7. Pythagorean theorem	I, *6*, Case B, Case C
8. Two points equidistant from the extremities of a line determine the perpendicular bisector of the line	I, *6*, Case A. III, Case A, 6
9. Two straight lines intersect at a point	I, *3*. VIII, *4*, 4
10. Horizontal projection	I, *5*. II, Case D. V, 2
11. A line from the apex to the mid-point of the base of an isosceles triangle is perpendicular to the base	I, *7 a, 9*
12. Parallel lines are equidistant from each other	I, *8 a, 8 b*. VII, 1
13. Isosceles triangle	VI, 4
14. Equilateral triangle	III, Case A, 7
15. The square of the perpendicular to the hypotenuse of a right triangle is equal to the product of the segments of the base	III, Case A, 10; Case B, 3
16. The diagonals of a parallelogram bisect each other	I, *8 c*
17. A line that divides two sides of a triangle proportionally is parallel to the third side	VI, 1

PROBLEMS CLASSIFIED BY MAIN GEOMETRIC FACTS (*Cont.*)

Main Geometric Fact	Section and Problem or Method*
18. Trigonometric ratios	Cosine formula: IV, Case A, 7. Sine formula: VI, 7. Tangent formula: VI, 7. The simple trigonometric ratios may be used in many of the problems in place of the given geometrical proportions.

*Problems are indicated by *italic*, methods by roman, type.

The exercises that follow offer practical work of this kind as well as historic information. They are grouped according to the nature of the problems; the methods are for the most part in historic order, not necessarily the best order for teaching purposes. They are so arranged that the teacher may have a fund of information to draw on as necessity requires. It is left to the individual teacher to pick out those methods which are considered most suitable, depending on the problem, the mathematical development of the students, and the instruments on hand; or, better still, to have the students think them out under the guidance of the teacher. The fundamental exercises in Section I should be performed by all students. Discussion of methods not used in actual field work may be advantageously carried on in the classroom, both for their geometric content and for their historic associations.

The accompanying classifications of those exercises suited to class use may be helpful to teachers in selecting appropriate work. The classification by main geometric facts shows the predominance of problems depending on similarity for their solution and again emphasizes the importance of this concept. Although the Pythagorean theorem is the primary concept in only two exercises, it enters into so many others indirectly that it is of fundamental importance and should not be slighted. Except for two methods (I, 7a and 9), the geometry of the circle is not used in these exercises; this, however, does not mean that it can be overlooked in school geometry, since it has many applications outside the field of elementary surveying.

PROBLEMS CLASSIFIED BY LEVELS OF DIFFICULTY

Section	Problem or Method*	
	Junior High School	Senior High School
I	1, 3, 4, 6, 7, 8, 9	2, 5
II	Case A: 1, 2, 3, 4, 5, 6, 8, 9, 11 a	Case A: 7, 10, 11 b; Case B; Case C
III	Case A: 1, 2, 3, 4, 5, 7; Case B: 1, 2, 4	Case A: 6, 8, 9, 10, 11, 12; Case B: 3
IV		Case A, Case B
V	1, 3, 4	5
VI	1, 2, 3, 4, 5, 6	
VII		2, 3, 4, 5
VIII	1; 4: 1, 2, 3	2; 3; 4: 4, 5, 6
IX	1, 3, 5	1, 2, 4, 5, 6

*Problems are indicated by *italic*, methods by roman, type.

SECTION I

FUNDAMENTAL EXERCISES

Problem 1. To mark out a straight line between two points visible from each other.

METHOD

a. Rods are placed vertically over the ends of the line at A and B (Figure 153). The observer, stationed behind the rod at A, sights along the line AB and indicates to his assistant where intermediate rods $C, D,$ etc., are to be placed so as to be in line with A and B. To accomplish this the assistant holds a rod vertically and, keeping his body out of the line of sight, moves in the direction indicated by the observer until the rod is on the line of sight, where it is set firmly in the ground.

b. In case no assistant is available, a rod C may be set up about mid-distance between A and B by trial. The observer then goes back of A and sees whether C is in line with A and B. If not, it must be moved and another trial made, a process which is then repeated for the intermediate distances.

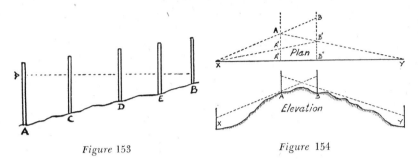

Figure 153   Figure 154

c. After the first rod C has been set up by one of the methods described above, the other rods may be lined in as follows: The observer goes beyond C and by trial finds the point at which the next rod D must be placed so as to be in line with AC; E is similarly placed in line with DCA; and so on. This latter method is also employed in the process of prolonging a line.

The method in c can be used to check the accuracy of lining in by removing the rod B as soon as C has been set up and requiring the student to prolong the line. The distance from B to the prolonged line checks the accuracy.

Remarks. The above exercise is necessary before measurement of horizontal distances can be carried on, since if the tape lengths are not kept in line, the measurement will be greater than the actual length. See Section I, Problem 4.

Problem 2. To mark out a straight line between two points not visible from each other.

METHOD

Let rods X and Y mark the extremities on opposite sides of a hill of the required line (Figure 154). Two observers A and B take up positions on the ridge, in approximate line with X and Y, so that each can see the other and the rod beyond him. A looks toward Y and lines in the rod which B carries, by Method a of Problem 1; B likewise lines in A with X. This is repeated until ABY and BAX are simultaneously in line.

Remarks. If because of topography this simple method is impossible, the general method, first described by Heron, may be employed (see p. 358). As Heron's method is somewhat compli-

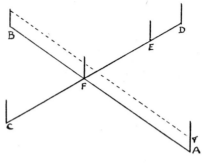

Figure 155

cated, it should be attempted only when the students have had some experience with the manipulation of instruments.

Problem 3. To find the intersection of two straight lines.

METHOD

Rods are set vertically on the two lines whose intersection is required, *AB, CD* (Figure 155). A third rod *E* is placed on line *CD* by Method *a* of Problem 1. Then, while the observer sights along the line *AB,* his assistant moves another rod along the line *CD* by lining in with *ED.* The assistant moves along *CD* until signaled by the observer at *A* that he is on the line *AB.* He then sets his rod *F* over the required point of intersection.

Remarks. For more difficult exercises on alignments with rods, see Hutton, *A Course in Mathematics in Two Volumes.*

Problem 4. To measure the distance between two points over ground approximately horizontal.

METHOD

Two range poles are set up about 500 ft. apart. Pupils should be asked to estimate the distance by eye. They then walk from one pole to the other, keeping in a straight line as far as possible, and count the number of natural paces in the distance. This exercise should be repeated several times and over varying distances. Such distances should then be taped, bearing in mind the following precautions. The student carrying the forward end of the tape, designated as the head tapeman, goes forward along the line with ten marking pins, while the rear tapeman, with one marking pin, remains at the beginning of the line. It is the duty of the rear tapeman to line in the head tapeman with the end of the line. This is done by having the head tapeman stand to one side of the tape when it is almost fully stretched out; holding a pin vertically near the ground in one hand, he is motioned by the rear tapeman to move to the right or left until the pin is in line with the rear range pole. When the head tapeman's pin is on line he presses it into the ground. The tape is then stretched taut in line with the pins, the rear tapeman holding the 100-ft. point of the tape beside the pin which he has inserted in the ground at the initial point, while the head tapeman removes his line pin and pushes it vertically into the ground opposite the zero graduation mark of the tape. When this operation is complete, the rear tapeman removes the pin at the end of the line and carries it along. The same process is repeated for the various other tape-lengths necessary. The number of pins which the rear tapeman collects corresponds to the number of whole tape-lengths measured. If the length of the line is over 1,000 ft. (scarcely desirable for school purposes) the rear tapeman passes on ten pins to the head tapeman after the first 1,000 ft. have been measured. When the last stretch of tape is not an exact number of feet, the decimal or fraction of a foot is read by the head tapeman, since the first foot of a surveyor's tape is the only one usually subdivided. In this case 1 ft. must be subtracted from the tape reading at the rear end. For instance, if the rear pin has the 46-ft. mark beside it, and the forward end reads 0.3 ft. at the end of the line, then the length of the last section is 45.7 ft.

Remarks. All linear measurements in surveying are reduced to two classes, horizontal and vertical. Vertical measurements are usually carried on by the process of leveling or by indirect measurement dependent on horizontal measurement. The most important and at the same time probably the most difficult operation in surveying is horizontal measurement. With young students care should be taken that the measurements are made along fairly level ground, in which case the tape may be laid along the ground. There is no need, for the standard of accuracy required in the following exercises, to explain in any detail the errors produced by change in temperature, sag, and pull. Errors due to lack of alignment and not holding the tape horizontally can be easily understood by beginners. But since these factors produce an error of only 0.1 ft. in a tape length of 100 ft. when 4.5 ft. off line, no elaborate precautions need be taken to avoid them.

The first objective of this exercise should be to have students acquire the habit of estimating distances. The relationship between his own pace and the standard units of length can be worked out by each student when he has both paced and taped several different lengths. It is not advisable that all this work be undertaken on the same day. As early as possible students should be introduced to the idea of the approximate nature of all measurement and the relative meaning of accuracy. For instance, when we say that a line, measured to the nearest tenth of a foot, is 57.4 ft. we mean that its length is nearer to 57.4 than to either 57.3 or 57.5 ft. While this degree of accuracy suffices for our present purpose, a surveyor under certain circumstances may measure the same line and determine its length as 57.36 ft., which shows that he is measuring to the nearest hundredth of a foot. The degree of accuracy which we set up for our measurement depends on the relative value of the measurement. For horizontal distances required in the remaining exercises there is no need of measuring closer than to the nearest tenth of a foot or even the nearest foot. It should be impressed on the students that any results obtained from calculations using measurements are no more accurate than the original measurements. For instance, if in Section II, Case A, Method 8, the horizontal line AX is measured as 56.4 ft., the calculated height of XY should not contain more than three significant figures, rounded off according to the recognized rules.[7]

Except in the sections on mapping and areas in the following exercises, the distances to be measured are usually less than 100 ft. and the system outlined in this problem is unnecessary unless a short tape is being used. More detailed information on horizontal measurement can be had by consulting any standard textbook on surveying. An interesting historical topic connected with this ex-

---

[7] A. Bakst, *Approximate Computation*, The National Council of Teachers of Mathematics, *Twelfth Yearbook* (New York, 1937), pp. 31 ff. C. N. Shuster, *A Study of the Problems in Teaching the Slide Rule* (New York, 1940), pp. 15 ff.

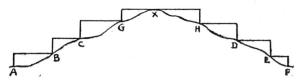

Figure 156

ercise is the development of our units of length. This has not been covered in the preceding chapters, since there already exists an extensive literature in English on the subject.[8]

Problem 5. To measure the distance between two points on sloping ground.

METHOD

This is a much more difficult exercise than that outlined in the previous problem, and for this reason should not be attempted until proficiency has been attained in taping over horizontal ground. Measuring downhill is usually less difficult than uphill. One end of the tape is held on or close to the ground, while the point on the ground perpendicularly below the other end when the tape is stretched horizontally must be determined by means of a plumb line. When the slope is steep, short tape sections must be taken. The easiest way to keep a record of the lengths is to enter them individually in a notebook. The line over the hill should first be determined as in Problem 2. The method of lining in is the same as in Problem 4 except that intermediate markers are used instead of the end range pole for sighting by the rear tapeman. To find the distance between *A* and *F* (Figure 156) it would be better to find first a point *X* on the summit visible from *A* and *F* and measure downhill from *X* to both *A* and *F*. Continuous measurement from *A* to *F* may then be tried and results compared.

Remarks. The horizontal distance on sloping ground is needed because the productive or useful area is always the horizontal projection of a sloping area. For example, no more corn can be grown

[8] D. E. Smith, *History of Mathematics* (Boston, 1923), Vol. 2, pp. 640 ff. R. T. Gunther, *Early Science in Oxford* (Oxford, 1923), Vol. 1. W. Hallock and H. Wade, *The Evolution of Weights and Measures and of the Metric System* (New York, 1906). On the subject of geodetic measurements, see A. R. Clark, *Geodesy* (Oxford, 1880). J. H. Gore, *Geodesy* (Boston, 1891).

on a sloping area than on the corresponding horizontal projection of this area. Among the Romans and during the Middle Ages this process of getting horizontal length in order to calculate horizontal areas was known as *cultellare*. It was carried out by using a

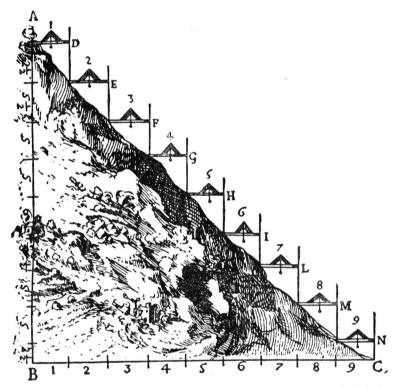

Figure 157. FINDING THE HORIZONTAL PROJECTION OF A SLOPE.
From Pomodoro's La Geometria Prattica.

long-dimensioned rod instead of a tape (Figure 157). The rod was placed horizontally, usually by means of a plumb-bob level, and the points on the ground corresponding to the ends of the rod were determined by means of vertical staffs. For beginners this would be a much easier way of carrying on the work.

References. Bettini (41), Progymnasma Secundum, Prop. 1. Leonardo Pisano (313), Vol. 2, pp. 107-108. Savasorda (439), pp. 125, 127. Blume, Lachmann, and Rudorff (54), Vol. I, pp. 33-34; Vol. II, p. 340. Cantor (92), p. 180. (Numbers in parentheses throughout the exercises indicate items in the Bibliography.)

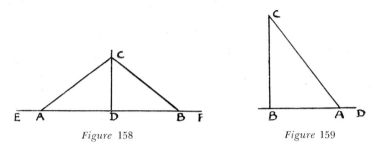

Figure 158   Figure 159

Problem 6. To erect a perpendicular from a point in a given line.

CASE A.   When the point is not near the end of the line.

METHOD

Let *EF* be the given line and *D* the given point (Figure 158). By means of a cord, equal distances *DA* and *DB* are marked off on each side of *D*. Then a length of cord greater than *AB* is taken and its mid-point found by folding. With the ends of the cord secured at *A* and *B*, the cord is stretched and the position of the mid-point *C* is marked on the ground. *CD* is the required perpendicular. (Note: If the ends of the cord are looped and pegs set in the ground at *A* and *B*, one student may carry out this exercise unaided; if not, the cooperation of three students is necessary).

References. The Indian Sulvasūtras (see p. 59). Schwenter (455), p. 305.

CASE B.   When the point is near the end of the line.

METHOD 1

Take a cord marked off in twelve equal units. Place the third division mark at *B* (Figure 159), the point at which the perpendicular is required, and stretch the first 3 units along the given line *BD* to *A*. The other end of the cord is also held at *A*. Then, holding the cord by the seventh division mark, *C*, pull the two sections taut and place a mark in the ground under *C*. *CB* is the required perpendicular.

References. Schwenter (455), p. 404. Le Clerc (310), p. 220. *Geometria Culmensis* (199), p. 33. Balbus: see Chapter II, note 23. Henrion (251), p. 164.

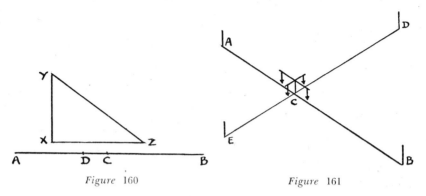

Figure 160   Figure 161

METHOD 2

Mark off any distance XZ from the given point X along the given line. Then take a cord AB whose length is twice that of the line XZ (Figure 160). By folding find the mid-point C of AB. By folding AC twice find D, so that DC = 1/4 AC. Then, if XZ is taken as a unit length, AD = 3/4 and DB = 5/4. Securing the ends of the cord at X and Z, stretch it, making D the apex of a triangle. The three points A, D, and B then correspond with the points X, Y, and Z. YX is the required perpendicular.

Reference. Baudhāyana (see p. 59).

CASE C.   When the point is anywhere on the line.

METHOD

The common method of solving this problem, fundamental to all early surveying methods, was to employ some one of the instruments especially devised for this purpose, such as the dioptra, the large wooden right triangle, the carpenter's square, the groma, or one of the various types of the surveyor's cross developed in the Middle Ages and Renaissance. The instrument was set up over the point on the given line (Figure 161). It was then turned in the horizontal plane until one pair of sights coincided with the direction of the given line. Then by setting a rod in line with the other pair of sights, the required line was marked out. See pp. 31-32.

Remarks. For the unhistoric legends connected with Case B,

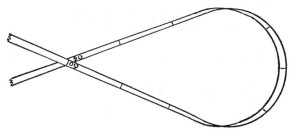

Figure 162

see p. 13. The process may be carried out as follows with the modern steel tape: Hold one end of the tape at *A* (Figure 159), 30 ft. from *B*, and the 90-ft. mark at *B*. Then, holding the 50-ft. mark *C,* stretch the two sections taut and place a mark in the ground under *C*. A more accurate determination of point *C* can be made by holding one end of the tape at *A,* the 100-ft. mark at *B,* and at *C* the 50- and 60-ft. marks, crossing the tape and leaving a loop above *C*. This eliminates the bend in the tape above *C* (Figure 162).

The importance of the right angle in all surveying work up to the end of the seventeenth century should be pointed out (see pp. 27 ff., 59 ff., and 143 ff.). These methods of constructing a right angle may well be employed in simple projects such as laying out a rectangle and checking the accuracy by measuring the diagonals, or laying out a baseball diamond, tennis court, or other playing field.

References. See pp. 29 ff.

Problem 7. To drop a perpendicular from a point to a line.

METHOD

a. One end of a cord is secured to a peg at *P* (Figure 163). The cord is then stretched to meet the given line *AB* at a point such as *C*. The length *PC* is then swung round to meet the given line *AB* at *D*. The mid-point *E* of *CD* is now found by taking a cord equal in length to *CD* and folding it. (The same construction, using practically the same process, can be carried out with a modern tape.) *PE* is the required perpendicular.

Reference. Leonardo Pisano (313), Vol. 2, p. 43.

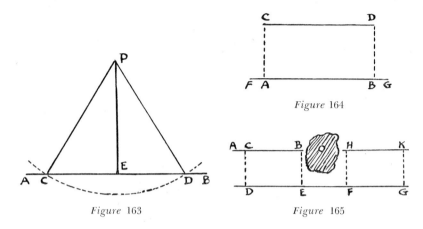

Figure 164

Figure 163

Figure 165

b. This problem can be solved by the right-angle instruments, but not so conveniently. Such instruments must be used, however, when the perpendicular is long. The instrument is set up on the given line with one pair of sights in alignment with the line. It must then be moved along the line until the given point is in line with the other pair of sights. The number of times the instrument has to be taken up and set down again makes the method inconvenient.

Reference. Geometria Culmensis (199), p. 31.

Problem 8. To establish a line parallel to a given line.

METHOD

a. From two points *A* and *B* on the given line *FG* (Figure 164) set out two perpendiculars to the given line. Measure equal distances on these perpendiculars. *AC = BD;* then *CD* is the required parallel.

b. If a right-angle instrument is used, only one perpendicular need be set out from the given line. The instrument is then moved along this perpendicular the required distance and the required line set out at right angles to the perpendicular.

Remarks. These methods may be used in prolonging a straight line through an obstacle. Let *AB* (Figure 165) be the given line which is intercepted by some obstacle *O*. At *C* and *B* erect equal perpendiculars *CD* and *BE* of sufficient length to clear the ob-

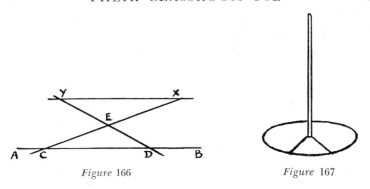

Figure 166   Figure 167

stacle. Prolong *DE* and erect at *F* and *G* perpendiculars *FH* and *GK,* making them equal in length to the original perpendiculars. Then *HK* is the prolongation of *AB*. For good alignment points *C* and *B* should be chosen far apart.

c. On the given line *AB* (Figure 166) set up rods at *C* and *D*. Take any convenient point *E*. Prolong the lines *CE* and *DE,* making *EX = EC* and *EY = ED*. Then *XY* is the required line.

Problem 9. To establish the direction of the meridian by the Indian circles method.

METHOD

The description in the *Sūrya-Siddhānta* reads (see Figure 167) :[9]

"1. On a stony surface, made water level, or upon hard plaster, there draw an even circle, of a radius equal to any required number of the digits of the gnomon.

"2. At its center set up the gnomon, of twelve digits of the measure fixed upon; and where the extremity of its shadow touches the circle in the former and after parts of the day.

"3. There fixing two points upon the circle, and calling them the forenoon and afternoon points, draw midway between them, by means of a fish-figure, a north and south line.

"4. Midway between the north and south directions draw, by a fish-figure, an east and west line; and in like manner also, by fish-figures between the four cardinal directions, draw the intermediate directions."

[9] E. Burgess, "Sūrya-Siddhānta," *Journal of the American Oriental Society,* Vol. 6, 1860, p. 239.

Remarks. The fish-figure refers to the method of bisection of a line by describing arcs from the extremities of the line with a radius equal to the line itself. For improvement on this method by al-'Urdī see p. 61. The establishment of the meridian line is a fundamental exercise in surveying, and this method is sufficiently accurate for school purposes. A check on the line established from the shadow of the sun could be carried out by lining in the North Star with a pair of vertical staffs at night, one staff being placed in the position corresponding to that of the daytime experiment. The only additional equipment needed is a flashlight.

References. Proclus Diodochus (403). Schwenter (455), p. 563. Gilbert (204), Bk. 4, Ch. 12. Atwell (21), Ch. 14.

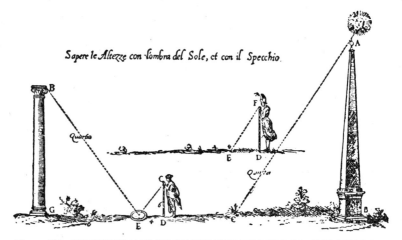

Figure 168. DETERMINATION OF HEIGHT BY MIRROR AND SHADOW METHODS. *From Pomodoro's* La Geometria Prattica.

SECTION II

Problem. To find the height of an object whose base is accessible.

CASE A. Observations made on a horizontal plane.

METHOD 1

a. Place a rod *AB* vertically in the ground (Figure 169). Observe when the length of the shadow *AC* is equal to the height of

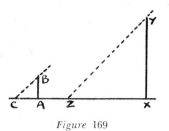

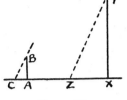

Figure 169   *Figure* 170

the rod. This may be best done by describing on the ground, in the direction of the shadow, an arc of a circle whose radius is equal to the height of the rod and whose center is at the foot of the rod. When the tip of the shadow meets the arc the shadow is equal in length to the height of the rod. Now measure the length of the shadow XZ of the flagpole, tree, or other tall object whose height is required. By similar triangles the height of the object XY equals the length of its shadow.

b. Instead of waiting until the shadow of the rod equals its height as in *a*, the following measurements may be made at any time: (1) height of rod, AB (Figure 170); (2) length of shadow of rod, AC; (3) length of shadow of object whose height is required, XZ. Then the required height is found by proportion from similar triangles. $XY = (AB \cdot XZ)/AC$.

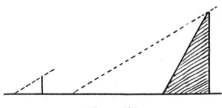

Figure 171

Remarks. Descriptions of these methods, as used by Thales in finding the height of a pyramid, are the earliest we have on any problem in applied geometry (see p. 38). In using these methods to find the height of a pyramid or any object whose base width is considerable as compared with its height, half the width of the base should be added to the length of the shadow (Figure 171). There is no mention of the use of such a correction by Thales.

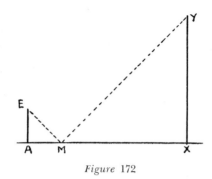

Figure 172

This shadow method was used by the Greeks to determine the height of mountains.[10]

References. This problem is to be found in practically all the works on applied geometry, a few of which will be mentioned here. Balbus: see Blume, Lachmann, and Rudorff (54), Vol. I, p. 93. Gerbert (200), Ch. 24. Mainardi (323), p. 357. Pacioli (386), Pr. 8. Finaeus (174), p. 14. Belli (36), p. 52. Hulsius (270), p. 22. Dou (147), p. 282. Schwenter (455), p. 447. Forestani (185), p. 325*v.* Digges (142), Ch. 9. Pomodoro (400), Pl. 44. Aryabhatta: Kaye (286). De Rojas (431), p. 157. Brahmagupta: Kaye (286). Bourdin (64), p. 32.

METHOD 2

A plane mirror *M* (Figure 172) is placed horizontally on the ground at some convenient distance from the object *XY* whose height is required. The observer moves back from the mirror and places a rod *AE* vertically in the ground, in such a position that by sighting over the top of the rod, he can see the image of the top of the object. Distances *AE, AM, MX* are then measured, and the required height *XY* is computed. $XY = (MX \cdot AE)/AM$.

Remarks. The earliest reference to this method is to be found in Euclid (*Optics,* 20, "To measure a height when the sun is not shining"). The method appears frequently in the practical geometries. Sometimes the use of the rod is omitted, and the height of the observer's eye when standing erect is substituted. This simple use of the mirror finally led through the transformation of the Jacob's staff to the development of the sextant (see p. 206). With more advanced students the effect of a non-horizontal mirror

[10] F. Cajori, "Determination of the Heights of Mountains," *Isis,* Vol. 12, 1929, p. 486.

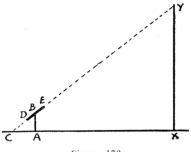

Figure 173

should be investigated. A simple explanation of the phenomenon of reflection of light from a plane surface is necessary before the geometrical properties of the problem are understood. A surface of still water is sometimes substituted for the mirror. This eliminates the problem of leveling the mirror.

References. Gerbert (200), Ch. 23. Pacioli (386), Pr. 9. Mainardi (323), p. 355. Finaeus (174), p. 15*v*. Köbel (297), p. 26. Pomodoro (400), Pl. 44. Münster (355), p. 52. Errard de Bar-le-Duc (160), p. 29. Digges (142), Ch. 16. Bartoli (31), p. 30*r*. Forestani (185), p. 326*r*. Arduser (16), p. 220*r*. Bourdin (64), p. 32.

METHOD 3

Place supporting rod *AB* (Figure 173) vertically in the ground. Turn the sighting rod until the line of sight *DE* passes through the top of the object *XY* whose height is required. The observer then moves to the other end of the sighting rod and finds point *C* where the reversed line of sight hits the ground. *AB, AX,* and *AC* are then measured. $XY = (AB \cdot CX)/AC$.

Remarks. The method is described by Sextus J. Africanus in Cestes V. See Vincent (518), p. 415. This combination of rods, with the sighter revolvable on the vertical rod, was known to the Romans as the *lychnia*. It is rarely mentioned in later times.

Reference. Pomodoro (400), Pl. 44.

METHOD 4

Holding vertically a large wooden right triangle, the observer moves back and forth until the line of sight along the hypotenuse *EB* (Figure 175) passes through *Y*, the top of the object to be

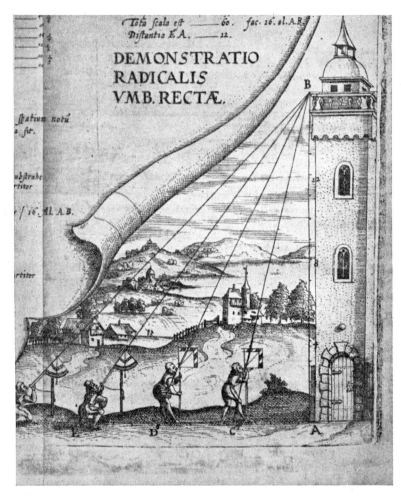

Figure 174. DETERMINATION OF HEIGHT BY QUADRANT AND GEOMETRIC SQUARE. *From Hulsius'* De Quadrante Geometrico.

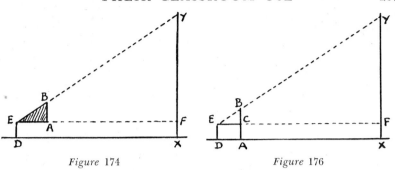

Figure 174 Figure 176

measured. *EA, ED, EF,* and *AB* are measured. Then $FY = (EF \cdot AB)/EA$, and $XY = FY + ED$.

Remarks. If an isosceles right triangle is used, $FY = EF$, and $XY = EF + ED$. For Leonardo Pisano's variation of this method by having the observer lie flat on the ground and hold a rod, equal in length to himself, between his feet, see p. 63. Instead of the solid wooden triangle, two short rods bound together at right angles were used in some cases.

References. Gerbert (200), Chs. 30, 31. Mainardi (323), p. 355. Honnecourt (261), p. 146. *Chou-pei:* Biot (47), p. 601. On the use of the triangle among the Romans, see Cantor (92), pp. 112 ff.

METHOD 5

The rod *AB* (Figure 176) is placed vertically in the ground at a convenient distance from *X,* the foot of the object whose height is required. The rod *EC* is held horizontally and moved up or down until such a position is reached that by sighting along the line *EB,* the point *Y* is seen. *AX, EC, BC,* and *AC* are then measured. $FY = (FE \cdot BC)/EC$, and $XY = FY + FX$.

Remarks. If a suitable double clamp is attached to the vertical rod, more flexibility will be given to the combination. Rods graduated in feet and inches or feet and tenths of a foot are more convenient than plain rods. No mention is made of graduated rods in any of the old descriptions of the solution of such problems by rod combinations.

References. Pomodoro (400), Pl. 44. Digges (142), Ch. 13. Pacioli (386), Pr. 3. Bartoli (31), p. 29r. Finaeus (174), p. 14. Peletier (391), p. 293. Belli (36), p. 63. De Suberville (486), pp. 92, 111. Bullet (83), p. 52.

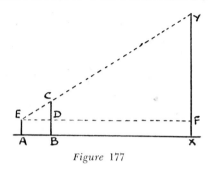

Figure 177

METHOD 6

The observer sets up vertically the rod *BC* (Figure 177), whose length is greater than his height, at any convenient distance from

Figure 178. DETERMINATION OF HEIGHT BY CARPENTER'S SQUARE.
From Bettini's Apiaria; *reproduced from Sanford's* A Short History of Mathematics, *by permission of the author.*

X, the foot of the object whose height is required. He then moves back from *B* and places the rod *AE* vertically in such a position that the line of sight across the tops of the rods, *EC*, passes through the top of the object, *Y*. The following measurements are then made: *AE*, *BC*, *AB*, *BX*. Then $FY = (FE \cdot CD)/AB$, and $XY = FY + AE$.

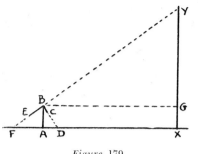

Figure 179

Remarks. Instead of a second rod, the observer's eye-level height was used in some cases, for instance, by Gerbert.

References. Hugo Physicus (269), p. 206. Ramus (410), p. 55. Schwenter (455), p. 451. Errard de Bar-le-Duc (160), p. 28. Gerbert (200), Ch. 26. Heron: Vincent (518), Chs. 12, 14. Pomodoro (400), Pl. 44.

METHOD 7

A large carpenter's square *EBC* (Figure 179) is attached by means of a screw to a vertical rod *AB*, which is set up at a convenient distance from the foot, *X*, of the object whose height is required. The square is revolved until the line of sight along the edge *EB* passes through the top of the object, *Y*. The point *D* where the line of sight of the other arm of the square hits the ground is then marked. *AB, AD,* and *AX* are measured. Then from the similar triangles *BAD* and *BGY, GY* = (*AD·BG*)/*AB* and *XY* = *GY* + *AB*.

Remarks. In some accounts the point *F* is found instead of *D*. The method is then the same as Method 3. In the solution with point *D*, the triangles have their corresponding sides perpendicular to each other.

References. Münster (355), pp. 40-41. Finaeus (174), Ch. 5, p. 7. Clavius (114), p. 94. Henrion (250), p. 29. Digges (142), Ch. 15.

METHOD 8

At a convenient distance from the object whose height is required, the observer places the geometric square *BCDE* (Figure 180) vertically. This may be done by holding it, or better, by

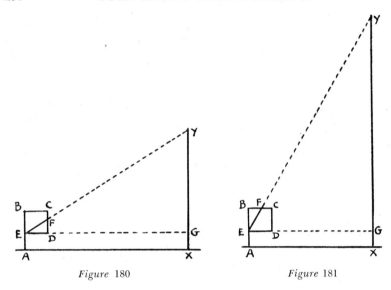

Figure 180   *Figure* 181

fastening it to a vertical rod *AE,* its verticality determined by means of a plumb line. The alidade is turned until the line of sight coincides with the top of the object *Y.* The distances *AX* and *AE* are measured. Then $YG = (FD \cdot EG)/ED$. If, as is assumed throughout these exercises, the side of the square is divided into 12 parts, and if $FD = n$ parts, then $YG = (n \cdot EG)/12$, and $XY = (n \cdot EG)/12 + AE$.

Remarks. In the above solution the line of sight crosses the umbra versa *CD.* If the line of sight crosses the umbra recta *BC* as in Figure 181, $YG = (12 \cdot EG)/n$, and $XY = (12 \cdot EG)/n + AE$.

If the line of sight falls along *EC,* then $XY = AX + GX$. It should be pointed out to the students that in all these cases we are really working with the tangent of the angle of elevation; in the early stages of development only the functions were considered and not the angles themselves.[11] Calculations may be simplified by using a square with sides divided into 100 parts.

References. Gerbert (200), Ch. 33; see Chapter III, note 114. Pacioli (386), Pr. 6. Mainardi (323), p. 362. Tartaglia (496), pp. 25-27. Schott (448), Pl. 4

[11] J. D. Bond, "The Development of Trigonometrical Methods down to the Close of the Fifteenth Century," *Isis,* Vol. 4, 1922, pp. 295-323. S. Gandz, "The Origin of Angle-Geometry," *Isis,* Vol. 12, 1929, pp. 452-481. D. E. Smith, *History of Mathematics* (Boston, 1923), Vol. 2, p. 620.

Figure 182. DETERMINATION OF HEIGHT BY ASTROLABE. *From*
Stöffler's Elucidatio Fabrica Ususque Astrolabii.

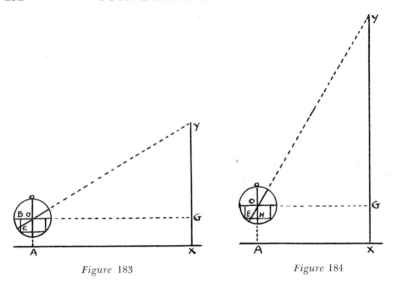

Figure 183   *Figure* 184

Belli (36), p. 46. Hulsius (270), pp. 8-13. Digges (142), Ch. 22. Bartoli (31), p. 16.

METHOD 9

The solution of this problem by means of the astrolabe is identical with the preceding method. The advantage of the astrolabe over the geometric square is that it can be held vertically more easily; its disadvantage lies in the smallness of the inscribed shadow square.

a. Where the alidade cuts across the umbra versa (Figure 183), $GY = (BE \cdot OG)/OB = (n \cdot OG)/12$, and $XY = GY + AO$.

b. Where the alidade cuts across the umbra recta (Figure 184), $GY = (OH \cdot OG)/EH = (12 \cdot OG)/n$, and $XY = GY + AO$.

c. If the alidade falls on the diagonal of the shadow square, then the height of the object = distance from object + height of center of instrument.

Remarks. The astrolabe was the most commonly used surveying instrument among the Muslims. From the references below it can be seen that its use for this purpose survived for a long period in Europe, even though in the meantime other instruments on which more accurate measurements could be taken had come into use. Though not used here as an angle-measuring instrument

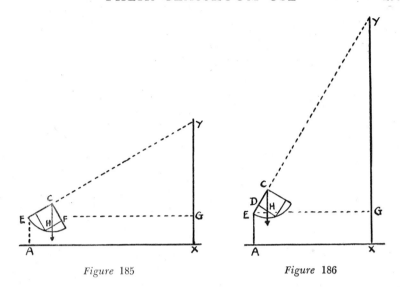

Figure 185   *Figure* 186

directly, it may be so employed if desired, and the height may be
found by using the tangent function. This affords an opportunity
to give students some information on the development of the
trigonometrical functions (see pp. 68 ff. and note 11 on p. 290).

References. Apian (14), p. 62. De Rojas (431), pp. 148-150. Hedraeus
(243), p. 16. Bartoli (31), p. 20. Henrion (250), p. 128. Schöner (447).
Stöffler (481), fol. 67. Danti (130), p. 124. Des Bordes (139), Ch. 6.

METHOD 10

a. If the plumb line falls across the umbra versa, the observer
takes up a suitable position at A (Figure 185), and either holding
the quadrant or suspending it from a staff in a vertical plane, he
turns the quadrant until the line of sight along the edge EC passes
through Y, the top of the object whose height is required. AX and
AE are measured. Then $GY = (HF \cdot EG)/CF = (n \cdot EG)/12$, and
$XY = GY + AE$.

b. If the plumb line falls across the umbra recta (Figure 186).
$GY = (CD \cdot EG)/DH = (12 \cdot EG)/n$, and $XY = GY + AE$.

c. If the plumb line falls as a diagonal of the shadow square,
then the required height $=$ the distance of the observer from
the foot of the object $+$ the height of the observer's eye.

Remarks. If sine lines are drawn on the quadrant. the method

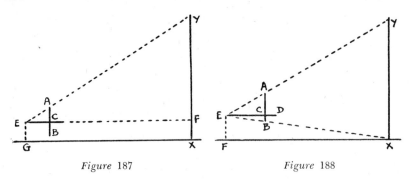

Figure 187   *Figure* 188

of using these indicated on pp. 70 and 81 may be used with the advantage of shortening the computations. The modern substitute for the sine-line quadrant is the hypsometer. On its use see Shuster (466), Ch. 8.

References. Robert Anglicus: see Tannery (493), pp. 34 ff. Pacioli (386), Pr. 7. Digges (142), Ch. 8. Cardan (94), fol. 611. Mainardi (323), p. 349. Leonardo Pisano (313), pp. 204-206. Bartoli (31), p. 25*v.* Finaeus (174), p. 13*v.* Rathborne (412), Bk. 3, Ch. 20.

METHOD 11

a. This method of solution by the Jacob's staff is essentially the same as Method 5. The observer holds the main staff until point Y comes into the line of sight EA (Figure 187). GX and EG are measured, and lengths EC and AC are read on the staff. Then $YF = (AC \cdot GX)/EC$, and $XY = YF + EG$.

b. In this case the whole cross-staff is used, unsymmetrically placed if necessary. In this solution the height of the observer is irrelevant. Holding the cross-staff horizontally, the observer moves into such a position that the two lines of sight EA and EB (Figure 188) strike the top Y, and the base X, of the object whose height is required. FX is measured. Then $XY = (AB \cdot FX)/EC$.

Remarks. This use of the Jacob's staff very seldom appears. Digges gives the following directions to the observer: "Also remember when you are appointed to measure any breadth or length (as shall be declared) it behooveth you to stand right with, and against that breadth, and the longer the breadth or larger the wideness or length is, the better the thing will come to passe. And for heights it is necessary (if you regard all preciseness) to have

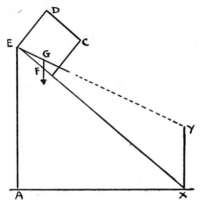

Figure 189

the height stand directly up. Ye must stand right up with your Body and Necke, your feete just together, your hands not much moving, the one eye closed, and ever marke your standing right with the midst of your feete."

References. Digges (141), p. 24. Gunter (219), Bk. I. Ramus (410), p. 62. Ryff (434), Bk. 3, Ch. 8. Reisch (424), Ch. 4. Ryff (433), p. 130.

CASE B. When the point of observation of known height is higher than the object.

METHOD

A plumb line is hung from the alidade of the geometric square. The lower edge of the square is sighted on the base, X (Figure 189), of the object, and the alidade is sighted on the top, Y. From similar triangles EXY and EFG, $XY = (FG \cdot EX)/EF$. Distances FG and EF are measured on the square. To find EX, the usual method given is $EX = \sqrt{EA^2 + AX^2}$. Distance AX is found by one of the methods given under Section III, Case B.

Remarks. This is one of the cases in which the solution depends on similar oblique triangles. After a sight has been taken along the base of the square, the instrument should be fixed in this position on its supporting staff. (According to the diagrams, the old-timers were able to take in both sights at once and hold the instrument by hand; too difficult an assignment for a beginner!) The measurement of the plumb-line length FG makes the method

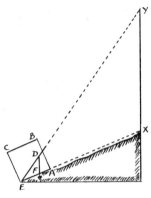

Figure 190

unreliable; at the same time it offers a rather simple solution to a complicated problem.

References. Finaeus (175), p. 74; (174), Ch. 13, p. 17*v*. Bartoli (31), p. 38*v*. Clavius (114), p. 118. De Suberville (486), p. 80.

CASE C. Where ground with constant slope separates the object from the observer.

METHOD

The geometric square is set up with its base parallel with the slope (Figure 190). A plumb line is suspended from the alidade. The alidade is sighted toward the top of the object, *Y*. From the similar triangles *EXY* and *EFD*, $XY = (FD \cdot EX)/EF$. The length of the slope must be measured.

Remarks. The main difficulty in this method is to set the square up with its base parallel to the slope. This may be done by taking the height of the base at *E* and sighting on a point of equal height on a rod some distance up the hill. Remarks made for Case B also hold true here. In the usual form in which this problem is found in modern trigonometry books, two observations of the angle of elevation of the top of the object are necessary from two points of known distance apart on the slope, and the result is obtained by the solution of two triangles, using the sine formula.

References. Finaeus (174), Ch. 15, p. 20. Dou (147), p. 292. Clavius (114), p. 118. De Suberville (486), p. 100. Forestani (185), p. 340*v*. Bartoli (31), p. 43. Pacioli (386), Pr. 5.

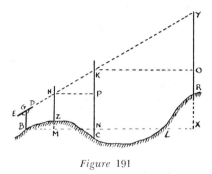

Figure 191

CASE D. When the observations have to be carried out over irregular ground.

METHOD

The earliest method is given by Heron as follows (see Figure 191):[12]

Problem: "From a point [elevated] which can be seen, let fall a perpendicular to a given horizontal plane, without approaching the point."

Solution: "Let Y be the elevated point and B a point in our plane [horizontal]. Place the dioptra at B and let BG be the support, and EGD the alidade along which sighting is done. Turn it toward Y, then, leaving it in that position, place between it and the point Y, in a vertical position, two rods of unequal height ZH and CK, of which the longer CK is the nearer to the point Y. Suppose that the ground follows a line such as BZCL, and take BL as the direction of our horizontal plane. Place the rods ZH and CK in such a manner that they appear to form only a single straight line passing through the point Y. Then with the alidade EGD at rest, let H be the sight on HZ and K that on KC. Prolong, in imagination, HZ and KC respectively to M and N, and draw HP and KO parallel to BL. With the aid of a level the height of Z above B can be found, since the points are near us, and consequently we shall know the length of ZM; and in the same way CN. But we know besides HZ and KC; therefore, we know the lines HM and KN, and consequently also their difference KP. We know also the distance HP, which is the horizontal projection of

[12] Heron, *On the Dioptra*, Ch. 12. Vincent or Schöne Edition.

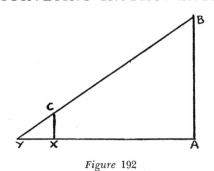

Figure 192

ZC; consequently, we can find the ratio *HP* : *KP*. Suppose, for example, that we have found *HP* equal to 5 times *KP*. By dropping the perpendicular *YORX* to our horizontal plane *BL,* we will also have *KO* equal to 5 times *YO*. But *KO* is known, because it is the distance *CR* reduced to the horizontal; we have therefore, also *YO*. And, since *OX* equals *KN,* it is also known; we have therefore, the total length of the perpendicular *YX* dropped to our horizontal."

Remarks. This is a complete solution which covers all ordinary conditions. The methods given by Heron for this and some other like cases are a remarkable tribute to Greek ingenuity. These solutions were in general avoided in the Renaissance textbooks. As an exercise it is probably too difficult for high school students; however, a discussion of its geometrical implications could be used to advantage.

SECTION III

Problem. To find the horizontal distance between two points, one being accessible.

CASE A. Observations made on a horizontal plane.

METHOD 1

The earliest solution is given by Heron as follows:[13]

"Let *X* and *Y* be the two given points, *X* near and *Y* in the distance [Figure 192]. Place at *X* the dioptra furnished with its

[13] *Ibid.,* Ch. 8. In Chapter 9 Heron employs this method to find the width of a river.

Figure 193. DETERMINATION OF DISTANCE TO AN INACCESSIBLE
POINT. *From Digges'* Pantometria.

vertical semi-circle, and revolve the alidade resting on the [diam-
eter of this] semi-circle, until Y comes into the line of sight. When
this is done, move to the other end of the instrument; then revolve
the semi-circle, all the other parts remaining fixed, and mark on
our side (on the ground) a point A in the direction XY. Erect by
means of the dioptra, at the points X and A, the two lines XC and
AB, perpendicular to YA; then take at random a point B on AB.
Next, the dioptra having been carried to B, place the alidade in
such a manner that it is possible to see, besides the point Y, the
point of intersection C of XC and YB. There will result a triangle
YBA, having its side AB parallel to XC. Now the distances AB
and XC must be measured horizontally. Suppose that AB equals
5 times XC, then YA equals 5 times XY, and it follows that AX
equals 4 times XY. Now, no more remains to be done than to
measure the horizontal distance XA, and XY will be found [by
taking the quarter of XA]."

Remark. Notice the vertical motion of the line of sight from the
instrument at X first to Y and then to A (see p. 34) .

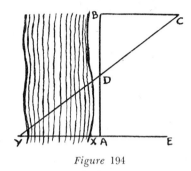

Figure 194

METHOD 2

The original description from M. Junius Nipsus reads as follows:[14]

"To find the width of a river.

"Bend at *A* the straight line *EX* which touches on the river, and where you have bent it lay out the right angle *EAB* [Figure 194]. Then transfer the groma, from the straight line *EAX* which meets the river, to the straight line *AB*, which you have laid out. Then move the groma [to *B*], and sighting along the straight line *BA* which you have laid out, make the angle *ABC* toward the right. Then go half-way along *AB* from the right angle at *B* [to the right angle at *A*], and divide that into two parts *AD* and *DB*, and erect a mark at *D*. Then place the groma on the mark *D* which divides the two parts *AD, DB* which you have divided. Having fixed the iron [foot of the groma] in the ground, set up the groma so that the plumb bob from the swinging arm falls over the mark *D*, and its line of sight corresponds with the line on the ground [*AB*], then sight on a mark *Y* which you have placed across the river. When you have carefully sighted, go to the other side of the groma, and without moving the groma lay out the line *DC*. Where your perpendicular *BC* meets the straight line *DC*, which you have laid out, place the mark *C*, and measure along *BC* from the mark *C* to the right angle *CBA*. Since the line *AB* whose center [at *D*] you have found shows two triangles *ADY* and *DBC*, and since the side *AD* is equal to the side *DB*, the base *AY* will equal the base *BC*. Whatever, therefore, is the number [of paces] of the base *BC*, over

[14] M. J. Nipsus, in F. Blume, K. Lachmann, and A. Rudorff, *Die Schriften der Römischen Feldmesser* (Berlin, 1848-1852).

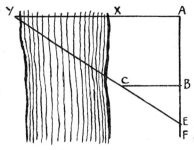

Figure 195

which you have traveled, of the same number is the side AY of the other triangle AYD whose side impinges on the river. And from that base which you have measured, take the number which you measure from the right angle to the river [AX]. What remains is the width of the river [XY]."

References. Blume, Lachmann, and Rudorff (54), pp. 285-286. Cantor (92), pp. 108-109. Schwenter (455), p. 46. Dou (147), p. 306. Pomodoro (400), Pl. 41.

METHOD 3

Let X be the accessible point, Y the inaccessible (Figure 195). At any convenient point A on the line YX prolonged, set out AF at right angles to AY. At a suitable point B on AF set out the line BC at right angles to AE. Erect a mark at C. Now move along the line AF until point E is reached, from which C and Y appear in a straight line. Measure AX, EB, BC, and AB. Then $AY = (AE \cdot BC)/BE$ and $XY = AY - AX$.

Remarks. This solution is analogous to Method 5, Section II. The earliest account is given by Sextus J. Africanus, in which he speaks of using a rod horizontally at BC. He does not mention what instrument was used in turning off the right angle, but it may be assumed that he had the groma in mind. In the seventeenth-century books, the angle AEY is measured in degrees and the distance AY calculated from the tangent function. A check can be established if both methods are used.

References. Sextus J. Africanus, Cestes IV: see Vincent (518), p. 413. Leonardo da Vinci (519), fol. 51v. Bettini (41), p. 45. Pomodoro (400), Pl. 41.

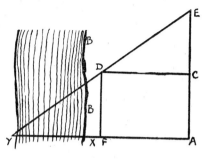

Figure 196

METHOD 4

The following is the original description given by **Sextus J.** Africanus for his method of measuring the horizontal **distance** to an inaccessible point.[15]

"To find the width of a river without crossing.

"Let Y be a point on the opposite bank, on the side of the enemy [Figure 196]; BB the bank on our side, on which the square must be placed. Set up the square on our side at a point A, situated in such a manner that its distance from the nearer bank may be greater than the width of the river, which is very simple to obtain, and sight two points at right angles; one on the opposite bank, such as a stone, a bush, or any other object easy to distinguish, let Y be this point; the other on our side, on the other branch of the square, and let E be this second point. Transporting the square to E, I sight the point Y, which forms a right triangle. I divide the side AE into two equal parts at point C, and through this point I lay out CD parallel to AY, and through point D the line DF parallel to AE. Then in the right triangle, the side AE is divided into two equal parts at point C, also CD is parallel to AY and finally DF is parallel to AE. Therefore, AY is divided into two equal parts at F. But it is easy to measure the distance AF, therefore the distance FY is known; subtract FX, the remainder is the width of the river."

Reference. Sextus J. Africanus, Cestes III: see Vincent (518), p. 411.

[15] A. J. H. Vincent, "Extraits des manuscrits rélatifs à la geométrie pratique des Grecs," *Notices et extraits des manuscrits de la bibliothèque imperiale*, 1858, Vol. 19, Part II, pp. 52-54.

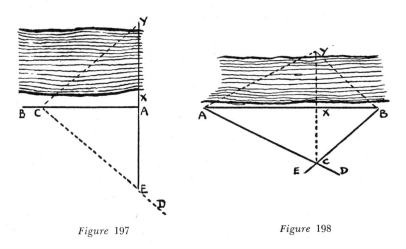

Figure 197   *Figure* 198

METHOD 5

From a convenient point A on the extension of YX lay out AB perpendicular to AY (Figure 197). At any convenient point C on AB measure angle ACY. Then lay out the line CD, making an angle equal to ACY with CA. Find the intersection E of YA produced with CD. AE can be measured; therefore AY is determined. $XY = AY - AX$.

Remarks. Medieval tradition associated this method with Thales. For the laying out of right and acute angles and the measurement of an acute angle any simple angle-measuring instrument may be employed. This exercise offers a good opportunity for angle measurement and at the same time provides for exercise in alignment and intersections.

Reference. Bettini (41), p. 43.

METHOD 6

Lay out the line AXB (Figure 198) at right angles to XY. With an angle-measuring instrument at A measure angle BAY and lay out angle BAD equal to it. Similarly make angle ABE equal to angle ABY. Locate C, the intersection of AD and BE. CX can be measured directly; hence XY is determined.

Remarks. The comment on Method 5 above applies also to Method 6.

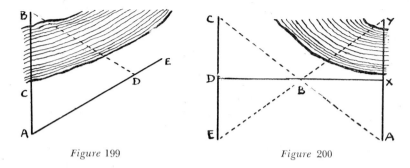

Figure 199   *Figure* 200

METHOD 7

At any convenient point *A* on *BC* prolonged, set out *AE* at an angle of 60° with *AB* (Figure 199). Move the instrument along this line until the point *D* is reached, whence the direction *DB* makes an angle of 60° with *DA*. *AB = DA*, which can be measured; and the required distance *BC = AB — AC*.

Remarks. This method is geometrically simple but not so convenient for actual field work because of the amount of territory required. Its difficulty and weakness as a practical exercise lie in the fact that point *D* has to be found by trial.

Reference. Bettini (41), Prog. I, Prop. 3.

METHOD 8

Prolong the line *XY* any convenient distance to *A* (Figure 200). Take point *B* in any suitable position. By means of rods and a tape prolong *AB* its own length to *C*. In like manner prolong *XB* its own length to *D*. Locate *E*, the intersection of *BY* and *CD* prolonged. Then *DE = XY*.

Remarks. This is a simple exercise using the techniques of intersection and prolongation of straight lines. It is not found in the Renaissance books.

Reference. Kröger (299), p. 68.

METHOD 9

Take a cord of suitable length and by folding find its mid-point. Tie the ends of the cord to pegs at the accessible end *X* and any other convenient point *B* on the prolongation of *XY* (Figure 201).

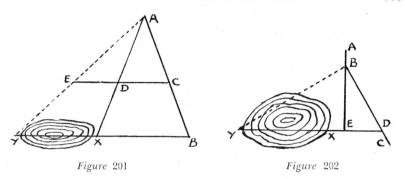

Figure 201   Figure 202

Stretch the cord, making A, its mid-point, the apex of an isosceles triangle. By means of the cord, mark off two equal lengths AD and AC on the lines AX and AB respectively. Then determine by means of rods the intersection, E, of CD prolonged and AY. Measure ED, AX, and AD. From these measurements XY is calculated: $XY = (AX \cdot ED)/AD$.

Remarks. If AD and AC are made equal to the halves of AX and AB respectively, then XY is double ED. This process simplifies the computation. For a more general solution the triangle AXB need not be made isosceles.

References. Errard de Bar-le-Duc (160), p. 26. Bourdin (64), p. 52.

METHOD 10

Set out EA perpendicular to EXY (Figure 202). At B, any convenient point on EA, lay off BC at right angles to BY. Find D, the intersection of XY prolonged and BC. Then $EY = (BE)^2/ED$, and $XY = EY - EX$.

Remarks. Any instrument for laying out a right angle may be used. This method is not in the Renaissance books.

METHOD 11

To find the distance AC (Figure 203), set up a triquetrum at A so that the apex a is vertically over A. (For ordinary school work this may be done by eye; there is no need of using a plumb bob.) When the instrument has been made fairly horizontal by means of a small spirit level or even a marble, sight the stationary arm or base toward any convenient point B. Then sight along the left

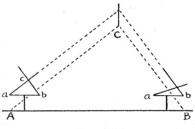

Figure 203

movable arm toward *C* and clamp it in position. Move the triquetrum to *B* and orient it by taking a backsight on *A*. Measure the
distance *AB*, and by moving the sighting arm at *B* lay off a distance on the base proportional to *AB*. Then sight the right moveable arm toward *C*, and clamp in position. There is then a triangle on the triquetrum proportional to the original triangle
ABC; hence $AC = (AB \cdot ac)/ab$.

Remarks. For the earliest account of this method by Münster
see pp. 220 ff. When the sides of *ABC* are large compared with
abc, the discrepancy caused by not having *a* and *b* vertically over

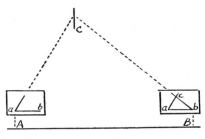

Figure 204

A and *B* is very slight and may be neglected. An important operation in this exercise is the orientation of the instrument; that is,
setting up the instrument in a second position so that its immov-
able parts are in directions parallel to those which they occupied
at the first position. This is easily accomplished by the method
of backsighting; that is, taking a sight from the opposite end of a
line and with the same parts of the instrument as on the original
sight. It may also be done by means of a compass, as described by
Münster.

Figure 205. DETERMINATION OF DISTANCE TO AN INACCESSIBLE
POINT. *From Bettini's* Apiaria; *reproduced from Sanford's* A Short
History of Mathematics, *by permission of the author.*

The basic principles of the modern range-finder are similar to
those of the triquetrum.

References. Stevin (479), p. 47. Zubler (556), Ch. 6.

METHOD 12

The plane table is set up horizontally over *A* (Figure 204). Fix
a point *a* on the paper to represent *A*. With the alidade sight
toward a convenient point *B*. Draw a line on the paper along the
edge of the alidade to represent the direction *AB*. Measure *AB*
and set off *ab* on the paper to any suitable scale. Sight the alidade
along *AC* and draw on the paper a line of indefinite length in this
direction. Move the table to *B* and set it up horizontally, with
point *b* fairly well over *B*. With the alidade along the line *ab*
backsight on *A* so as to orient the table. Now sight the alidade
along *BC* and draw a line on the paper in this direction. The
intersection of the two lines fixes the relative position of *C* to *A*
and *B*. The length of *AC* is then determined from the scale.

Remarks. The plane table is a simple instrument to operate
and can be easily used by young students. A table such as that
depicted by Zubler (Figure 245) with a very simple alidade is

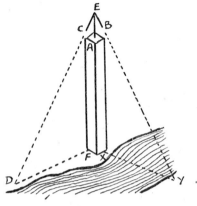

Figure 206

quite sufficient for high school purposes. As in the last exercise the exact setting of the point on the instrument over the point on the ground is unimportant. When pupils have acquired facility with the use of the plane table in exercises such as this, they will have no trouble in carrying out exercises such as Section VIII, Problem 4, Method 6, which is the type usually solved by the instrument.

References. Digges (142), 1591 Edition, p. 55. Leybourn (316), Ch. 4. Stevin (479), p. 28. Bourdin (64), p. 36. Arduser (16), p. 231r. Sturm (483), Fig. 14. Bramer (73), p. 75, turns the plane of observation into the vertical and uses the same method to find the height of a cloud.

CASE B.   Observations made from a height above the accessible point.

METHOD 1

From the elevation *A* (Figure 206) the observer sights the distant object *Y*, whose distance from the foot of the elevation, *X*, is required, and records, if necessary, the angle *AEB*. Then revolving his instrument on its vertical axis through a convenient angle, he observes an accessible point *D*, making the same angle with the vertical as *AEB*. *DF* is measured, and so *XY* is known.

Remarks. Tradition has it that Thales used this method to find the distance of a ship from the shore.[16] This method of solution •

[16] T. Heath, *A History of Greek Mathematics* (Oxford, 1921), Bk. I, p. 133.

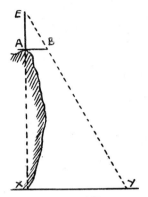

Figure 207

is of frequent occurrence in the practical geometries. Practically the whole gamut of instruments was used, the astrolabe being most common; even the peak of the observer's cap was used as a means of determining the line of sight.[17]

References. Schwenter (455), p. 38. Pomodoro (400), Pl. 43. Clavius (114), p. 95. Errard de Bar-le-Duc (160), p. 23. Belli (36), p. 22. Hedraeus (243), Pr. 25. Bettini (41), p. 45. Hulsius (270), p. 36. Bourdin (64), p. 32.

METHOD 2

The observer stands at a point of known elevation, sighting the object Y over the top of a vertical rod (Figure 207). At the same time he moves a horizontal rod back and forth until its end B comes into the line of sight. Lengths EA and AB are measured. Then $XY = (EX \cdot AB)/EA$.

Remarks. This solution has been ascribed to Thales by Eudemus according to Proclus Diodochus in his commentary on Euclid, Book I.[18] In some descriptions of this method the observer stands on the same level as the required distance. Figures 208 and 209, showing solutions from Gerbert, are self-explanatory. Such methods are not of much practical value, as the length of the unknown distance would have to be comparatively short.

[17] Belli and Bettini use the peak of the cap (see Figure 205). A recent textbook ascribes the same method to an officer in Napoleon's army.
[18] *Procli Diodochi in primum Euclidis elementorum librum commentarii,* Edited by G. Friedlein (Leipzig, 1873), p. 92.

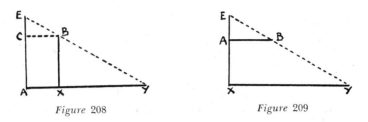

Figure 208   *Figure* 209

References. Gerbert (200), Chs. 35, 38. Errard de Bar-le-Duc (160), p. 20. Hedraeus (243), Pr. 24. Pomodoro (400), Pl. 43. De Suberville (486), pp. 58, 63. Oddi (380), p. 125.

METHOD 3

The carpenter's square is set up on a vertical rod *EC* (Figure 210) over the accessible end *X* of the distance whose length is required. The observer, sighting along the long leg, revolves the square until the line of sight passes through *Y*, the inaccessible point. The point *F* where the line of sight of the short leg meets the horizontal plane through the point *X* is then determined. *CX* is known beforehand, and *FX* is measured. $XY = (EX)^2/FX$.

Remarks. The distance *XY* that can be measured in this way is limited by the height of point *E* above the plane *XY*. In most of

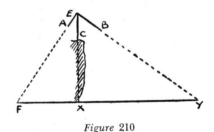

Figure 210

the practical geometries the supporting rod, which could not be conveniently more than about 5 ft. high, is placed on the ground at point *X*. Under this condition the method is not very practical. For instance, suppose in Figure 210 that *XY* is 300 ft. and *EX* is 5 ft., then *FX* should equal 1 in., too fine a measurement to be made under the circumstances. Notwithstanding this limitation the method is of frequent occurrence.

References. Finaeus (174), p. 7. Errard de Bar-le-Duc (160), p. 24. Digges (142), Ch. 15. Clavius (114), p. 94. Bettini (41), p. 41. Bartoli (31), p. 13.

METHOD 4

The observer stands at a known height above the accessible end of the line, X (Figure 211), raises the geometric square to eye level or, better, has it set up on a vertical staff, and revolves the

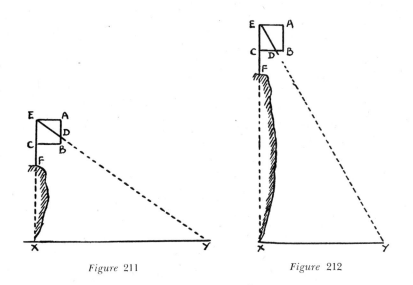

Figure 211   *Figure* 212

alidade until the line of sight passes through Y. The height of eye level FE must be known. If the alidade rests on the umbra versa, then $XY : XE :: EA : AD$, or $XY = (12 \cdot XE)/m$, where $m =$ number of divisions in AD. If the alidade came to rest at D on the umbra recta (Figure 212), then $XY = (XE \cdot m)/12$. If the alidade passes through B, then $XY = XE$.

Remarks. The same method can be used with the shadow square of the astrolabe or the quadrant.

References. Geometric square: Gerbert (200), Ch. 33. Pacioli (386), Pr. 10. Belli (36), p. 18. Hulsius (270), p. 33. Clavius (114), p. 64. Schott (448), Pl. 4. Bartoli (31), p. 9. Bourdin (64), p. 32. Astrolabe: Apian (14), p. 62. Bartoli (31), p. 11. De Rojas (431), p. 179. Henrion (250), p. 110. Stöffler (481), fol. 65. Quadrant: Clavius (114), p. 50. Bartoli (31), p. 13. Finaeus (174), p. 6. Hulsius (270), p. 37.

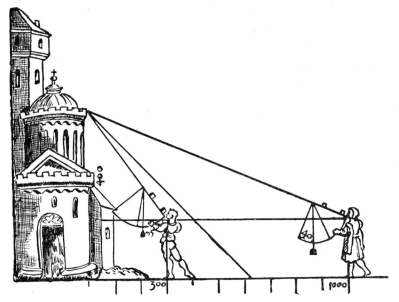

Figure 213. DETERMINATION OF HEIGHT, TWO-POSITION METHOD, USING QUADRANT. *From W. Ryff's* Der furnembsten . . . Kunst.

SECTION IV

Problem. To find the height of an object whose base is inaccessible.

CASE A. When the observations are made on the same horizontal plane as the base of the object.

This problem can be solved by successive operations as outlined in the two preceding sections. The distance to the base can be found by one of the methods given in Section II; using this information and one of the methods of Section III, the required height can be obtained. This was probably the general procedure in early times. The more powerful and compact method of two positions of observation seems to have originated with the Hindus and was the common method adopted by the Muslims and later by the Europeans.[19] A fantastic method is given by Gerbert for

[19] See p. 62. For early Chinese solutions using this method see L. van Hee, S.J., "La classique de l'ile maritime, ouvrage chinois du III⁰ siècle," *Quellen und Studien zur Geschichte der Mathematik*, Abt. B, Bd. 2, 1932-1933, pp. 255-280.

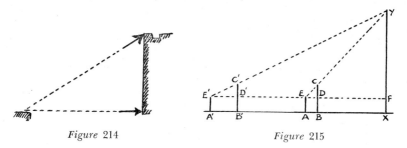

Figure 214   *Figure* 215

short distances, such as the width of a moat. Two arrows with strings attached were to be discharged, one toward the base (horizontal), the other toward the top of the wall (Figure 214). The two arrows were then to be pulled back, and from the lengths of string used a right triangle was to be formed, congruent with that made by the strings and the wall. In this way the height of the wall was to be determined.

METHOD 1

Using a rod greater than his own height, the observer sets it up vertically in any convenient position such as BC (Figure 215). He then moves backward to position A, so that the line of sight from the top of a short vertical rod AE passing through C meets the top Y of the object whose height is required. It follows that

$$AX = \frac{AB \cdot FY}{CD}. \tag{1}$$

Then, setting the rod farther back in such a position as $B'C'$ and performing the same operations,

$$A'X = \frac{A'B' \cdot FY}{C'D'}. \tag{2}$$

Subtracting (1) from (2),

$$AA' = \left(\frac{A'B'}{C'D'} - \frac{AB}{CD}\right) FY$$

$$= \frac{(A'B' - AB) FY}{CD}, \text{ since } CD = C'D';$$

therefore

$$FY = \frac{CD \cdot AA'}{A'B' - AB}$$

$$= \frac{\text{(Difference in height of rods) (Distance between stations)}}{\text{Difference in distance between rods}}$$

and

$$XY = FY + AE.$$

Remarks. If the difference between the lengths of the rods is equal to a unit of length, then $FY = AA'/(A'B' - AB)$ in the same units. In the above method, which is the one usually de-

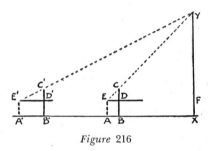

Figure 216

scribed, the position of rod AE is governed by the arbitrary position of rod BC; this makes the process of observation simple but leads to a complicated computation. If the difference in height between the two rods and the distance between the rods at any observation are arbitrarily chosen, the reverse holds true: the computation is simplified but the observations are made more tedious. For instance, suppose that at the first station $ED = DC$, and at the second $E'D' = 2D'C'$, then it follows that $FY = AA'$. This operation may be carried on more conveniently by using a combination horizontal and vertical rod as shown in Figure 216. At the first station $DC = ED$ and the position of B is found by trial, then the combination is changed so that $E'D' = 2C'D'$ and the new position B' is found. Points A and A' are determined by means of a plumb-bob line. This was the method usually employed when the Jacob's staff was used in making the observations. See Method 5.

References. Aryabhatta, Brahmagupta, Bhāskara: see pp. 62 ff. For Muslim references see Wiedemann (see Chapter III, note 67, p. 63), pp. 21-22. Gerbert (200), Ch. 32. Mainardi (323), p. 361. Errard de Bar-le-Duc (160), p. 25. Da Vinci (519), fol. 131. Schwenter (455), p. 451.

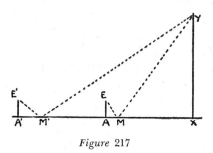

Figure 217

METHOD 2

The mirror M (Figure 217) is placed horizontally on the ground at a convenient distance from X, the foot of the object. The observer stands some distance back from M so that he can sight, either standing erect or over a vertical rod AE, the image of Y, the top of the object. The mirror is then moved to position M', and like observations are taken. The distances AM, $A'M'$, $M'M$, and AE are then measured. The necessary computation is the same as that given in Method 1.

$$MX = \frac{XY \cdot AM}{AE} \tag{1}$$

$$M'X' = \frac{XY \cdot A'M'}{A'E'}. \tag{2}$$

Subtracting (1) from (2),

$$M'M = XY \left(\frac{A'M'}{A'E'} - \frac{AM}{AE} \right).$$

But

$$AE = A'E';$$

therefore

$$XY = \frac{M'M \cdot AE}{A'M' - AM}.$$

Remarks. A simplification similar to that given in Method 1 could also be worked out here by placing the rod AE at a distance equal to itself from the mirror in the first observation and twice that distance in the second observation. But the difficulty of plac-

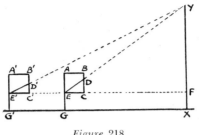

Figure 218

ing the mirror in the proper position under these conditions is
not compensated for by the simplification of the computations.

References. Gerbert (200), Ch. 37. Mainardi (323), p. 361. Errard de Bar-
le-Duc (160), p. 26. Clavius (114), p. 95.

METHOD 3

Observations are made from two stations with the geometric
square, keeping it at the same height for each observation (Figure 218). As in Section II, Methods 8, 9, and 10, three cases will be
considered.

a. At both stations the alidade falls on the *latus versum.* From
observations taken at *G,*

$$FY : EF :: DC : CE$$

or

$$EF = \frac{12 \cdot FY}{n}. \tag{1}$$

Similarly, at position *G'*

$$FY : E'F :: D'C' : C'E'$$

or

$$E'F = \frac{12 \cdot FY}{n'}. \tag{2}$$

Subtracting (1) from (2),

$$GG' = \left(\frac{12}{n'} - \frac{12}{n}\right) FY;$$

therefore

$$FY = \frac{GG'}{\dfrac{12}{n'} - \dfrac{12}{n}},$$

and

$$XY = \frac{\text{Distance between stations}}{\dfrac{12}{n'} - \dfrac{12}{n}} + \text{Eye-level height.}$$

b. If the first station is chosen so that D falls on the *latus rectum*, while D' remains as before, then

$$XY = \frac{\text{Distance between stations}}{\dfrac{12}{n'} - \dfrac{n}{12}} + \text{Eye-level height.}$$

c. If for both stations the alidade falls on the latus rectum, then

$$XY = \frac{\text{Distance between stations}}{\dfrac{n'}{12} - \dfrac{n}{12}} + \text{Eye-level height.}$$

Remarks. This is the most frequently described method in the old practical geometries. The geometric square, astrolabe, or quadrant was employed for the observations (see Figure 213). If the angles are measured and their trigonometrical ratios used, the three formulas given above become

$$XY = \frac{\text{Distance between stations}}{\text{Cot } E' - \text{Cot } E} + \text{Eye-level height.}$$

Where E and E' are the observed angles of elevation, the usual method of solution in modern textbooks requires the solution of two triangles using the sine formula.

References. Geometric square: Gerbert (200), Ch. 17. Belli (36), p. 54. Metius (336), p. 142. Tartaglia (496), p. 29. Hulsius (270), p. 24. Bourdin (64), p. 34. Astrolabe: Hedraeus (243), Pr. 6. Stöffler (481), fol. 67. Apian (14), p. 64. Bartoli (31), p. 35. De Rojas (431), p. 171. Metius (336), p. 139. Quadrant: Clavius (114), p. 43. Cardan (94), fol. 611, Pr. 5. Mainardi (323), p. 359. Digges (142), Ch. 11. Henrion (251), p. 113. Oddi (380), p. 167.

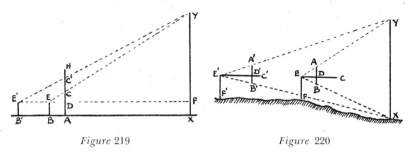

Figure 219   Figure 220

METHOD 4

Having set up a long rod *AH* in a suitable position such as *A* (Figure 219), the observer moves backward to a position such as *B*, sights toward *Y* over a vertical rod *BE*, and determines where the line of sight intersects the rod *AH*. Moving back to position *B'*, he repeats the same observations. *BB'*, *CD*, and *C'D* are measured. Then

$$BX = \frac{AB \cdot FY}{CD},\tag{1}$$

and

$$B'X = \frac{AB' \cdot FY}{C'D}.\tag{2}$$

Subtracting (1) from (2),

$$BB' = \left(\frac{AB'}{C'D} - \frac{AB}{CD}\right) FY;$$

therefore

$$FY = \frac{BB' \cdot C'D \cdot CD}{AB' \cdot CD - AB \cdot C'D}.$$

Remarks. This solution is offered by Gerbert (200), Ch. 36, "Sine mutatione hastae." No mention is made of a sighting instrument at *E* or of a dimensioned rod. If these are used the method is simplified and more accurate results may be obtained.

METHOD 5

The usual method described for the use of the Jacob's staff in this problem is depicted in Figure 220. Equal division instruments

Figure 221. DETERMINATION OF HEIGHT, TWO-POSITION METHOD, USING JACOB'S STAFF. *From W. Ryff's* Der furnembsten . . . Kunst.

were used, in which the cross-staff was equal to a division of the main staff. The crosspiece was fixed on any convenient division mark, and the observer took up such a position that when sighting, the crosspiece *AB* just covered the object *XY*. He then moved the crosspiece one unit farther from the eye end of the main staff and walked backward until a position was found where the crosspiece again covered the object. The distance between the two positions was then equal to the required height.

Remarks. This solution is more theoretical than practical for the following reasons. With a balanced crosspiece the eye level of observation should be equal to half the height of the object being measured, and, again, the elevations of the two points of observation should be the same. Neither of these conditions is usually present in reality, notwithstanding the naïve way in which they are represented in some of the old books. For explanation of the geometry involved see Section VII, Method 3.

References. Digges (141), p. 24. Belli (36), p. 43. Gunter (219), Bk. 1, Pr. 6. Ryff (434), Bk. 3, Ch. 8.

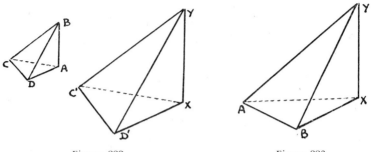

Figure 222   *Figure* 223

METHOD 6

A rod *AB* (Figure 222) is set up vertically on horizontal ground. The tip *C* of its shadow and the tip *C'* of the shadow of the object whose height is required are marked on the ground at the same time. After a lapse of some time, the tips are again marked, *D* and *D'*. *CD* and *C'D'* are measured. Then $XY : AB :: XC' : AC :: C'D' : CD$; therefore $XY = (AB \cdot C'D')/CD$.

Remarks. This is a simple and interesting solution depending on the proportionality of similar triangles set up by the parallel light rays from the sun. A lapse of a few hours should be allowed between the two observations, so that *CD* and *C'D'* may not be too small compared with *AB* and *XY*. The solution does not appear in the Renaissance geometries; it is too slow for practical purposes but interesting for a geometry class.

Reference. Ibn-Jūnus: see Schmidt (442), p. 236.

METHOD 7

A convenient distance *AB* is measured on horizontal ground (Figure 223). At *A* the angles *XAY* and *BAX* are measured. At *B* angle *XBA* is measured. Side *AX* is calculated from triangle *ABX*, and then *XY* is calculated from triangle *AXY*.

Remarks. This method offers a good opportunity for practice with a simple transit and tape. Both horizontal and vertical angles have to be measured and the required distances computed by trigonometric formulas. If angle *XBY* is also measured, a check computation may be used.

References. Hedraeus (243), Pr. 11. Cagnoli (88), p. 161.

METHOD 8

In case the object whose height is required is elevated above the plane of observation, three positions of observation are usually indicated, although only two are necessary. From observations at positions A and A' (Figure 224) the height ZX is calculated according to Method 3. Similarly from observations at A' and A'' the height ZY is calculated. Then the required height $XY = ZY - ZX$.

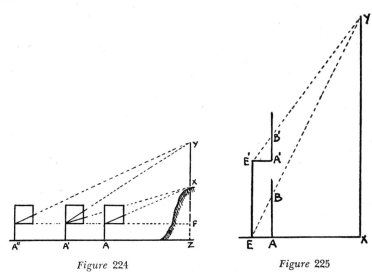

| Figure 224 | Figure 225 |

Remarks. Various instruments are used in descriptions of this method. The only advantage to be seen in the use of the third position of observation is that it gives a more convenient angle of elevation to the point Y, if Y is much higher than X.

References. Hulsius (270), p. 30. Belli (36), p. 85. Bartoli (31), p. 44. Hedraeus (243), p. 7. Clavius (114), p. 60. Metius (336), p. 136.

CASE B. When the positions of observation are taken vertically over each other.

METHOD

With a simple combination of horizontal and vertical staffs two observations are taken as indicated in Figure 225. Let L represent the inaccessible distance from E to X and H the known vertical distance EE'.

Then

$$\frac{AB}{AE} = \frac{XY}{L}, \qquad \text{or} \qquad L = \frac{XY \cdot AE}{AB},$$

and

$$\frac{A'B'}{A'E'} = \frac{XY - H}{L}, \qquad \text{or} \qquad L = \frac{A'E'\,(XY - H)}{A'B'};$$

therefore

$$\frac{A'E'\,(XY - H)}{A'B'} = \frac{XY \cdot AE}{AB}.$$

But

$$A'E' = AE;$$

therefore

$$\frac{XY - H}{A'B'} = \frac{XY}{AB};$$

therefore

$$XY = \frac{AB \cdot H}{AB - A'B'}.$$

Remarks. This method is equivalent to Case A, Method 1. The solution has been simplified by keeping the horizontal staff of constant length. The earliest account of this method is given by Bhāskara in the *Siddhānta-Śiromaṇī*. It occurs frequently in the Renaissance texts, where various instruments are used for the observations.

References. Clavius (114), Pr. 15. Hulsius (270), p. 26. Belli (36), p. 80. Bartoli (31), p. 36v. Mainardi (323), p. 360.

SECTION V

Problem. To determine depth.

METHOD 1

Let the required depth be XY (Figure 227). The observer stands at a point such as A, so that by sighting from E he sees the

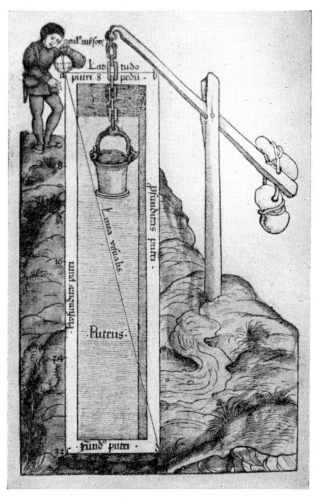

Figure 226. DETERMINATION OF DEPTH, USING ASTROLABE. *From*
Stöffler's Elucidatio Fabrica Ususque Astrolabii.

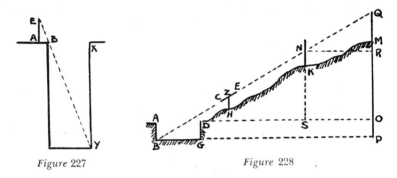

Figure 227   *Figure 228*

point Y, just over the edge B. XB, AB, and AE are measured. Then $XY = (XB \cdot AE)/AB$.

Remarks. The earliest treatment of this problem, as outlined above, is to be found in Euclid (*Optics*, 21). He speaks in terms of no particular instrument, merely giving the geometric properties involved. This problem of depth, usually put in the form of finding the depth of a well, is to be found in nearly all the old works on practical geometry. The methods of solution with different instruments vary very little from the fundamental form laid down by Euclid. The most complete general solution was given by Heron (see Method 2).

METHOD 2

Heron's complete solution is as follows (see Figure 228):[20]

Problem: "Given a ditch, to determine the depth, that is to say, to measure the length of the perpendicular drawn from a point situated at the bottom of the ditch to our horizontal plane, or to any other plane parallel to the horizontal."

Solution: "Let $ABGD$ be the given ditch, and B the point on the bottom. Let the dioptra be set up at D or otherwise at H; let HZ be the pedestal of the instrument, and EC the alidade, which we will incline in such a manner as to sight the point B along it. Imagine that the surface of the ground follows the line $DHKM$ and that the horizontal plane on which we are situated is represented by the straight line $ADSO$. Place vertically on the ground two rods KN, MQ, in line with the alidade CE and suppose that

[20] Heron, *op. cit.*, Ch. 14.

the line of sight CE meets KN at N and MQ at Q. It is necessary to determine the length of the perpendicular drawn from point B to our horizontal plane, that is to the line ADO; that is the line which we have represented by BA. Imagine the horizontal plane which passes through B; then let the rod QM be prolonged to P and the rod NK prolonged to S: finally let the line NR be drawn parallel to DO through N. From this it follows that NR is the distance between the points K and M, measured on the horizontal projection, a distance which can be determined as also KS and MO. As for the length QR, it is the difference between the lengths QRO and NS; and it is equally possible to determine it, as we have done in (XII) where we have shown how to draw a perpendicular to any point by means of two rods. Suppose that we have found, for example, that NR is four times RQ, it follows that BP is similarly four times QP. But it is possible to determine BP that is to say AO; because this distance is also a horizontal projection. Therefore it is equally possible to obtain QP which is the quarter of BP. Besides we know the length of QO, therefore, we will have OP, that is to say the perpendicular AB."

Remarks. For Heron's reference to Chapter XII see Section II, Case D.

METHOD 3

The observer stands on the edge of the well and places a rod under his foot in the direction from X to C (Figure 229). He moves the rod back and forth until he sights the point D, at the foot of the opposite wall, over the end point A. XC and XA are measured. EX is the height of the observer's eye, or if a vertical staff is used, as described in many books, EX is the height of the staff. From the similar right triangles,

$$EY = \frac{EX \cdot YD}{XA}$$

$$= \frac{EX \cdot XC}{XA};$$

therefore

$$XY = EY - EX.$$

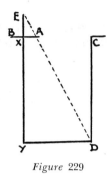

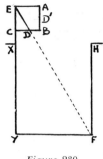

Figure 229   *Figure* 230

Remarks. Sometimes the horizontal rod is placed all the way across the mouth of the well, and the point of intersection of the line of sight *ED* is noted. Ramus substitutes a Jacob's staff for the rod combination.

References. Gerbert (200), Chs. 29, 34. Hugo Physicus (269), p. 213. Mainardi (323), p. 365. Ramus (410), p. 68. De Suberville (486), p. 117. Bullet (83), p. 56. Bourdin (64), p. 34.

METHOD 4

The observer stands on the edge of the well, brings the geometric square to eye level, and revolves the alidade until the line of sight hits *F* (Figure 230). If the alidade rests at *D* on the umbra versa,

$$EY : YF :: EC : CD;$$

therefore

$$EY = \frac{12}{m} \cdot YF$$

$$XY = \frac{12}{m} \cdot XH - XE.$$

If the alidade rests at *B*:

$$XY = XH - XE.$$

Suppose the alidade falls on *D′* on the umbra recta, then

$$EY : YF :: AD' : EA$$

$$EY = \frac{m}{12} \cdot XH$$

$$XY = \frac{m}{12} \cdot XH - XE.$$

Remarks. The geometric square, astrolabe, and quadrant were the most frequently used instruments in the solution of this problem, the methods of solution being similar. See Figure 226.

References. Pacioli (386), Pr. 18. Belli (36), p. 105. Hulsius (270), p. 39. Münster (355), p. 53. Bartoli (31), pp. 44, 45, 46. Gerbert (200), Ch. 20. Bourdin (64), p. 34. De Rojas (431), p. 181. Danti (130), p. 134. Digges (142), Ch. 17. Bettini (41), p. 78. Finaeus (174), p. 22v. Cardan (94), fol. 612.

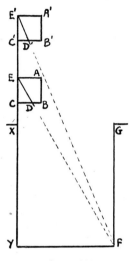

Figure 231

METHOD 5

In case the width of a chasm or canyon could not be measured directly and its depth was required, recourse was had to the two-position method. This solution is essentially the same as that given in Section IV, Method 3. Suppose two sights can be taken, as in Figure 231, one perpendicularly above the other; then from the first observation we have:

$$EY = \frac{12}{m} FY \qquad (1)$$

where the side of the square is 12 units and $CD = m$ units. Similarly, from the second observation:

$$E'Y = \frac{12}{m'} FY. \qquad (2)$$

Figure 232. DETERMINATION OF INACCESSIBLE DISTANCE. *From* Zubler's Novum Instrumentum Geometricum.

Subtracting (1) from (2),

$$EE' = \left(\frac{12}{m'} - \frac{12}{m}\right) FY;$$

therefore

$$FY = \frac{EE'}{\dfrac{12}{m'} - \dfrac{12}{m}}.$$

Similar relations may be worked out for the other cases, as in Section IV, Method 3.

Remarks. Such a method might be used to find the width of a playground or park or the distance of any object on the same horizontal plane from a school building, by taking observations from a pair of windows on different floors. The distance between the points of observation could be easily measured by means of a tape or cord.

References. Belli (36), p. 110. Clavius (114), p. 60. Mainardi (323), p. 360.

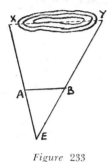

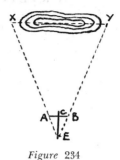

Figure 233   Figure 234

SECTION VI

Problem. To find the horizontal distance between two points, each inaccessible from the other but both accessible from a third point.

METHOD 1

Let XY (Figure 233) be the required distance and EX and EY measurable directly. The distances from E to X and Y are measured. Convenient distances EA and EB are marked off so that $EA/EX = EB/EY$. Line AB is measured directly. Then $XY/AB = EX/EA$, and $XY = (EX \cdot AB)/EA$.

Remarks. This offers a good exercise in taping and alignment. The earliest account of it comes from Euclid (*Optics*, 22), but he makes no mention of instruments. See Method 2 in Section VII for the more general case of this solution as given by Heron.

References. Schwenter (455), p. 397. Kröger (299), p. 68.

METHOD 2

A sight is taken with the Jacob's staff from a convenient position such as E (Figure 234), so that the crosspiece covers the required length. XE is measured directly. Then

$$\frac{XY}{XE} = \frac{AB}{AE} = \frac{AB}{\sqrt{AC^2 + CE^2}};$$

therefore

$$XY = \frac{AB \cdot XE}{\sqrt{AC^2 + CE^2}}.$$

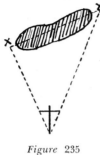

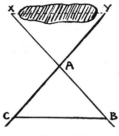

Figure 235   Figure 236

Remarks. Care must be taken that the crosspiece is held as parallel as possible to the required distance, for otherwise the proportion expressed above does not hold. The incorrect use of the cross-staff in this exercise is to be found in a few books, *e.g.*, Münster (355), fol. 48 (Figure 235). Because of the difficulty of keeping the instrument in a correct position, this method is unreliable.[21]

References. Apian (14), p. 60. Reisch (424), Bk. 6. Finaeus (174), Ch. 6. Köbel (297), p. 22. Digges (141), p. 24. Ryff (433), p. 125. Gunter (219), Bk. 1, Pr. 7.

METHOD 3

From a convenient point A the distances AX and AY are measured directly. AX is then prolonged, and AB is measured equal to AX; similarly AC is made equal to AY on its prolongation. Then CB is measured directly, and $CB = XY$. (Figure 236.)

Remarks. AB and AC may also be marked off in lengths proportional to AX and AY respectively. This is the method outlined in the earliest record (Heron (518), Ch. 10) and is probably more practicable than the method outlined above under ordinary conditions, since less territory is required for its accomplishment.

References. Heron (518), Ch. 10. Kröger (299), p. 26.

METHOD 4

At X lay off XC making an angle of 120° with AX, the prolongation of YX (Figure 237). Locate by trial point D on XC such that

---

[21] See E. M. Horsburgh, "The Cross-staff and Its Use in Navigation," *Scottish Geographical Magazine*, 1930, pp. 92-100.

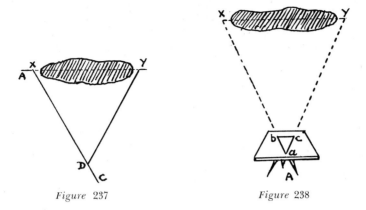

Figure 237   Figure 238

a line from D making an angle of 60° with XC passes through Y. In the equilateral triangle thus formed $XY = XD$, which can be measured directly.

Remarks. This method may be found in many modern geometries. For school purposes the angles may be measured by any simple angle-measuring instrument, such as a simplified form of the astrolabe set up horizontally. Because of the difficulty of locating point D, this method is not of much practical value. If another angle of 120° were set out at Y, point D could be located more conveniently.

METHOD 5

The plane table is set up over a convenient point A (Figure 238). Above A on the paper, point a is marked and a pin inserted. With the edge of the alidade against the pin a sight is taken on point X, and line ab is drawn on the paper. A similar sighting on Y gives line ac. AX and AY are then taped, and these distances are scaled off on ab and ac respectively. By scaling the line bc, the inaccessible distance XY is known.

Remarks. This offers a very simple graphical solution, a type which became very popular after the development of the plane table. As with all graphical solutions, its accuracy depends to a great extent on the scale used.

References. Zubler (555), Ch. 1. Rathborne (412), Bk. 3, Ch. 3. Leybourn (316), Ch. 4. Bramer (73), Ch. 1. Sturm (483), Pr. 13. Bourdin (64), p. 35.

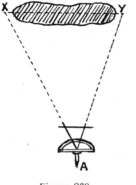

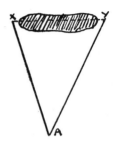

Figure 239   Figure 240

METHOD 6

Erect at a convenient point A (Figure 239) an instrument of the same type as the novum instrumentum geometricum of Zubler (Figure 232). Set one arm along the direction AX and the other along AY. Measure AX and AY. Then lay the detached ruler across the two arms, cutting off distances proportional to the lengths of AX and AY. The distance XY can then be read to scale on the detached ruler.

Remarks. This method is even simpler than the plane-table method and is admirably suited for beginners.

References. Zubler (555), Ch. 6. Arduser (16), p. 218. Leybourn (316), Ch. 4. Bramer (73), Ch. 1.

METHOD 7

In modern trigonometry texts the problem is usually solved as follows: From the convenient point A the lengths AX and AY are measured and angle XAY is determined. (Figure 240.) From these data XY is found by using the law of tangents formula and the law of sines.

Remarks. The calculations involved in this solution are much more complicated than in the preceding methods. As an exercise in surveying the solution is no more accurate or convenient than Methods 3 and 4; nevertheless it gets far more recognition, possibly because our textbook writers want to give some practice in the law of tangents.

Figure 241. DOUBLE-POSITION METHOD WITH JACOB'S STAFF FOR DETERMINING INACCESSIBLE DISTANCE. *From W. Ryff's* Der furnembsten . . . Kunst.

SECTION VII

Problem. To find the horizontal distance between two points, each inaccessible from the other and from any third point.

METHOD 1

The earliest description is given by Heron (see Figure 242):[22] "Let X and Y be the two given points. I set up the dioptra in the place where I am, for example at G, and I direct the alidade in such a way as to sight the point Y on its prolongment. The line of sight will be the straight line GY. I lay out, with the dioptra, the straight line GD perpendicular to GY and I move the instrument to a point E on the straight line GD, whence it is possible to sight the point X on EX perpendicular to GD: YG will be parallel to XE. I determine the distance from Y to G [Section III, Case A, Method 1] and in the same way that from E to X. If GY is equal to XE, XY will equal GE and I can measure this last line since it is situated near me. But suppose that XE is greater than YG; for example by 20 cubits, I take starting from E on EX which is on

[22] Heron, *op. cit.,* Ch. 10.

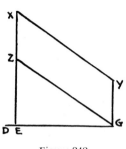

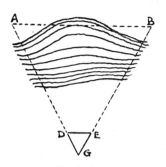

Figure 242   Figure 243

my side *EZ* equal to 20 cubits: *ZX* will be equal to *GY*, and moreover, it is parallel to it, consequently also *XY* will be equal and
parallel to it. Since this latter can be measured, it is clear that
we know at the same time the position of *XY*, since we have found
a line which is parallel to it."

Remarks. This historically interesting method of Heron for
what is considered the most difficult of the problems in the measurement of distances is sufficiently simple for school purposes. It
does not seem to appear in the Middle Ages and Renaissance texts.

Reference. Heron of Byzantium: see Vincent (518), p. 363.

METHOD 2

a. The earliest description is given by Heron (see Figure 243):[23]
"I place the dioptra where I wish, for example at G. By means
of it, I set out two lines *GA* and *GB,* and I measure them (Ch. 8).
I make *GD* equal to a certain portion of *GA*, for example, the
tenth part, and *GE* equal to a similar portion of *GB*. If *DE* is
joined this straight line will also be the tenth part of *AB* and parallel to it. But I can measure *DE* which is near me; I have therefore also the measure and the position of *AB*."

Remarks. The reference to Chapter 8 is to a method of determining the length of a line when one end is accessible (see
Section III, Case A, Method 1). Heron uses the dioptra in the
exercise only to establish a straight line.

References. Hyginus: see Blume, Lachmann, and Rudorff (54), p. 193.
Heron of Byzantium: see Vincent (518), p. 357.

[23] *Ibid.*

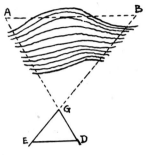

Figure 244

b. The earliest description is given by Heron (see Figure 244):[24]

"Having placed the dioptra at *G,* I lay out in a straight line with *GA,* a certain portion *GD* of that line; and in the same way, in line with *GB* a corresponding portion *GE* of *GB.* Then *DE* will be in the same proportion to *AB* at the same time that it will be parallel to it. But it is possible to measure *DE:* the position and size of *AB* are therefore known."

Remarks. Heron fails to mention here that *GA* and *GB* must also be measured indirectly by the method referred to in *a,* on p. 334.

Reference. Heron of Byzantium: see Vincent (518), p. 359.

METHOD 3

In this double-position method of determining horizontal distance when the two points are inaccessible from each other and from any third point, the Jacob's staff is used for sighting. Two observations are made on the inaccessible distance *XY* from convenient points such as *E* and *E'* (Figure 246). The precautions mentioned in Section VI, Method 2 should be observed. Unless the crosspiece is held in the proper position parallel to the required distance, the proportions cited will not hold. The distance between the two stations is measured. This gives immediately the distance *XY* if for the second observation the cross-staff is moved a distance equal to its own length along the main staff from the position it occupied at the first observation.

[24] *Ibid.*

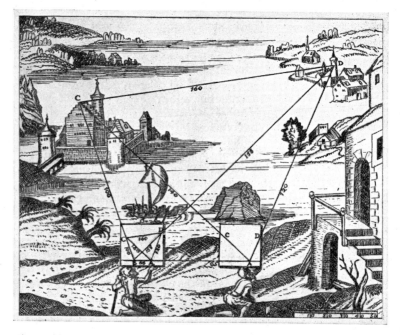

Figure 245. METHOD OF INTERSECTIONS, USING PLANE TABLE.
From Zubler's Fabrica et Usus Instrumenti Chorographici.

This method allows only one position of observation to be chosen at will.

Proof that $EE' = XY$ under the conditions mentioned above is as follows:

Since triangle ADE is similar to $EE'X$, and triangle $A'E'B'$ is similar to $XE'Y$,

$$\frac{XY}{A'B'} = \frac{E'X}{E'A'} = \frac{E'X}{AD} = \frac{EE'}{DE};$$

therefore

$$XY = \frac{EE' \cdot A'B'}{DE}.$$

But

$$DE = A'B';$$

therefore

$$XY = EE'.$$

Hence if $AB = CD$, that is, if a division on the main staff is equal

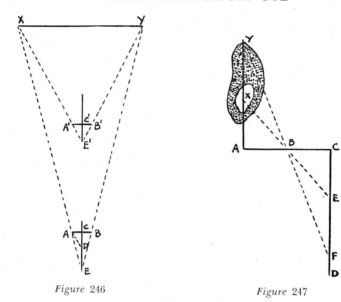

Figure 246   Figure 247

to the length of the crosspiece, then XY = Distance between points of observation.

Remarks. Jacob's staffs graduated as indicated above were in common use among surveyors chiefly because of the ease with which such staffs could be used in solving the above problem. This is the commonest solution to the problem in the Renaissance books. The setting of the cross-staff for the first observation depends on the position chosen by the observer; whereas the position of the observer for the second observation depends on the changed setting of the cross-staff. See Figure 241.

References. Ramus (410), p. 72. Finaeus (174), p. 8. Bettini (41), pp. 69-74. Bartoli (31), p. 15. Belli (36), p. 53. Gunter (219), Bk. 1, Pr. 8. Ryff (434), Bk. 3, Ch. 8. Digges (141), p. 26. Münster (355), pp. 48-51. Ryff (433), p. 130.

METHOD 4

Establish a point A on the prolongation of XY (Figure 247). Stake out line AC of convenient length perpendicular to AY. Set up a range pole at its mid-point B. Stake out CD perpendicular to AC. Find point E, the intersection of XB prolonged, with CD. Similarly find F, the intersection of YB prolonged, with CD. Measure EF, which equals XY. If inconvenient to make $BC = AB$, BC

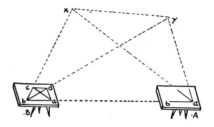

Figure 248

may be marked off as any convenient fractional part of *AB;* then *EF* will be an equal fractional part of *XY*.

Remarks. This method offers interesting exercises in the staking out of lines and finding intersections as given in Section I, Problems 1 and 3. The method is not in the Renaissance books.

Reference. Kröger (299), p. 27.

METHOD 5

Two convenient points *A* and *B* are chosen and the distance between them is measured (Figure 248). A plane table is set up at *A* and a point on the paper vertically above *A* is marked *a*. A sight is taken on *B* and the line *ab* drawn to suitable scale. Sights are then taken on *X* and *Y* and the corresponding lines drawn on the paper. The instrument is then set up at *B* and oriented by sighting back on *A* with the alidade along the line *ba*. Sights are again taken on *X* and *Y* and the corresponding lines drawn on the paper. The intersection *c* of the two rays drawn toward *X* from *a* and *b* determine the relative position of *X* on the scale drawing. Similarly *d* represents the position of *Y*. The distance *cd,* measured to scale, is equal to the required distance *XY*.

Remarks. By making similar observations with a transit or other horizontal angle-measuring instrument, the distance *XY* may be calculated. *BX* of the triangle *ABX* and *BY* of the triangle *ABY* are calculated by using the sine formula. Then in triangle *BXY*, *XY* is calculated by the cosine formula. This is the usual modern method of solving the problem.

References. Plane table: Belli (36), p. 46. Sturm (483), Fig. 14. Bourdin (64), p. 36. Angle-measuring instrument: Hedraeus (243), Pr. 19. Day (135), Pr. 7. Henrion (251), p. 116.

SCALE DRAWING, MAPPING, AREAS

Scale Drawing

Scale drawing should form a very important part in the practical geometry carried on in schools. From their experience with pictures and maps young students form intuitive ideas on the advantages of scales. These intuitive ideas offer a good basis on which to build some of the fundamental properties of similarity. The proportionality between the corresponding linear dimensions of an object and its picture can be easily established by experiment. After a series of such experiments, the fundamental property of the proportionality of corresponding parts between an object and its picture is identified as the scale of the picture. The necessity for scales, either for enlarging or for diminishing, can readily be made clear by a few appropriate examples. Factors that govern the choice of scale should be explained; in particular for map-drawing it will depend on the relative sizes of the district to be mapped and the paper on which the map is to be drawn. From a variety of maps the students should be shown how scales vary, how to find the scale, and how to use the scale. In the solution of many of the previous exercises scale drawings may be employed. In such solutions the student should be led to pick out a suitable scale, make a drawing of it, then draw the geometric figure to this scale, and finally determine the value of the answer from the scale. With beginners simple line scales, such as Figure 250, are sufficient. The method of subdivision of the first unit is easily made acceptable to students without their full comprehension of the underlying geometry. More advanced students should be introduced to the construction and use of the diagonal scale (for its historical connections with the Jacob's staff, Tycho Brahe, etc., see pp. 178 ff.) and the straight line vernier (for its historical development see pp. 175 ff). Instruction might also be advantageously given in the use and geometric principles of the proportional compasses and various mechanical devices for enlarging or reducing to scale, such as the pantograph.

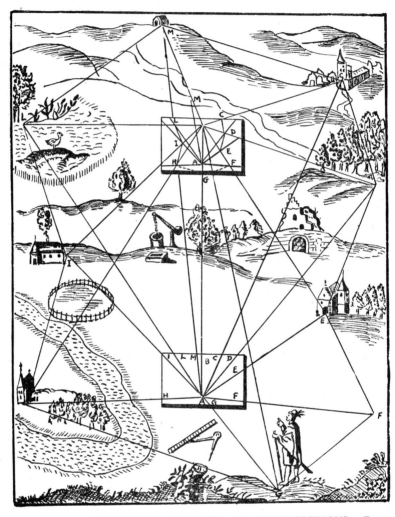

Figure 249. PLANE-TABLE MAPPING BY INTERSECTIONS. *From*
Schott's Pantometrum Kircherianum.

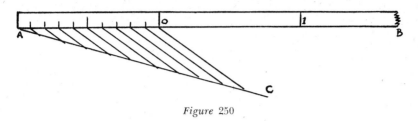

Figure 250

Problem 1. To construct a simple scale (Figure 250).

METHOD

Draw line *AB* 6 in. long and divide it into inches by means of a ruler. From *A* draw *AC,* making any angle with *AB* (about 30° or 40° is most suitable). Step off on *AC,* beginning from point *A,* any convenient distance 10 times. Join the last point with *O* and through the other division points draw parallels to this line. These parallels divide the first main division into ten equal parts, each of which represents one-tenth of a main division of the scale.

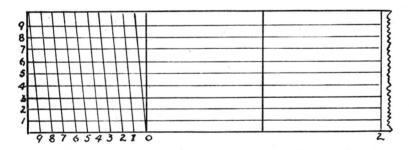

Figure 251

Problem 2. To construct a diagonal scale to read to 1/100 of the main division (Figure 251).

METHOD

Draw a series of 11 horizontal parallels equally spaced. Mark off the main divisions and the primary subdivisions in the first unit of the required scale on the upper and lower parallels. Join the corresponding main division points by perpendicular lines; then join the subdivision points as follows: 0-1, 1-2, 2-3, etc. The uses, advantages, and geometric principles should be explained.

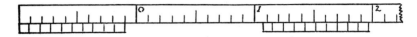

Figure 252

Problem 3. To construct a vernier scale (Figure 252).

METHOD

Along one edge of a piece of white cardboard construct a simple scale with all primary units subdivided into 10 equal parts. On another piece of cardboard draw a line equal in length to 9 of these subdivisions and subdivide this again into 10 equal parts. Each division on this scale is 1/10 of a primary subdivision shorter than a primary subdivision. Therefore when the zero of the secondary scale coincides with the zero of the main scale, the first division of the secondary scale is 1/100 of the main unit shorter than the first primary subdivision of the main scale. This value is known as the least count of the vernier. Similarly the length of the first two subdivisions of the secondary scale is 2/100 of a main unit shorter than the length of the first two primary subdivisions of the main scale, and so on. Now if the secondary scale or vernier is moved until its fourth division coincides with the fourth primary subdivision of the main scale, then the initial point of the vernier has moved 4/100 of a main division. In general the division of the vernier which coincides with a division mark on the main scale gives the reading of the second decimal place on such a scale.

Remarks. With the type of instruments proposed for use in school surveying as outlined here, there is no need to use a vernier. However, some explanation of its construction and history and practice in reading from a large model are to be recommended for senior students. The following rule for finding the least count of a vernier may easily be verified: divide the smallest subdivision of the main scale by the number of divisions into which the main vernier division is divided. Work on scale drawing should not be given *in toto* at some particular part of the course; rather, it should be developed gradually as the need for such knowledge arises. For information on the history of early map-making see Raisz (409) and Reeves (417).

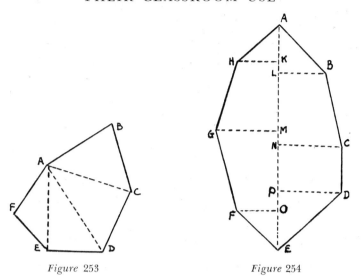

Figure 253   Figure 254

Mapping

Problem 4. To map an area bounded by straight sides.

METHOD 1

The area is divided into a number of triangles by lining out all the diagonals from one corner, such as *A* in Figure 253. The lengths of all sides are then measured directly. After selection of a suitable scale, the map is developed by constructing triangles in the same order as those in the field, with sides proportional to the actual measurements. As a check on the accuracy of the work, some other line, such as *CE,* may be measured in the field and then scaled off on the map.

Remarks. This simple method of determining an outline should help to impress on students the importance of linear measurement, since by this means alone sufficient data can be gathered to determine completely any geometrical polygon.

References. Leybourn (316), Chs. 13 ff. Rathborne (412), Bk. 3. Bourdin (64), p. 48.

METHOD 2

One diagonal such as *AE* (Figure 254) is staked out; then the perpendicular distance from each apex to the diagonal and the

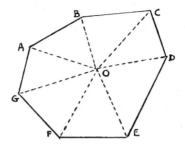

Figure 255

distance to the foot of the perpendicular from one end of the diagonal are determined. These measurements may be made by tape alone or in coordination with an instrument for setting out right angles. In Figure 254 the required measurements are *BL, CN, DP, FO, GM, HK, AK, AL, AM, AN, AO, AP.* To produce the required map *AE* is drawn to suitable scale and points *K, L, M, N, O, P,* are marked on it. Perpendiculars are erected at these points and the measured lengths of the perpendiculars scaled off. The work may be checked as in the preceding method.

References. Digges (142), Chs. 23-25. Hulsius (270), p. 53. Pomodoro (400), Pl. 24.

METHOD 3

A compass is set up within the field at a convenient point from which all corners are visible. The bearings of all the radial lines are determined from the compass and their horizontal distances measured by tape. To reproduce these data on a map two methods may be employed.

a. A point is fixed on the paper to represent *O,* the position of the compass. Through *O* an assumed meridian line is drawn, and the bearings of the radial lines are then marked off relative to this meridian by means of a protractor. The lengths of the radial lines are set off to scale; by joining the end points the figure is completed. (Figure 255.)

b. One radial line, such as *OA,* is set out to scale. Then the angle *AOB,* determined from the bearings of *OA* and *OB,* is marked off by means of a protractor from *OA,* and *OB* is marked

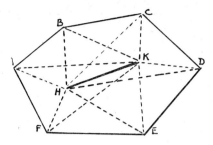

Figure 256

off to scale. The other apexes are found similarly. As a check, use may be made of the fact that the sum of the angles at *O* should be 360°; the check given in Method 1 may also be used.

Remarks. Any simple angle-measuring instrument may be substituted for the compass, and the size of the angles between adjacent radial lines may be measured directly. To orient any compass survey with the true N-S, the angle of declination must be known. This can be determined by setting out a N-S line by the Indian circles method and then determining the bearing of this line with the magnetic meridian.

References. De Rojas (431), p. 182. Leybourn (316), Bk. 4, Ch. 13. Pomodoro (400), Pl. 24. Metius (336), p. 152. Heron (518), Ch. 26.

METHOD 4

This is the method of triangulation or of intersections. Two points *H* and *K* (Figure 256) are chosen from which all the corners within a field are visible. The length of the line *HK* is carefully measured. Setting the compass over *H*, the bearings of *HK* and of all radial lines from *H* are noted; the same observations are made from *K*. From the bearings the angles between the radial lines and *HK* are calculated. The line *HK* is set down to scale on paper, and the radial lines from *H* and *K* are marked out by means of a protractor. The intersection of a pair of radial lines from *H* and *K* fixes the position of each corner. The checks given in the preceding method may be applied here also.

Remarks. This is a fast method, since it employs only one linear measurement, but not so exact as the preceding unless the angles can be measured and set down on paper with great accuracy; and

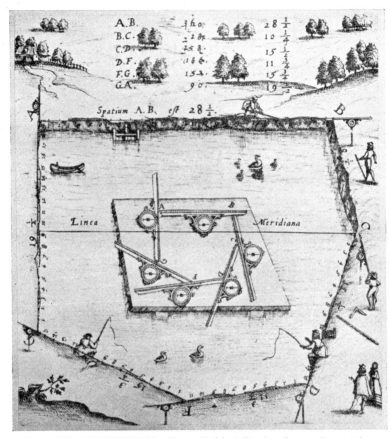

Figure 257. TRAVERSING. *From Hulsius'* De Quadrante Geometrico.

this is not possible with simple instruments. It is the basic process of all large-scale map-drawing and the most practical method
when the required points are inaccessible. Besides the use of the
compass as described above, the more common method in later
times was to employ some form of triangulation instrument. In
case the plane table is used, the map is made in the field as the observations are being taken. (See Figure 249.) See p. 158 and corresponding Appendix quotations on the earliest exposition of the
triangulation method by Gemma Frisius. For a brief account of
the subsequent large-scale triangulation projects of the seventeenth
and eighteenth centuries undertaken by Snellius, Picard, Roy, the
Cassinis, and others, see Kirby and Laurson (293).

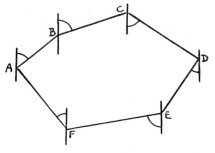

Figure 258

METHOD 5

This method employs the compass traverse. In this method the length and bearing of each side of the field have to be determined. The usual direction of traversing is clockwise. The compass is set up over each corner, such as A, and the forward bearing of the side, AB, determined (Figure 258). The length of the side, AB, is then taped, and the same process is repeated at the other corners. In mapping the data an arbitrary direction is taken to represent the magnetic meridian, and the angles are set out with reference to this meridian, the lengths of the sides being measured to scale. As a check on the forward bearings the back bearings may also be recorded. In all work with the compass it is important that tapes and pins be kept at a distance from the instrument when readings are being taken. The area over which this work is to be done should be free from local attraction, which would bring about complications better avoided in elementary work.

Remarks. The method of traversing is the common one employed over small areas since 1724, when a method of calculating areas from the observations of this method was evolved (see p. 144). All the early farm surveys of this country were traverse surveys by compass. In case it was impossible to work along the exact boundaries, lines parallel to these were run either outside or inside. To set out these parallels the surveyor's cross was employed, and this was the main reason for the survival of this right-angle instrument into modern times. If a simple angle-measuring instrument is employed in this method, the interior angle at each corner is determined and the directions of the sides on the map are set out

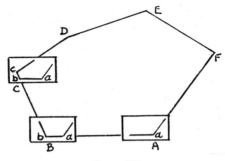

Figure 259

accordingly. The modern method of traversing by the determination of azimuth angles is too difficult for high school work.

References. Hulsius (270), p. 58; (271), p. 52. Digges (142), p. 59.

METHOD 6

This is the plane-table traverse (Figure 259). Set up the table over corner *A* and and mark point *a* vertically above on the paper to represent *A*. Care must be taken in choosing the position of *a* on the paper to allow sufficient space so that all sides of the figure can be conveniently drawn on the paper. With the edge of the alidade on *a*, sight on point *B* and draw the line *ab* to represent the direction of *AB*. Measure *AB* and set off this distance to scale. When the instrument is moved to *B*, a backsight is taken on *A* in order to orient the instrument. Then a forward sight is taken on *C* and the same process repeated as at *A*. This method is repeated at each corner. When a sight is taken from the last corner *F* toward *A*, it should pass through the original point fixed on the paper.

Remarks. This method of using the plane table is not very commonly employed, Method 4 being likely to produce more accurate results.

References. Hulsius (270), p. 60. Rathborne (412), Bk. 3, Ch. 3. Zubler (555), Ch. 1. Leybourn (316), Ch. 4.

Calculation of Areas

When the area of a triangle is to be calculated by application of the formula $A = 1/2\ bh$, the perpendicular distance from an apex of the triangle to the opposite side must be determined. This may be done by Section I, Problem 7, Method *a;* or, in case the perpendicular is too long to use cord or tape, Method *b* may be employed. In the case of a short perpendicular, its length can be determined immediately by the tape, making use of the fact that the perpendicular is the shortest distance from a point to a line. Altitudes of trapezoids are found by the same methods.

Remarks. Our earliest records testify to the fact that the Babylonians and Egyptians used the square as the unit of area. The commonest method employed in finding the area of a triangle was to use the formula $A = 1/2\ bh$. In finding the area of all other rectilinear figures, the method employed up to 1724 (see Chapter IV, note 103) was to break them up into squares, rectangles, triangles, and trapezoids, calculate the areas of the individual figures, and add up the areas. This method was first completely expounded by Heron.

The preliminary work for finding areas is similar to that described in the preceding methods of traversing. Heron's method of finding the area of a triangle when the length of the three sides is known is included here, as it may be of interest in a trigonometry class where the formula is derived by other methods. His general method for finding irregular areas is still in common use and is an exercise suitable for advanced students.

References. Bartoli (31), pp. 63-71. Metius (336), pp. 165-172. Finaeus (174), Bk. 2. Hulsius (271), Ch. 16. Digges (142), Chs. 16-21.

Problem 5. To find the area of a horizontal plot bounded by irregular sides.

METHOD

The earliest account is that of Heron. His original description follows (see Figure 260):[25]

"Let the given field have for contour the irregular line *ABGD-EZHC.* . . . Since we have learned how to lay out, by means of the dioptra conveniently placed, a perpendicular to any given line, I take a point *B* on the boundary line of the field, and I lay out at random with the dioptra the straight line *BH,* also *BG* perpen-

[25] *Ibid.,* Ch. 23.

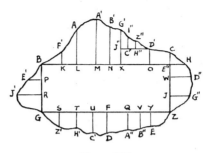

Figure 260

dicular to *BH;* then another perpendicular *GZ* and similarly to *GZ* the perpendicular *ZC.* Then I take on the lines thus laid out, a series of points such as *K, L, M, N, X, O* on *BH; P, R,* on *BG; S, T, U, F, Q, V, Y,* on *GZ;* finally *J, W,* on *ZC.* Then, through the points thus chosen I lay out, from the lines on which they lie, the perpendiculars *KF', LA, MA', NB', XG', OD', PE', RJ', SZ', TH', UC, FD, QA", VB", YE, JG", WD",* and that in such a manner that the portions of the contour of the figure which will be contained between the extremities of the perpendiculars laid out first [from the sides of the inscribed parallelogram] may be taken approximately for parts of straight lines; and when that is done the field can be measured. First, the parallelogram *BGZE"* is rectangular; therefore, by measuring its sides with a chain or a well-tested rope, that is to say, one which cannot elongate [by the effect of pull] nor contract, we have the area of this parallelogram. Then, in the same way, we measure the triangles, rectangles and trapezoids outside the parallelogram, which will be easy since we know all the sides: the triangles are *BKF', BPE', GRJ', GSZ', ZYE, ZJG", CHE";* there remain but trapezoids. The triangles are measured by multiplying one side by the other of the right angle and taking half the result; as for the trapezoids, it is by multiplying the semi-sum of the parallel sides by the line which is perpendicular to them: for example [*KF'AL*], the half of *KF'* plus *AL* is found and multiplied by *KL;* the others are worked similarly. Therefore, the whole field is measured by the parallelogram in the middle and the exterior triangles and trapezoids.

"But if there happens to be some portion of the contour, contained between the perpendiculars drawn to the sides of the par-

Figure 261. LEVELING WITH QUADRANT. *From W. Ryff's* Der furnembsten . . . Kunst.

allelogram, which cannot be approximated as a straight line, but
rather as an arc of a circle, as for example the arc *G'D'* contained
between the perpendiculars *XG'*, *OD'*, it is necessary then to manage as follows. Lay out from *OD'* the perpendicular *D'J''*; then,
on this line, take the points *C''H''* and lay out the perpendiculars
C''I'', *H''Z''* in such manner that between their extremities there
will be at least approximate straight lines; then we will have to
measure as above a parallelogram *J''XOD'*, a triangle *H''X''D'*, a
trapezoid *G'J''C''I''* and another trapezoid [*I''C''H''Z''*] and we
will obtain thus the size of the space bounded by the curve
G'I''Z''D' and the straight lines *G'X*, *OD'*, *OX*, and as a result the
entire field."

Problem 6. Given the sides of a triangle, to find its area.

METHOD

The earliest description is that of Heron (see Figure 262):[26]
"Let *ABG* be the proposed triangle, and let each of its sides be

[26] *Ibid.*, Ch. 30.

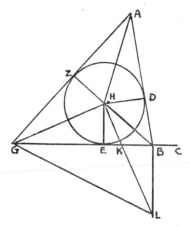

Figure 262

given, required to find its area. Inscribe in the given triangle the circle *DEZ* of which the center is *H*, and draw *HA, HB, HD, HE, HG, HZ.* The product *BG* × *HE* will be the double of the triangle *BHG; AB* × *HD* will be the double of the triangle *AHB;* and finally *AG* × *HZ* will be the double of triangle *AHG.* Therefore the product of the perimeter of the triangle *ABG* by the radius *HE* of the circle *DEZ* is double the triangle *ABG.* Prolong *GB* and make *BC* equal to *AD: GC* will be half of the perimeter. Therefore the product *GC* × *HE* [or the square root of the product *GC²* × *HE²*] will be the area of the triangle. Draw *HKL* perpendicular to *HG,* also *BL* perpendicular to *BG,* and join *GL.* Since each of the two angles *GHL, GBL* is right, the points *G, H, B, L* are all four on the same circumference of a circle: and the angles *GHB, GLB* form a sum equal to two right angles. Therefore, since the lines *HA, HB, HG* divide into two equal parts the three angles formed around the point *H* [by the radii of the inscribed circle], the angle *AHD* is equal to the angle *GLB,* and the triangle *HAD* is similar to the triangle *GLB.* Therefore, *GB* : *BL* :: *AD* : *DH,* or :: *BC* : *HE,* by alternation, *GB* : *BC* :: *BL* : *HE,* or :: *BK* : *KE,* and by composition *GC* : *BC* :: *EB* : *EK.* In such a way that we have again *GC²* : *GC* × *BC* :: *GE* × *EB* : *GE* × *EK* or *HE².* From which it follows that the product *GC* × *BC* × *GE* × *EB* is equal to *GC²* × *HE²,* of which the square root measures the area. Since the four lines which form

Figure 263. LEVELING WITH PLANE TABLE. *From Le Clerc's* Traité de
géométrie.

the product are known: indeed *GC* is half the perimeter; *BC* is
the excess of the semi-perimeter over the side *BG;* *GE* the excess
of the semi-perimeter over the side *AB;* and finally *EB* is the excess over the side *AG*. Therefore, by summing up, the area of the
triangle is given.

"Let us take an example: Let *AB* equal 13, *BG* equal 14, *GA*
equal 15. Adding the sides we have 42, of which the half is 21.
Take away 13, there remains 8; then 14, there remains 7; then 15,
there remains 6. Multiply the four numbers 21 · 8 · 7 · 6; the
result is 7056 of which the square root is 84. Therefore the area
of the triangle is 84."

SECTION IX

LEVELING AND MISCELLANEOUS PROBLEMS

Leveling

Leveling is the process of determining how much one point on
the earth's surface is higher or lower than another point. Depending on the difference in elevation and the nature of the intervening terrain, the process of leveling between two points is carried
on by various methods. For the purpose of carrying on simple

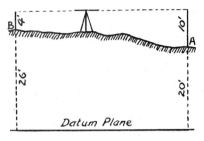

Figure 264

leveling in school many of the simple instruments spoken of in the previous chapters are suitable; there is no need of using an expensive modern bubble tube level. Perhaps the best simple instrument would be a simple open-water-tube level of the type quite common in France in the eighteenth century. The fundamental principle of ordinary leveling is made clear in Figure 264. The height of point *A* above an arbitrarily chosen horizontal plane (the datum plane) is assumed. A level instrument is set up in such a position that sights can be taken on a rod held at *A* and *B*. All the lines of sight from the instrument at any fixed height determine a horizontal plane. Suppose that the sight on *A* reads 10 ft., while that on *B* reads 4 ft. Then the horizontal plane of sight is 10 ft. above *A* or 30 ft. above the datum plane; therefore *B*, which is 4 ft. below the plane of sight, must be 26 ft. above the datum plane, and the difference in elevation between *A* and *B* is 6 ft. $= (26 - 20) = (10 - 4)$.

When the two points whose difference in elevation is required are so far apart that they are not both visible from one position of the instrument, then the result has to be obtained by finding the elevations of intermediate points by repetitions of the same process outlined in the previous paragraph. In order to simplify the process of keeping records the following method may be easily demonstrated by diagram. If a sight on a point of assumed or known elevation is designated as a | sight and a sight on an unknown elevation as a — sight, then the difference in elevation between any two points is equal to the sum of all the + sights less the sum of all the — sights.

Since the instruments proposed for use here are without tele-

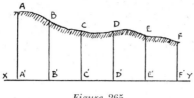

Figure 265

scopes, the rod-reading will have to be done by the rod man, who moves a target up and down the rod, as signaled by the level man, until it is on the line of sight. The distance from the rod to the level should not be more than 30 ft. at any time. With the open-water-tube level (see Figure 7) sighting is done across the top of the water in each tube; as an aid in determining the lines of sight the water may be colored. A plumb-bob level may be used in the same manner as that outlined in Section I, Problem 5. A home-made leveling rod about 7 or 8 ft. in length with target or the common Philadelphia rod may also be used. Figures 261 and 263 show how the quadrant and plane table were used as levels.

Problem 1. To determine a series of elevations and draw a profile map.

METHOD

Assuming the elevation of point *A* (Figure 265), the elevations of *B, C,* etc., are determined as outlined above. The points *A, B, C,* etc. should be on the same straight line, such as the center line of a road. The horizontal distances between points are taped. It may be better to tape off equal distances first to determine the points *A, B, C,* etc. The elevations are calculated as the work proceeds. Practice at downhill leveling should precede uphill leveling. To construct a profile, a line *XY* is drawn to represent the datum plane. On this are laid off to scale the horizontal distances between points *A, B, C,* etc. Perpendiculars are erected at these points and on these perpendiculars are scaled off the calculated elevations. It is necessary to explain why the scale for vertical distances must in general be larger than the scale for horizontal distances and what effect this has on the shape of the profile. Explanation should also be given of some of the uses of profile maps.

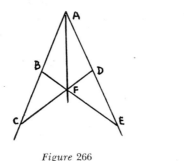

Figure 266

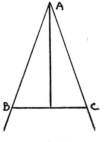

Figure 267

Problem 2. To produce a contour map.

METHOD

This exercise requires time and the coordination of a number of students. The plot for which it is proposed to make a contour should have a suitably undulating surface. This surface must first be divided into a number of squares, 10 or 20 ft. on the side, by setting out two sets of lines at right angles to each other. Wooden stakes should be driven into the ground to mark the corners of the squares. If one set of lines is numbered and the other denoted by letters of the alphabet, the designation of the corners is simplified; for example 1C,4E, etc., meaning the points of intersection of lines 1 and C, and lines 4 and E, etc. The level is set up and the height of one corner assumed. Sights are taken on as many corners as possible and their elevations calculated as in the previous exercise. The instrument is then moved to another location and a sight is first taken on one of the corners whose elevation has already been calculated. Then sights are taken on another set of corners; this process is repeated until all the required elevations have been calculated. In this or the preceding exercise there is no need for the elaborate system of note-keeping practiced by the regular surveyor. The corners are then located on a sheet of square paper and the elevations inserted. Pupils must be instructed on how to draw contours by interpolation between the elevations marked on the corners.[27] A series of contour maps should be on hand, which the teacher can use to explain how information as to topography is derived from contours.

[27] C. N. Shuster, F. L. Bedford, *Field Work in Mathematics* (New York, 1935), p. 128.

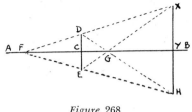

Figure 268

Miscellaneous

Problem 3. To bisect an angle.

METHOD

From the apex *A* (Figure 266) mark off any convenient distances *AB, AC* on one side of the angle. Mark off equal distances on the other side, *AD, AE*. Find *F*, the intersection of *CD* and *BE*. *AF* is the required bisector.

Problem 4. To determine the size of an angle, using a tape.

METHOD

On each side of the angle tape off a distance of 100 ft. from the apex *A* (Figure 267). Measure the distance *BC*. Then, since sin 1/2 $A = 1/2 \ BC/AB$, the value of 1/2 *A* can be determined from a table of sines, and hence the value of *A* is determined.

Problem 5. To establish the perpendicular to a given line from an inaccessible point.

METHOD

In Figure 268 let *X* represent the inaccessible point and *AB* the given line. At any point *C* on *AB* set out the perpendicular *CD* of any convenient length. Prolong it on the other side of *AB* for the same distance, *CE*. Mark on *AB* a point *F* in line with *D* and *X* and also a point *G* in line with *E* and *X*. Find *H*, the intersection of *DG* and *FE* prolonged. Find *Y*, the intersection of *HX* and *AB*. *XY* is the required perpendicular. Care should be taken to choose point *D* so that *DG* and *FE* will not be almost parallel. For good intersections, angle *DXG* should be at least 30°.

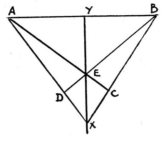

Figure 269

Problem 6. To set out a perpendicular from a given point to a given inaccessible line.

METHOD

In Figure 269 let X be the given point and *AB* the inaccessible line. Establish the directions of *XA* and *XB* and of the perpendiculars from *A* and *B* to *XB* and *XA* respectively. Determine *E*, the intersection of these perpendiculars. Then the line *XEY* is the required perpendicular.

Problem 7. To lay out the direction of the straight line joining two points hidden from each other.

METHOD

The earliest account is given by Heron (see Figure 270):[28]
"Let *A* and *B* be the two given points. Let the dioptra be set up in such a manner that it is possible to sight in two directions perpendicular to each other. Place the instrument at *A* and by means of it, mark on the plane a straight line *AG* of arbitrary length. Then carry the dioptra to G and lay out the line *GD* perpendicular to *AG* of any length. Again carry the dioptra to *D* and lay out *DE* making a right angle with *GD*. In the same way carry the dioptra to *E;* lay off the perpendicular *EZ*, and fix the point Z. Lay out the perpendicular *ZH*, and fix the point *H;* then, on *ZH*, the perpendicular *HC*, and fix the point *C;* then, on *HC*, the perpendicular *CK*, and fix the point *K;* then, on *CK*, the perpendicular *KL;* and continue thus until the point *B* is sighted. Sup-

[28] *Ibid.,* Ch. 7.

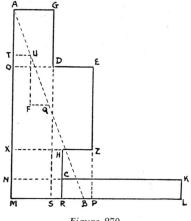

Figure 270

pose such a point has been reached, move the dioptra along the
direction *KL*, until at the point *L* in this direction, the point *B*
can be seen in a direction at right angles. Finally suppose *B* can
be sighted as soon as the dioptra reaches *L*.

"While making these observations, they are to be written on a
paper or on a tablet, that is to say the figure of the outline is drawn
on it, indicating the totals of the broken line and the lengths of
the various parts.

	AG	20	cubits		*GD*	22	cubits
	DE	16	"		*EZ*	30	"
[—]	*ZH*	14	"		*HC*	12	"
	CK	60	"		*KL*	8	"
[—]	*LB*	50	"			72	"
		32	"				

"Imagine that there is drawn, perpendicular to *AG*, the straight
line *AM*, also that the directions *LB*, *KC*, *ZH*, *ED* are prolonged
to the points *M*, *N*, *X*, *O* and the directions *EZ*, *HC*, *GD* to the
points *P*, *R*, *S*. The result will be according to the preceding
values that *AO* equals 22 cubits as *GD*, *OX* equals 30 as *EZ*, *NX*
equals 12 as *HC*, and *MN* equals 8 as *KL*. For this reason the en-

tire line AM equals 72. In the same way, MS equals 20 cubits as AG, PS equals 16 as DE, PR 14 as ZH; and finally the remainder RS equals 2 cubits, and the sum RM equals 22. Then RL equals 60 as CK, of which PR equals 14; therefore the remainder LP equals 46 and the total of LB equals 50; therefore the remainder PB equals 4 cubits and the remainder BR equals 10. But RM equals 22; therefore the whole line MB equals 32; and as, moreover, AM equals 72, it follows that $AM : MB :: 72 : 32$.

"Having obtained this result, mark off on AM a part AT of arbitrary length, for example, 9 cubits. Erect TU perpendicular to AT, and let $72 : 32 :: 9 : TU$, from which TU equals 4 and the point U will lie exactly on the line which joins the two points A and B. In the same way set off from TU the perpendicular UF and make it, for example, 18 cubits in length; then lay out FQ perpendicular to UF; and since $72 : 32 :: 18 : 8$, make FQ equal to 8; the point Q will lie on the direction which joins the two points A and B. Continue to work thus with the dioptra and by always observing the same proportionality, successive points on the required direction AB are obtained."

Appendix

Chapter II, note 72, p. 42.

Corpus Inscriptionum Latinarum, Vol. 8, No. 2728, p. 323.

. . . [Varius Clemens Valerio] Etrusco: 'et Salditana civitas splendidissima et ego cum Salditanis rogamus te, domine, uti Nonium Datum, veteranum leg[ionis] III Aug[ustae] libratorem, horteris veniat Saldas, ut quod relicum est ex opere eius perficiat.' 'Profectus sum et inter vias lattrones sum passus; nudus saucius evasi cum meis; Saldas veni; Clementem procuratorem conveni. Ad montem me perduxit, ube cuniculum dubii operis flebant, quasi reliquendus habebatur, ideo quot perforatio operis cuniculi longior erat effect[a] quam montis spatium. Apparuit fossuras a rigorem errasse, adeo ut superior fossura dextram petit ad meridiem versus, inferior similiter dextram suam petit ad septentrionem: duae ergo partes relicto rigore errabant. Rigor autem depalatus erat supra montem ab orientem in occidentem. Ne quis tamen legenti error fiat de fossuris, quot est scriptum 'superior' et 'inferior', sic intellegamus: superior est pars, qua cuniculus aquam recipit, inferior, qua emittit. Cum opus adsignar[em], ut scirent, quis quem modum suum perforationis haber[et], certamen operis inter classicos milites et gaesates dedi et sic ad compertusionem montis convenerunt. Ergo, ego qui primus libram feceram, ductum atsignaveram, fieri institueram secundum formam, quam Petronio Celeri pro[curatori] dederam, opus [effeci]. Effectum aqua missa dedicavit Varius Clemens pro[curator]. Ut lucidius labor meus circa duc[tum] hoc Saldense pareret, aliquas epistulas subieci.'

Porci Vetustini ad Crispinum: 'Benignissime, domine, fecisti et pro cetera humanitate ac benivolentia tua, quod misisti ad me Nonium Datum evocatum, uti tractare[m] cum eo de operibus, quae curanda suscepit. Et ideo, quamquam tempore urguerer et Caesaream festinarem, tamen Saldas excucurri et aquae ductum bene inchoatum, sed magni operis inspexi et quod absolvi sine curam Noni Dati non potest, qui it simul diligenter et fideliter tractavit. Et ideo rogaturus eram, concedere nobis, uti mensibus aliquis rei agendae immoraretur, nisi incidisset [in] infirmitatem contractam [ex laboribus]. . . .'

Chapter III, note 160, p. 97.

"Constitutionum Comunis et Populi Civitatis Massae."

Item [ordinamus] quod omnia partita stantiala posita et ponenda inter aliquas foveas, tam per magistros quam arbitros et arbitratores et amicos comunes electos a partiariis de voluntate et concordia partium, debeant calamitari et cum calamita signari, post quam posita et facta erunt, et scribantur in instrumento sententiae ad quem ventum partita respiciunt, et ut, si dicta partita mutarentur, possint refici et reformari in pristinum statum; quae calamita et artificium cum quo calamitabit stare debeat penes Camerarios Comunis, in camera Comunis Massani pro praestando et exhibendo, quando et quocies necesse fuerit ad praedicta partita ponenda et scribi facienda, et videre ad quem ventum partiantur.

Chapter III, note 165, p. 99.

Geometria Culmensis, pp. 36-37.

Idem quod proponit procedens per tres virgas rectas sive gnomone campo triangulari similes non quantitate sed proporcione et numero invenire.

Sic triangulas *ABC* cuius omnia latera sunt nota: Accipe tres virgas rectas, in quantitate seu longitudine sicut placet et sint tales virge divise equaliter in iquales porciones, ut 30, 40, 80 vel plures aut pauciores. De hiis tribus virgis duas coniunge simul cum clavo, ut iugiter firme permaneant mobiles cum consistant, et tercia habeatur absolute ut possit applicari ad libitum. De his tribus virgis numero similes quantitate et proporcione sicut fuerunt latera trianguli *ABC* propositi recipias et applica dictas virgas angulariter ad invicem, ut fiat triangulas similis omnino triangulo *ABC* in proporcione laterum et angulorum. Et tunc illorum duorum triangulorum cunctorum laterum se respiciencium est proporcio una, igitur anguli contenti hiis equalibus lateribus sunt equales, ut patet per quintam sexti Euclidis. Igitur per diffinicionem similium superficierum positans in principio eiusdem sexti dicti trianguli habent superficies equales et, scita tunc quantitate parvi trianguli, scitur et quantitas maioris, quia eadem est utrobique, ut probatum est.

Chapter IV, note 32, p. 114.

Sebastian Münster, *Rudimenta Mathematica,* pp. 28-31.

Hanc hypotenusam potissimum observare debent artifices, qui igniuomis et saxiuomis utuntur machinis aut etiam catapultis aliisque similibus ballistis. Hi enim non recte in altum torquent solides aut in directum, potissimum qui inculantur ignes aut lapides per catapultarum nervos, quin et bombardii, qui conantur res in alto sitas deijecere, nullam ex triangulo rectangulo observant lineam praeter unam hypotenusam. Atque ob id necesse est ut machinis adhibeant quadrantes, sciant potentiam et vim illarum, habeant certa pondera saxorum, ne illa nimis gravia in itinere hypotenusae languescant et non perveniant ad destinatum terminum a quo perpendiculariter cadentia, subiectum locum aut incendant aut concutiant. In eiaculatione tamen bombardarum non intendimus finem cursus, sed summam vim, quae in ipso medio et violento cursu ictum rei demoliendae inferat, advertimus. Cum itaque globum igneum quis eijecere conatur et per perpendicularem contendit tangere certum scopum, oportet illum in primis scire vim illius iaculatoriae machinae, atque deinde distantiam loci quem cupit igne uexare. Cognitis duabus distantiis, basi scilicet et hypotenusa, inclinanda est machina iuxta affixi quadrantis normulam, ut globus piceus hypotenus et ramitem recte incedat, atque deficiens in cursu suo, descendendo cadat in destinatum locum.

Chapter IV, note 33, p. 115.

Daniel Santbech, *Problematum Astronomicorum et Geometricorum*, p. 223.

Constituamus igitur totam vim tormenti posse deferre globum per *CL*, quae sit 1000 passuum, distantia vero *CO* sit 600, altitudo *NO* 100. Quaeritur hic primum, an vis tormenti possit extorquere globum aut ignem eiusque, ut in aliqua parte contingat *LN* cathetum. Primum multiplico *CL* quadrante, hinc consurgit 1,000,000, deinde quadratum 600 est 360,000, quo sublato ex priori, remanet quadratum catheti 640,000, cuius radix est 800 passuum, quae cum 100 exuperet, non est de eventu dubitandum. Constat igitur in hac constitutione sphaeram ex aere delabi per 700 fere passuum intervallum, donec attingat punctum *M*. Iam vero superest, ut investigemus quantitatem circumferentiae *FR* in quadrante ad quam debet elevari media tormenti linea *CF*, id quod facillime expediemus per sinuum tabulas.

Chapter IV, note 36, p. 117.

Jacques de Rojas, *Commentarium in Astrolabium quod Planisphaerium vocant*, p. 199.

Quae in longitudinem moventur res, maxime si a distanti loco conspiciantur, saepenumero accedantne an recedant a nobis propter visus imbecillitatem in dubium trahimur. Id quod in felicissima tua Carole maxime in Tunetu expeditione videre licuit, cum Maurorum copiae circumquaque suo more discurrentes, ob loci distantiam fugiebantne an nostros insequabantur vix cerneres. Erit igitur operae pretium nosse, qua id indubitata ratione possit subinde cognosci, ut vel de insequendo fugiente hoste, vel de instantium impetu repellendo consilium maturet. Suspensa igitur ab hasta, ut firmior sit aut a re aliqua immobili sphaera, dioptram in hostem dirigemus. Post pauxillum vero temporis, sphaera, dioptraque immotis, eandem rem rursus per pinnularum foramina, aut earum saltem latera conspiciemus: statimque accessisse aut retrocessisse hostes cognoscemus. Si autem immota [ut diximus] dioptra semel et iterum hostes per eius pinnularum foramina conspexerimus, neque accedere eos neque recedere, sed potius se a loco non movisse colligemus.

Chapter IV, note 91, p. 138.

Levinus Hulsius, *Tractati Instrumentorum Mechanicorum*, Tractatus Secundus, Ch. 7, p. 9. De formanoui Quadrantis Tormentarii.

Forma vera noui Quadrantis Tormentarii, hic in figura tibi iuxta magnitudinem suam repraesentatur. Constat ex aera inaurato, habetq; capsulam magneticam libere pendentem duas etiam alas, quarum quaelibet in 50 gradus, interius distributa est. In medio numeri alarum scrobiculus est cera repletus. Capsula magnetica interne sub acu, etiam in 64 partes distributa est, per numeros 4 : 8 : 12 etc. habetque circumcirca quoque scrobiculum cera refertum. In inferiori parte huius Quadrantis atque sunt foramina visoria, num 1, 2, 3 designata. Est etiam perpendiculum prope *A.* et in capite eius horologium solare, indicans diei horam a 6 matutina ad eandem vespertinam, cuius usus deinceps indicabitur.

Chapter IV, note 93, p. 140.

Christopher Clavius, *Operum Mathematicorum,* Tomus Secundus, *Geometria Practica.*

Quando oblatum spatium non est valde magnum, excogitavit Ioannes Ferrerius Hispanus nobilis Architectus et Mathematicus, instrumentum percommodum pro librationibus, hoc modo. Compingantur duae regulae *AB, AC,* ex ligno aliquo solido, ac duro, aequalium crurum, quae longitudinem habeant satis longam, ita ut distantiae inter extrema *B, C* contineat 10 palmos praecise, aut etiam plures. Deinde ducta recta *AG* ad *BC* perpendiculari, describatur ex *A,* semicirculus quantuscumque *IDK,* cuius semidiameter *AD,* in tot aequales partes secetur, quot palmi in distantia *BC,* comprehenduntur. Descripto quoque circa *AD,* semicirculo occulto *AED,* transferantur ex *D,* in eius peripheriam omnia intervalla inter *D,* et puncta rectae *AD:* ac tandem ex *A,* per singula puncta semicirculi *AED,* rectae occultae emittantur, notenturque intersectiones earum cum peripheria *DI,* atque in alteram peripheriam *DK,* transportentur. Si namque ex *A* filum cum perpendiculo egriatur, et omnes partes exscindantur, relictis solum cruribus instrumenti *AB, AC,* una cum peripheria semicirculi *IDK,* constructum erit instrumentum ad librationes peropportunum.

Chapter IV, note 139, p. 158.

Peter Apian, *Cosmographia,* Werner's Edition, fols. 58, 59. Gemma Frisius on triangulation.

Primum in assere plano confice instrumentum tale, fiat circulus qui in quatuor quadrantes dissecetur, quadrante quolibet rursus quolibet diviso [ut solet] in 90 gradus. Postea affigatur per centrum index cum perspicillis aut pinnulis quemadmodum in dorso astrolabii. Hoc instrumento facto, opus erit etiam instrumento nautico [quod compassum appellamus] non ab illo fere tota res pendet, quibus habitis ita procedite. Pone instrumentum planimetrum primum in plano, et super ipsum compassum ita ut latus compassi quadrangularis adjacet lineae meridinae instrumenti inferioris. Deinde verte instrumentum cum compasso eo usque, quo index compassi correspondeat sibi subscripto indici, et post haec instrumento ita manente, compassum, tamquam [per]-functum suo officio remove. Si nunc angulum positionis alterius loci a tuo

scire velis, manente instrumento immoto, volve indice donec per perspicilla
eius videas locum alium, videbis mox angulum positionis a meridie vel septin-
trione secundum ipsius indicis remotionem ab eis. Sed quorsum haec? roget
aliquis, etiam si habeam ab uno loco positionis vel situs omnium locorum, si
non adsit distantia nota, nihil profuerit. Verum dicis ab uno loco, nam nisi ab
duobus locis habeas angulos positionum, non poteris describere tertium. Igitur
si nunc provinciam totam depingere placet, investiga primum ab uno oppido,
a quo placet incipere omnium circumiacentium locorum situs: eosque trahe
in plano descripto primum circulo ex uno puncto posito ad libitum, eoque
diviso in 360 gradus ut est ipsum instrumentum planimetrum et cuique lineae
positionis adsigna suum nomen. Ut autem evites multam peregrinationem
ascende turrim oppidi altissimam, atque inde quasi e specula circumspice.
Post haec proficiscere ad aliud oppidum, atque ibi similiter agito cum angulis
positionum omnium circumiacentium locorum: quos ubi habueris, pone
punctum ipsius oppidi a priori puncto in quacumque velis distantia, super
tamen sua linea positionis, atque ex hoc puncto trahe circulum obscurum et
meridianum distantem a priori meridiano undique aequaliter. Demum trahe
ex hoc puncto lineas positionum locorum iam inventas, et ubi tunc sit inter-
sectio lineae alicujus cum prioribus ejusdem loci, ibi notula ponenda est pro
tali loco. Haud dissimili ratione ages cum omnibus locis alicujus regni, pro-
ficiscendo eo usque donec omnia quae describere decrevisti, bis in tuum con-
spectum venerint, atque omnium duas lineas habeas positionum.

Translation from the beginning to ". . . tota res pendet" will be found on
p. 158. The passage continues:

This done proceed as follows. First place the instrument planimeter on a
level surface, and over it the compass so that one side of the four sided compass [box] lies along the N-S line of the lower instrument. Next turn the instrument and compass until the needle corresponds with the mark below itself.
[This refers to the declination mark engraved on the compass card.] After this,
the instrument remaining thus, remove the compass, which has now performed
its duty. If you now wish to determine the angular position of another place
from you, keeping the position of the instrument unchanged, turn the pointer
[alidade] until you see the other position through the sights. You will now see
the angular position from the north or the south according to the movement
of the alidade from them. But why this? Someone may ask, even if I were to
have from one position the bearings or directions of all points, should the
distances be unknown, there is no advantage. True for you with regards one
position, for unless you have the angular positions from two points you cannot
determine a third. So now, if it is desired to map out a whole province, investigate first from one town, whence you desire to begin [noting] the positions
of all the surrounding places: draw them in a plane circle first described from
any point you please: this having been divided into 360° as is the instrument
planimeter itself, and to each line assign the name of its position. To avoid,

however, much walking around, ascend the highest tower in the town and thence as it were from a watch tower look around. After this proceed to another town and act similarly with the angular positions of all the surrounding places: when you have got them, place the position of the town itself at whatever distance you like from the first point and on its own positional line, and from this point draw a light circle and a meridian line parallel to the first meridian. Finally from this point draw the bearing lines of the positions just found and then wherever there is an intersection of these lines with the former lines of the same place, there a mark is made for such a position. By a similar method you will deal with all places in any area, not moving from it until all the places you have decided to map have been sighted twice and you have two lines for all positions.

Chapter IV, note 143, p. 158.

William Cuningham, *The Cosmographical Glasse,* fols. 135 ff. On triangulation.

This description is in the form of a conversation between the scholar, Spoudeus, and the teacher, Philonicus.

Sp. Ther now remaineth to speke of the describing of a perticuler card for any region or country, without knowinge their longitues and latitudes.

Ph. That is well remembered, and ther be divers, and sondri waies to performe this work, of which I will shew you but one; that is by an instrument, serving properly to this use. But like as this waie is more easier then that whiche is performed by Longitude, and Latitude, and may be put in practice at all times: so in like condition, the worke is not so exacte, and perfaite, as by Longitude and Latitudes, which require longe and diligent observation.

Sp. In what form is th'instrument made by which so much utilitie may spring as to describe by it, a country.

Ph. It is made much like the backeparte of an Astrolabe, conteininge in the circuite 360 degrees [Figure 86], and hathe a ruler with two sightes, whiche we move to and fro, as occasion is ministred, untill thorowe them we see the place desired. But it differeth from an Astrolabe, in that it hath a Diall, with a Needle fixed in it, and also that th'instrument is divided into two and thirtie partes, like as a Shipmans compasse. As this figure before placed, doth apparantly set out.

Sp. This Instrument is easye to be provided, yea, and that without great expence, and is not troublous in carriage: but in what sorte may I by it describe a Country?

Ph. I will in fewe wordes make it to you evident. With youre Instrumente you shall ascende on some hie towre, Steaple, or Mountayne, so that you may on every part se the townes and Villagies, aboute you adjacent in your Horizont. Then placing your Instrument (which I name a Geographicall plaine Sphere) Flat and levell, tourninge it from one parte unto another,

until the nedle fall on the Meridian Line, in thy Geographicall plaine
Spheare, then it remaininge stedfaste: directe the ruler with hys two sights
unto anye one place that you do see, and marke diligently th' Angle of sight,
(Gemma Frisius calleth it) Angulus positionis.

SP. I praye you be not·offended althoughe at thys presente I interrupte you,
and or you further procede shewe me what you call the Angle of sight.

PH. I am nothynge displeased, but much reioyse that you will not negligentlye
suffer thinges to escape you, untill you be satisfied touchinge their true
meaninge. You shall note that the Angle of Sighte, is that Arke or portion
of the Horizont of anye place, comprehended betwixte two Merridiane
Circles and drawne by the verticalle Circle of the first place, unto the Meridian of the seconde, whose distaunce you seke out.

SP. Then, you in this place call that Arke of the Horizont, the Angle of Sight,
whiche is lesser than a perfait angle, conteininge 90 degrees.

PH. I do so, for if it be 90 degrees, the place is under the same Parallele of
Latitude, but yet differeth in Longitude, and therefore is dirictly East or
West, as also if there be no Angle of Sight, it hatte the same Longitude and
meridiane Line, and is plaine North or South from you.

SP. Then I pray you proceade with your precept, you saye, I shall take the
Angles of Sight of everye place that I can see in the Horizont of my place
where I begin my worke.

PH. Yea verelye, and then you shall make in some Paper a great Circle, and
devide it into 360 partes, as your Geographicall plaine Sphere is, writing the
foure coastes of the countrey East, South, West and North, in your paper,
then draw right lines from the Center of your circle, (whiche representeth
your place where you take th'Angles of sight of other townes, and villagies
adiacent) unto suche Angles of sighte as you have founde oute by your
Geographicall plaine Sphere.

SP. But this shall little (as I coniecture) avayle: yea althoughe I might have
th'Angles of sight of all places in a Region, from my place, if I have not the
trewe distaunce of them?

PH. I confesse no lesse: for if you have not th'Angles of sight from ij places,
you can not gather the distaunce of the thirde. Therefore when as you have
placed in the Paper all the Townes, Villages, or notable hils, that you can
se in that Horizont: you shall take your instrument and Paper, travelinge
unto some other town, where in like manner you shall go up into the hiest
place of the same, and there placinge your instrumente as before, observe
th'Angles of sight of such Townes and Villagies as are in that Horizont.
Which ended you shall describe in the Paper another Circle as before (as
farre distaunte from th'other, as you thinke conveniente, marking dili-
gentlye that the Center of the second Circle, be in the line of sighte drawne
from the Center of the firste Circle, it beinge also devided into 360 partes)
drawing such Angles of sight as you can finde. And so procede from place to
place, until every Towne or Village have come twise in your sight. And
where that anye line of the second Circle, Crosseth the like line in the first

Circle make there a Sterre, or like marke, for that thirde place (so call I the towne observed twise) and so in like manner you shall do with other places, until you have drawn the hole region you desire.

Sp. Than it is expedient for me to observe the Angle of sighte of everye Towne, from ij several places, so I shall finde oute the difference of one of them from the other or of the thirde from them both, as it must be placed in the Card.

Ph. Yea, and not only in the Card, but that being knowen, you shall easely finde out the distaunce in miles of one of them from the other.

Sp. That semeth very mervelous, seying that you have not theyr Longitudes and Latitudes.

Ph. Yet the worke is right easie (as I doubt not but that you will confesse) for knowing the distance in miles of anye Townes, or Villagies, you shall knowe the true distaunce of all the Townes in a Region, one from an other.

Chapter IV, note 173, p. 169.

Pedro Nuñez, *De Crepusculis,* Prop. III.

Construatur enim Astrolabium quam exacte fieri possit: dioptramque; habeat, hoc est regulam que super centro volvitur, quam rectissimam: ad hanc tabellae ut fieri solet erectae sint: quarum meatus maiores non sint quam ut per ea lucidiora fixa sydera distincte videre possint. Esto exempli gratia huius modi astrolabii plana una atque circularis superficies *abcd,* diametrisque *ac, bd,* in quadrantes divisa: eius centrum sit *e,* punctum. Super hoc intra ipsam circumferentiam, quantouis intervallo (pari aut impari nihil refert) alius intra alium circulorum quadrantes describantur numero 44. Exterior quadrans ut *ab,* in nonaginta aequales partes dividatur. Interiorum vero ei propinquior in partes aequales 89. Sequens deinde in 88, et qui hunc proxime sequitur in 87; et ita deinceps hoc ordine progrediatur, donec ad ultimum interiorum minimumque; perveniatur, qui in partes aequales 46, secabitur. In quolibet quadrante singulo denae partes tenuissimis quibusdam lineolis, parum circumferenciam praetergredientibus notentur. Nam nisi Astrolabium ingentis magnitudinis esset, si quinae aut denae partes numeris distinguerentur, prae nimia intervallorum angustia, magna confusio accideret. Numerus autem partium quas unusquisque; quadrans habet, prope unum eius extremum iuxta semidiametrum scribatur. Ut si supputatio fiat ab *a* versus *b,* super ipso *b* puncto 90, scribantur notis algoristicis: Subtus vero iuxta diametrum *eb,* reliqui numeri suis debitisque; locis collocabuntur. Igitur hac arte numerus graduum nonaginta quem unus quisque quadrans etiam interior habere intelligitur, etsi in pauciores partes divisus proponatur, omnem aliquotam partem actu habet, quae a quouis numero nonaginta minori denominatur: nempe dimidiam partem totius, tertiam, quartam, quintam, sextam, septimam, octavam, nonam, decimam, undecimam, duodecimam et reliquis singulatim usque nonagessimam, quam exterior quadrans actu habet. Nam quod a minoribus partibus ad maiores progrediendo usque ad quadragessimam sextam, aliquotas partes habeat, videlicet nonagessimam, octogessimam nonam, octogessimam octavam et reliquas, nemo insiciabitur. At quod et caeteras quoque habeat, quae ab iis numeris denominantur, qui inter unitatem sunt atque 46, huic facile constare poterit, quod qui numerum aliquem in numerum dividit, dividit et in subduplum, subquadruplum, caeterosque numeros submultiplices quos dividens numerus habet: ut qui dividit in nonaginta dividit etiam in quadraginta quinque et qui in 88, dividit et in 44 et ita deinceps in caeteris. Atque singuli numeri a 23, usque 45, subdupli sunt eorum qui in serie numerorum disponuntur a 46 usque 90, uno semper intermisso: et hi quoque aliorum minorum multiplices sunt, et ita in reliquis, alii ad alios eodem modo se habebant, usque ad unitatem. Igitur numerus ipse gradum nonaginta quem in unoquoque quadrante contineri intelligimus, per praedictas divisiones omnem aliquotam partem habet a dimidia usque ad nonagessimam. Hactenus de instrumenti structura: usus vero perquam facilis erit.

Chapter IV, note 174, p. 171.

Tycho Brahe's letter to Rothmann.

. . . At cum postea per Quadrantes, Altitudines etiam Siderum perscrutari inciperem, et in minoribus Instrumentis vulgarem divisionem minimis portiunculis non sufficere satis experiter, ad Nonnianam illam, quam Propositione tertia de Crepusculis tradit, subtilitatem me converti eademque adhuc exactionem pluribus subdivisionibus reddidi, supputatis etiam Tabulis, e quibuslibet puncti altitudo scrupulose sine mora cognosceretur. Cumque res ipsa doceret, ne hoc quidem inventum Nonnianum id habere in recessu, quod in accessu pollicebatur, caepi cogitare an divisio illa praedicta, quam linea recta subtilissime per puncta transversalia in minores secatur particulas, etiam curvis et circularibus applicari possit. . . .

Chapter IV, note 177, p. 173.

Christopher Clavius, *Operum Mathematicorum,* Tomus Secundus. A modification of the nonius.

Descriptis ex *A,* centro quadrantis *BC,* intra eundem quadrantem aliis 39 quadrantibus aequaliter, si placet, inter se distantibus, ut venustior appareat figura: ita ut in universum sint 40. quadrantes, quorum extimus in 90. gradus more solito facetur: proximus deinde in 128. partes aequales, primum videlicet in duas, et utraque pars rursus in duas, et quaelibet harum quatuor partium iterum in duas et ita deinceps, donec 7. divisiones absolutae sint, atque adeo totus quadrans in 128. partes aequales distributus. Post haec producantur alii quadrantes ultra semidiametrum *AB,* ut dictum est, ille quidem, qui tertius est ab extremo *BC,* usque ad gradum 91. extremi quadrantis *CB,* producti, hoc est, usque ad lineam ex *A,* ad gradum 91. ductam: sequens deinde usque ad gradum 92. et insequens ad gradum 93: atque ita deinceps usque ad alios gradus, ita ut quadragesimus quadrans usque ad gradum 128. producatur. Hi arcus ita producti dividantur singuli in 128. partes aequales, sicuti quadrans extimo quadranti proximus, qua divisione peracta, partes supra semidiametrum *AB,* resecentur, tanquam supervacaneae.

Chapter IV, note 180, p. 174.

Christopher Clavius, *Operum Mathematicorum,* Tomus Secundus. A modification of the nonius.

Quando intra Quadratem non descripti sunt plures quadrantes, sed unicus tantum adest in 90. gradus exquisite distributus, cognoscemus solo circini beneficio, quot Minuta, ac secunda in quavis gradus particula contineantur: id quod etiam in Astrolabio fecimus, hoc scilicet modo. Sit data verbi gratia particula *t u,* in gradu 20. superioris Quadrantis *BC.* Sumatur ea diligentissime beneficio circini, et a principio Quadrantis, id est, a puncto *C,* incipiendo, eadem apertura circini accipiantur 60. aequales particulae usque ad punctum *X,* ita ut arcus *CX,* sexagecuplus sit arcus *t u:* Quot enim gradus integri in hoc arcu sexagecuplo comprehenduntur, tot minuta complectetur particula data *t u.* Et si ultra gradus integros in arcu *CX* supersit aliqua particula, accipiatur ea sexagies quoque, initio facto a puncto *C.* Nam quot gradus integri in hoc arcu sexagecuplo continentur, tot secunda ultra Minuta inventa continebuntur in data particula *t u.* Quod si adhuc aliquid supersit, reperietur eodem modo Tertia, etc. Itaque cum in arcu *CX,* qui sexagecuplus est particulae *t u,* contineantur 40. gradus integri, comprehendet particula *t u* quadraginta Minuta, et insuper tot secunda, quot gradus continentur in arcu, qui sexagecuplus sit particulae ultra 40 gradus in arcu *CX* contentae, etc.

Chapter IV, note 182, p. 175.

Christopher Clavius, *Operum Mathematicorum,* Tomus Secundus. On the first approach to the straight-line vernier.

Quae Num. 10. 11. 12. et 13 precedentibus diximus, perbelle etiam quadrant in lineas rectas. Nam eadem rationem cognoscem, si linea recta in quotius partes aequales secetur, quantam fractionem quaelibet particula unius partis contineat: Et vicissim quo pacto ex una parte abscindenda sit quaecumque; fractio proposita. Quae res incredibile est, quantam utilitatem cum aliis rebus Geometricus: tum vero maxime Dimensionibus, quae per scalam altimetram fieri solet, afferat, ut lib. 3. cum de Quadrato Geometrico, ubi scalae altimetrae usus apparebit, perspicuum erit. Sit enim recta linea *AB,* ut ad pedem Quadrantis superioris vides, secta in 10. partes aequales, (In tot *n.* partes libet tam umbram rectam, quam versam scalae altimetrae distribuere: quamvis ab aliis utraque; in 12 dividatur: quod per illam divisionem facilius Dimensiones perficiantur, ut suo loco patebit. Magis tamen probarem, si utrumque: umbrae latus in 100 partes secaretur, si id magnitudo instrumenti commode permittit) propositumque; sit, quot partes decimas contineat *DC,* partis quintae beneficio circini sumpta particula *DC,* decupletur ab *A,* usque ad *E.* Et quoniam in *AE,*

continentur sex partes totius lineae *AB,* continebit propterea particula *DC,*
6/10. unius partis decimae, hoc est, 6/100. totius lineae. Ita ut si recta *AB,*
divisa cogitetur in 100 partes, tribuendo singulis decimis partib (us) denas
particulas, segmentum *AC,* comprehendat 46/100. Quia vero ultra 6/10
superest adhuc particula *FE,* unius decimae, si ea rursum decupletur ab *A*
usque ad *G,* reperientur in *AG,* octo partes totius lineae *AB.* Continet ergo
particula *FE* 8/10. unius decimae (unius inquam decimae ex illis 6/10. quas
in particula *DC,* diximus comprehendit) nimirum 8/100. unius partis, si sin-
gulae partes decimae rectae *AB,* divisae essent in 100. particulas; atque: adeo,
si recta *AB,* secta intelligatur in 1000 partes.

Chapter IV, note 183, p. 176.

Pierre Vernier, *La construction, l'usage et les propriétéz du quadrant nouveau
de mathématique.* On the vernier.

L'Instrument estant d'un pied de demy diametre, il sera composé de deux
parties; la premiere et principale desquelles est une Planche, relevée d'un bord
ou limbe circulaire; sur lequel la quatriéme partie d'un Cercle est exactement
divisée en nonante portions esgales; ou bien en terme de l'art, en nonante
degrés: et de rechef chasque portions, en deux: à fin d'y veoir les demy degrés.
Tellement que laditte quatriéme partie contiendra cent octante portions
esgales, pour concevoir le cercle entier, divisé à l'ordinaire en trois cents
soixante degrés, ou bien sept cents vingt demy degrés, selon que tous les
Mathematiciens le conçoivent.

Laditte planche sera appelée du nom de base fixe à cause qu'elle sera
tousiours fixe et arrestée es operations de l'Instrument; laquelle quarte partie
de cercle sera enclose et enfermée par deux lignes droites, s'entrecoupans en un
poinct au centre dudict Instrument; lesques lignes se nommeront demy
diametres d'iceluy.

La division des degrés et demy degrés, cy dessus declarée, se colloquera sur
la partie interieure du bord ou limbe de la base, et à l'extremité d'iceluy:
laquelle division sera distinguée par nombres, de cinq en cinq degrés sur la
partie extérieure dudict bord; commençant laditte division depuis le demy
diametre senestre de la base, tirant au dextre.

La seconde partie de l'Instrument est une planche construicte en la forme
et figure d'un secteur de cercle, la circonferance de laquelle comprendra iuste-
ment un angle de trente et un demy degrés; non toutefois formés ny descris
mais bien divisé en trente partes esgales seulement: laquelle circonferance sera
enfermée et enclose par deux lignes droittes se rencontrant en un poinct au
centre d'icelle; formant ledict angle de trente et un demy degrés; c'est à dire
de quinze degrés trente minutes, comme a esté dict cy devant: En sorte qu'icelle
seconde partie estant appliquée et ajustée sur la première appelée base, et les
centres des deux demeurans communs, la portion extreme et exterieure de
Cercle de division, la laditte partie seconde, responde et soit contigue à la portion extreme et interieure du Cercle de division de laditte base.

La division de laditte partie seconde sera distinguée par nombres de cinq en cinq, commenceant à compter à dextre en tirant à senestre d'iceluy et une chacune portion des trentes, de laditte division, vaudra en operation une minute de degré du cercle.

Laditte seconde partie sera appelée Secteur mobile de l'Instrument; parcequ'elle se meut tantost à dextre, tantost à senestre sur la base, lorsque l'un veut faire quelque operation. Audict Secteur mobile, les deux lignes droittes se rencontrans au centre et comprenans trente et un degrés du Cercle, s'appelleront lignes de foy: sur une chascune desquelles seront apposées deux lamules percées et fendues en sorte que les rayons visuels puissent estre exactement recognens et observés, lesdittes lignes ainsi appelées, à raison que l'on adjuste foy au rencontre qu'elles font sur les degrés de la base; et qu'elles representent une partie des rayons visuels, qui causent l'angle desiré aux operations.

Chapter IV, note 196, p. 186.

Aaron Rathborne, *The Surveyor*, Bk. 3, Ch. 2. On the "theodelite."

This Instrument consisteth of foure severall parts; As first, the Planisphere or Circle, whose limbe is divided into 360.equall parts or divisions, called degrees, without which it is fitting equidistantly to draw and describe sixe concentricke lines of circles with crosse Diagonals, by whose intersections are had the parts of a degree upon which *Planisphere,* and within the divisions before specified, there is described the *Geometricall Square,* being the second part thereof both which together, or eyther of them severally serve to excellent purpose, for the dimension of lengthes, bredthes and distances. The third part is a Semicircle or Quadrant perpendicularly raysed, and artificially placed on the former Planisphere (or more properly on the Index thereof) to be moved about circularly at pleasure on all occasions, which semicircle or quadrant hath the limbe thereof equally divided into parts or degrees, with like concentricke Circles and Diagonals to those of the *Planisphere.* And the fourth and last part is a *Scale,* described within the same Semicircle or Quadrant, whose sides are divided into divers equal parts, the more the better, and to best purpose; which two later parts serve chiefly for the mensuration of altitudes and profundities. All which together composed, make an excellent Instrument meete for many purposes, especially for the description of Regions and Countries, or other spacious workes.

Chapter IV, note 210, p. 195.

Peter Apian, *Cosmographia,* Werner's Edition. On the construction of the Jacob's staff.

Antequam rem ipsam aggrediar, fustis seu baculi fabricam Geometrica ratione consulto praedicere decrevimus. Fiat igitur semicirculus super *F*, centro, qui sit *A, B, C:* Et ex *F*, signo seu centro, orthoganalis excitetur ad circumferentiam usque in longitudine 5. 6. aut 7 pedum, (quia secundum eius longitudinem debet fieri baculus seu fustis ex ligno solido et glandoso grossitudine digiti) et tangat circulum in puncto *B*, sic erit semicirculus divisus in duos quadrantes, scilicet *A, B*, et *B, C*. Quibus sic dispositis, pone unum circini pedem in *F*, signu reliquum ad plani latum extende, et fac mobili pede notas duas, unam vers *A*, ibidem fiat nota *G*. Reliqua versus *C*, ubi notetur *H*. Circino sic immoto manente, ponetur unus pes in *B*, altero mobili describe circulum occultum ad quem ducendae sunt contingentes ex utrisque punctis circa *F*, eruntque ipsae lineae *G, D*, et *H, E*, aequidistantes seu parallelae *FB*. Deinde quadrantem *AB* similiter *BC*, divide in 90 partes aut gradus, hoc modo; primo in tres partes aequas et iterum quamlibet partem in tres: tertio quamlibet in duas: postremo et ultimo in quinque. Quibus et centro *F*, applica regulam et trahe lineas occultas per omnes gradus; et ubi iam productae lineae dispescunt *G, D* et *H, E*, lineis, notentur signa. Quo facto, protrahe lineas a punctis *G, D*, lineae usque ad opposita puncta lineae *HE*. Quae quidem lineae transversae interscindunt *FB*, semidiametrum. Deinde fiat Baculus in longitudine *FB*, habens aequales divisiones *FB* lineae. Numeri itaque gradum ab *B* versus *F*, secundum exigentiam divisionis sunt aptandi. Deinceps fac tabulam versatilem seu pinnacidum in longitudine *GH*, vel *DE*: eiusque; in medio fac foramen seu rimulam aut fissuram, in qua idem baculus ad angulos rectos moveri possit et paratus erit Baculus.

Chapter IV, note 261, p. 220.

Sebastian Münster, *Rudimenta Mathematica*. On the construction and use of the trigonus.

Fac tibi instrumentum quale hic vides descriptum in tabula aliqua cum duabus mobilibus regulis et adiuncto quadrato compasso. Tres huius trigoni lineae habent similes divisiones. Immobilis finitur 24 sectionibus, duae mobiles vero non coguntur ad certum sectionum numerum Reliqua tu ipse tuo marte facile adscribes. Vsus huius instrumenti est talis. Vis scire quam tumarbor aliqua, castrum aut turris bombardis uexanda, aut res alia a te distet, aut quanta sit latitudo alicuius praetereuntis fluvii, operaberis sic. [Figure 209.]

Pone instrumentum super truncum aliquem aut lapidem et gyra ipsum quousque per pinnulas seu centra *BA* videris rem, cuius a te distantia scire cupis, manenteque instrumento in eo situ respicies ad dextram vel ad sinistram, et deliges tibi signum aliquod, ad quod comode ventre queas, quodque a te aliquot distet passibus, triginta scilicet aut quadraginta aut etiam pluribus, nam quo angulum illum maiorem feceris, eo certius operaberis in inquisitione distantiae rei, cuius a te intervallum quaeris. Versus autem signum illud dextrum vel sinistrum diriges regula *BC* donec per foramen pinnulae *B* et aciem erectam in *C* videas observatum signum. Advertes etiam intersectionem huius regulae et circuli in cuius centro regula *BC* voluit. Nam in secunda statione necesse erit regulam eundem tangere circuli punctum. Pones etiam compassum super instrumentum anteque ipsum tollas ex statione prima, latus scilicet compassi meridianum adaptando lineae instrumenti *AB* et videbis quam horam aut quod aliud punctum inter horarum divisiones tangat compassi lingua mobilis, aut si spendet sol, adverte quam horam tangat gromonis umbra et punctum illud indicis aut umbrae diligenter serva, qua oportet te instrumentum in hoc situ rursum in observato laterali signo (ubi secunda erit statio) ponere, id qd citra compassi officium facere non potes. Hac prima statione expedita, transibis ad observatum laterale signum, ubi secunda erit statio et inter eundem numerabis per pedes vel per passus spacium inter duas stationes comprehensum annotabisque diligenter numerum pedum aut passuum interceptum, quia erunt unum latus trianguli dimensum, ex quo ad cognitionem reliquorum duorum laterum venies eo modo quo iam sum dicturus. Ubi itaque perveneris ad signum laterale a te in prima statione observatum et cuius intervallum es dimensus, pones instrumentum super re aliqua elevata a terra, applicatoque compasso statues ipsum in eo situ quem habuit in prima statione. Quo facto non indigebis amplius officio compassi. Figes etiam regulam BC in eo situ quem habuit in prima statione. Postea move regulam DA super regula BC donec per pinnulas eius videas rem illam cuius a te distantiam quaeris, et observaque puncta ab scindantur in regula DA per regulam BC et habebis triangula euisque tres lineas per aequalia puncta divisas. Deinde operaberis per regulam de tri in hunc modum. Pone primo puncta regulae BC, deinde numerum pedum vel passum quos numerasti a prima statione usque ad secundam tertio pone numerum lineae AB, qui semper est 24 et duc secundum in tertum productumque divide per primum et haberis pedes vel passus a statione prima usque ad rem visam. Quod si distantia quoque illa que est a statione secunda ad rem visam habere cupis, pone numerum punctorum regulae DA quae abscindit regula BC, tertio loco et operare ut prius.

Chapter IV, note 269, p. 228.

Abel Foullon, *Usaige et description de l'holomêtre,* Italian Edition of S. Ziletti.

[L'Holomêtre] contiene sei pezzi notabili solamente i quali sono la Tauola il Rettore, la Base, le duc Verghe e il Piede.

La Tauola è quella, che sostiene la Base, e le due Verghe, e ne serue di forma piana per prendere giustamente le misure. Al mezzo della qual Tauola ha una aguglia tale, quale si mette ai quadranti da Sole: la quale aguglia è attorniata di Segni, che ne rappresentano i venti. . . . Et ne serue qui per prender le lunghezze solamentez affin che trasportando l'Holometro d'un luogo nell'altro, si possa rimettere, come era per auāti; per lo giudicio di quella.

. . . Il Rettore è un pezzo composto di un circolo, e di un Regoletto. Il circolo diviso in quattro quarti, e ciascū quarto in ventiquattro portioni eguali. Io dico eguali; ma io intendo sopra la linea perpendiculare, doue elle sono tirate verso il centro del detto circolo, e non altramente perche non ostante che le dette portioni siano diseguali su il circolo; tut tavia elle sono di pari grandezza sopra la linea dritta. Et seruira questa divisione per conoscere la quantita di tutte le altezze, e profondita. Ma il Regoletto (altrimenti alhidada) ha alle due cime due traguardi, o pinnulle, per riguarder per loro le cose, che si ha proposto di misurare; il qual Regoletto è con giunto al Rettor per lo mezzo, e centro, del detto circolo. Et è questo pezzo appellato Rettore; percio che ello regge, e gouvernale Verghe, e la Base perche per saper la misura delle cose lontane egli bi sogna piantar un Rettore a piombo sopra ciascuna delle dette Verghe; e a fin di non fallir a metter il Rettor perpendicolarmete sopra di quelle Verghe, egli è bisogno di pendere un picciol piombo per lo cĕtro del dett circolo. Che essendo il fil del piōbo sopra il perpendicolo del Rettore, egli ne segue, che la Tavola dell'instrumento sia similmĕte a livello. . . . La Base è un pezzo mobile messo a coda di rondine entro una incastratura. . . . Et serue la detta incastratura per allungar, o accorciar la Base, quanto ne è bisogno. I quali pezzi cosi Base, come incastratura sono graduati di segni egualmente distanti. Et è questo ferro appellato Base, perioche ella fa il fondamento di un Triangolo.

La Verghe sono due rami dritti, i quali sono tutti allungo graduati di segni equalmente distanti, come la Base, e la incastratura. L'una delle quali (che noi appelliam Verga destra) è conguinta con un nodo al capo della detta Base, affinche la detta Verga destra, e la Base si possano serrare, e aprire, come un compasso, per lo mezzo del detto modo. L'altra Verga (che noi appelliamo sinistra) è similmente annodata con un piccola pezzo mobile. Detto mobile, perioche si muoue per di sotto de la Base per mezzo di una fessura, che è allungo della detta incastratura. Et ne serve questo pezzo mobile, per auuicinar, o allungar la Verge sinistra dalla destra, quanto ne sera bisogno; similmente per chui derla, e aprirla con la Base, e con la Verga destra. Et non bisogna scordarsi, che il pezzo mobile è attaccato con il quarto di un circolo segnato in venti quattro parti, le quali sono di tal misura, come quel le del circolo intero del Rettore.

Chapter IV, note 274, p. 231.

Aaron Rathborne, *The Surveyor,* Bk. 3, Ch. 3. On the "playne table."

This table it selfe is divided into five parts, or small bords, whereof three are in the bredth, and the other two imployed as ledges in the length to keepe the rest together, whereunto a ioynted frame is artificially applyed, for the fastning and keeping playne thereon, an ordinarie sheet of paper for use in the fields; of which length and bredth or rather lesse, as 14 1/2 inches in length and 11 in bredth, the whole Table together should consist. But for my purpose, I would have made of these three boords in bredth, with helpe of ledges to be thereon glued, to the back-side thereof, and strong ioynts or gemmoves fastning them together, an artificial boxe; which at any instant being opened, and the ledges fastened on, is fit for use in the Fields, and afterwards those ledges taken away, may be as instantly turned backwards, and inclosed as before, fit for the keeping of loose papers and small tooles, till further occasion.

Bibliography

1. ABEL, T., *Subtensial Plain Trigonometry* (Philadelphia, 1761).
2. ABŪ'L WEFĀ. See Suter, H.
3. AGRICOLA, GEORG (1495-1555), *De Re Metallica* (Basel, 1556). English translation by H. C. Hoover and L. H. Hoover (London, 1912).
4. AIRY, W., "The History of Land Measurement in England," *Engineering*, 1909, pp. 341 ff.
5. AL-BATTĀNĪ. See Nallino, C. A.
6. AL-BĪRŪNĪ. See Wiedemann, E.; Wright, R. R.
7. ALBRICHT, M., "Astronomische Orientierungen in der römischen Geodäsie," *Weltall*, Vol. 5, 1904, pp. 53-63.
8. AL-CHĀZINĪ. See Khanikoff, N.
9. AL-CHWĀRIZMĪ. See Frank, J.
10. ALFONSO X OF CASTILE (1223-1284), *Libros de Saber de Astronomia del Rey Alfonso X de Castillia*, Edited by D. M. Sinobas (Madrid, 1863-1867).
11. AL-MIZZĪ. See Morley, W. H.; Dorn, B.
12. AL-'URDĪ. See Seeman, H.
13. APIAN, PETER (1495-1552), *Cosmographia*, Werner's Edition (Ingolstadt, 1524).
14. APIAN, PETER, *Instrument-Buch* (Ingolstadt, 1533).
15. ARCHIBALD, R. C., "Babylonian Mathematics," *The Mathematics Teacher*, Vol. 29, 1936, pp. 209-219.
16. ARDUSER, JOHANN (*fl.* 1620), *Geometricae, Theoricae et Practicae* (Zurich, 1627).
17. ARISTOTLE, *Metaphysics*, Translated by H. Tredemick, Loeb Library Edition (Cambridge, Mass., 1933).
18. ARNOLD, BR., F.S.C., *The Letter of Petrus Peregrinus on the Magnet, A.D. 1269*, Translation (New York, McGraw-Hill Book Co., 1904).
19. ARTZ, F. B., "Les débuts de l'éducation technique en France 1500-1700," *Revue d'Histoire Moderne*, September-December, 1937.
20. ARYABHATTA, *The Aryabhatuja of Aryabhatta*, Edited by W. E. Clarke (Chicago, University of Chicago Press, 1930).
21. ATWELL, GEORGE (*fl.* 1660), *The Faithfull Surveyour* (London, 1658).
22. AVEZAC, D', M., "Anciens témoignages historiques relatifs à la boussole," *Bulletin de la société de géographie de Paris*, 1858.
23. AVEZAC, D', M., "Aperçus historiques sur la boussole." *Bulletin de la société de géographie*, 1860.

24. BAGUETTE, A., *Die Bedeutung des Astrolabiums* (Bonn, 1909).
25. BAKST, A., *Approximate Computation*, The National Council of Teachers of Mathematics, *Twelfth Yearbook* (New York, 1937).
26. BARBER, H. C., "Random Notes on Geometry Teaching," *The Mathematics Teacher*, Vol. 30, 1937, pp. 338-339.

27. BARBOSA, A., "Instrumente nauticos da epoca dos descobrimentos maritimos: sua importancia historica," *O instituto, revista scientifica e literaria,* Vol. 74, 1927, pp. 470-534.
28. BARLOWE, WILLIAM (d. 1625), *Magnetical Advertisements* (London, 1616).
29. BARLOWE, WILLIAM, *The Navigator's Supply* (London, 1597).
30. BARROS, DE, J., *Decades de Asia* (Lisbon, 1552).
31. BARTOLI, COSIMO (1503-1572), *Del modo di misurare* (Venice, 1564).
32. BASSERMANN-JORDAN, VON, E., *Alte Uhren und ihre Meister* (Leipzig, 1926).
33. BAUER, L. A., "The Beginnings of Magnetic Observation." *Terrestrial Magnetism and Atmospheric Electricity,* Vol. 4, No. 2, 1889. Translated from the German of G. Hellmann.
34. BAUER, L. A., "The Earliest Values of the Magnetic Declination," *Terrestrial Magnetism and Atmospheric Electricity,* Vol. 13, No. 3, 1908, pp. 97-104.
35. BELIDOR, DE, B. F., *Nouveau cours de mathématique,* Second Edition (Paris, 1757).
36. BELLI, SILVIO (fl. 1560), *Libro del misurar con la vista* (Venice, 1566).
37. BENESE, DE, RICHARD (fl. 1530), *The Boke of Measuring of Lande* (London, 1537).
38. BENSAUDE, J., *Histoire de la science nautique portuguaise, résumé* (Geneva, 1917).
39. BENSAUDE, J., *L'Astronomie nautique au Portugal à l'époque des grandes découvertes* (Bern, 1912).
40. BERT, P., *First Lessons of Experimental Geometry,* Translated from the French (London, 1886).
41. BETTINI, MARIO, S.J. (fl. 1640), *Apiaria Universae Philosophiae Mathematicae* (Bonn, 1645).
42. BETZ, W., "The Present Situation in Secondary Mathematics," *The Mathematics Teacher,* Vol. 33, 1940, pp. 339-360.
43. BETZ, W., *The Teaching of Intuitive Geometry. A Study of Its Aims, Development, Content and Method,* The National Council of Teachers of Mathematics, *Eighth Yearbook* (New York, 1933).
44. BHĀSKARA, *Līlāvatī, A Treatise on Mensuration by Bhaskara,* Edited by M. S. Dvivedi (Benares, 1912). *See also* Colebrooke, H. T.
45. BION, NICOLAS (fl. 1700), *Traité de la construction et des principeaux usages des instruments de mathématique* (Paris, 1709). English translation by E. Stone (London, 1724).
46. BIOT, E., *Le Tcheou-Li ou Rites de Tcheou* (Paris, 1851).
47. BIOT, E., "Traduction et examen d'un ancien ouvrage chinois intitulé Tcheou-pei," *Journal Asiatique,* Series 3, Vol. 11, 1841, pp. 593-639.
48. BIRKHOFF, G. D., AND BEATLEY, R., *A New Approach to Elementary Geometry.* The National Council of Teachers of Mathematics, *Fifth Yearbook* (New York, Bureau of Publications, Teachers College, Columbia University, 1930).
49. BIRKHOFF, G. D., AND BEATLEY, R., *Basic Geometry* (New York, Scott, Foresman and Co., 1941).
50. BJORNBO, A. A. *See* Hoops, J.
51. BLAEU, WILLIAM J. (1571-1638), *Seespiegel* (Amsterdam, 1631).
52. BLAGRAVE, JOHN (d. 1611), *The Familiar Staff* (London, 1590).
53. BLONDEL, FRANÇOIS (fl. 1680), *L'Art de jetter les bombes* (The Hague, 1683).
54. BLUME, F., LACHMANN, K., AND RUDORFF, A., *Die Schriften der römischen Feldmesser* (Berlin, 1848-1852). 2 vols.
55. BLUNDEVIL, THOMAS (fl. 1580), *His Exercises* (London, 1594).
56. BONCOMPAGNI, B. *See* Leonardo Pisano.

57. BOND, J. D., "The Development of Trigonometrical Methods down to the Close of the Fifteenth Century," *Isis*, Vol. 4, 1922, pp. 295-323.

58. BORCHARDT, L., "Die altägyptische Zeitmessung," *Die Geschichte der Zeitmessung und der Uhren*, Edited by E. von Bassermann-Jordan, Vol. 1, 1920.

59. BORCHARDT, L., "Ein altägyptisches astronomisches Instrument," *Zeitschrift für ägyptische Sprache*, Vol. 37, 1899, pp. 10-17.

60. BORCHARDT, L., "Längen und Richtungen der vier Grundkanten der grossen Pyramide bei Gise," *Beiträge zur ägyptischen Bauforschung und Altertumskunde*, Vol. 1, 1926.

61. BORCHARDT, L., "Wie wurden die Boschungen der Pyramiden bestimmt?" *Zeitschrift für ägyptische Sprache*, Vol. 31, 1893, pp. 9-17.

62. BOULENGER, JEAN (d. 1636), *La géométrie pratique* (Paris, 1623).

63. BOULLES, DE, CHARLES (1470-1553), *Livre singulier et utilé, touchant l'art et pratique de géométrie*, Latin Edition (1511); French Edition (1542).

64. BOURDIN, P., *Le Cours de mathématique*, Third Edition (Paris, 1661).

65. BOURLET, C., *Cours abrégé de géométria*, Second Edition (Paris, 1908).

66. BOURNE, WILLIAM (*fl.* 1560), *A Regiment for the Sea* (London, 1573).

67. BOURNE, WILLIAM, *Inventions and Devices* (London, 1578).

68. BOURNE, WILLIAM, *The Art of Shooting Great Ordnance* (London, 1587).

69. BRAHE, TYCHO (1546-1601), *Astronomiae Instauratae Mechanica* (Wandesburg, 1598).

70. BRAHMAGUPTA. *See* Colebrooke, H. T.

71. BRAMER, BENJAMIN (1588-1649), *Bericht über Jobst Bürgii geometrische Triangularinstrument* (Cassel, 1648).

72. BRAMER, BENJAMIN, *Beschreibunge . . . eines neuen . . . Instruments zum Grundlegung* (Marburg, 1616).

73. BRAMER, BENJAMIN, *Trigonometria Planorum Mechanica* (Marburg, 1617).

74. BREAKS, T., *A Complete System of Land Surveying* (Newcastle-on-Tyne, 1771).

75. BREASTED, J. H., *Ancient Records* (Chicago, University of Chicago Press, 1906).

76. BREEN, VAN, JOST (*fl.* 1660), *Stiermanns Gemack ofte eene korte Beschryvinge van de Konst der Stierlieden* (Graven-Hage, 1662).

77. BRESLICH, E. R., "The Nature and Place of Objectives in Teaching Geometry," *The Mathematics Teacher*, Vol. 31, 1938.

78. BRETSCHNEIDER, C. A., *Die Geometrie und die Geometer vor Euklides* (Leipzig, 1870).

79. BUBNOV, N. *See* Gerbert.

80. BUCHNER, JOHANN (*fl.* 1680), *Theoria et Praxis Artilleriae* (Nürnberg, 1682).

81. BÜRK, A., "Das Āpastamba-Sūlba-Sūtra II: Übersetzung," *Zeitschrift der deutsch Morgenland Gesellschaften*, Vol. 56, 1902.

82. BUGGE, T., *Gründliche und vollständige theoretisch-practische Anleitung zum Feldmessen*, Translated from the Danish of L. H. Jobiesen (Altona, 1798).

83. BULLET, PIERRE (1639-1716), *Traité de l'usage du pantomêtre* (Paris, 1675).

84. BURGESS, E., "Sūrya-Siddhānta," *Journal of the American Oriental Society*, Vol. 6, 1860. English translation.

85. BURGH, THOMAS, *A Method to Determine the Areas of Right-Lined Figures Universally* (Dublin, 1724).

86. BURGH, DE, W. G., *The Legacy of the Ancient World* (New York, The Macmillan Co., 1924).

87. BUTEO, JOHANNES (*c.* 1490-*c.* 1565), *Opera Geometrica* (Lyons, 1554).

88. CAGNOLI, M., *Traité de trigonomètre*, Translated from the Italian by M. Chompré (Paris, 1786).

89. CAJORI, F., *A History of Mathematics* (New York, The Macmillan Co., 1922).

90. CAJORI, F., *The Teaching and History of Mathematics in the United States* (Washington, D. C., 1890).

91. CAMPBELL, W. T., *Observational Geometry* (New York, Harper Bros., 1899).

92. CANTOR, M., *Die römischen Agrimensoren und ihre Stellung in der Geschichte der Feldmesskunst* (Leipzig, 1875).

93. CANTOR, M., *Vorlesungen über Geschichte der Mathematik* (Leipzig, 1880).

94. CARDAN, GIROLAMO (1501-1576), *Opera*, Tomus Quartus (Lyons, 1663).

95. CASSIODORUS, F. M. A. (fl. 500), *Variarum Epistularum, Libri XII*, English Translation by T. Hodgkin (London, 1886).

96. CATANEO, GIROLAMO (fl. 1555), *Dell'art del misurare* (Brescia, 1572).

97. CATANEO, GIROLAMO, *Opera nuova di fortificare* (Brescia, 1564).

98. CESPEDES, DE, GARCIA (fl. 1600), *Libro de instrumentos nuevos de geometria* (Madrid, 1606).

99. CESPEDES, DE, GARCIA, *Regimento de navegacion* (Madrid, 1606).

100. CHACE, A. B., MANNING, H. P., ARCHIBALD, R. C., *The Rhind Mathematical Papyrus* (Oberlin, Ohio, 1927).

101. CHALES, DE, CLAUDE (1621-1678), *Mundus Mathematicus* (Leyden, 1674). English translation by Reeve Williams (London, 1685).

102. CHAPPELL, J., "The Early History of Magnetism," *Nature*, Vol. 14, 1877.

103. CHASLES, M., *Aperçu historique des méthodes en géométrie* (Paris, 1875).

104. CHAUCER, G., *Tractatus de Conclusionibus Astrolabii, 1391*, Edited by W. W. Skeat (London, 1872).

105. CHAUVET, JACQUES (fl. 1575), *Instruction et usage du cosmomètre* (Paris, 1585).

106. CHAUVET, JACQUES, *La pratique universelle de géométrie* (Paris, 1585).

107. CHAUVET, JACQUES, *La pratique universelle de l'arpenterie* (Paris, 1583).

108. CHÉZY, DE, A., "Mémoire sur quelque instruments propre à niveler, nommés niveaux," *Mémoires de l'académie des sciences*, Vol. 5, 1768.

109. CICERO, M. T., *Tusculanarum Disputationes*.

110. CLAIRAUT, A. C., *Eléméns de géométrie* (Paris, 1741).

111. CLARAMONTIUS, SCIPIO (1565-1652), *Opuscula varia mathematica* (Bonn, 1653).

112. CLARK, A. R., *Geodesy* (Oxford, 1880).

113. CLARKE, S., AND ENGELBACH, R., *Ancient Egyptian Masonry* (Oxford, Oxford University Press, 1930).

114. CLAVIUS, CHRISTOPHER, S.J. (1537-1612), *Operum Mathematicorum*, Tomus Secundus, Geometria Practica (Moguntiae, 1611).

115. *Codex Arcerianus.* See Cantor, M.; Blume, F., Lachmann, K., and Rudorff, A.

116. COIGNET, MICHEL (fl. 1575), *Instruction nouvelle des poincts plus excellents et nécessaires touchant l'art de naviguer* (Antwerp, 1581).

117. COLE, J. H., "Determination of the Exact Size and Orientation of the Great Pyramid of Giza," *Survey of Egypt* (Cairo, 1925), Paper No. 39.

118. COLEBROOKE, H. T., *Algebra, Arithmetic with Mensuration of Brahmegupta and Bhascara* (London, 1817).

119. COLEMAN, R., *The Development of Informal Geometry* (New York, Bureau of Publications, Teachers College, Columbia University, 1943).

120. "Constitutionum Comunis et Populi Civitatis Massae," *Archivo storico italiano*, Vol. 8, 1845, Appendix No. 27. Edited by F. Bonaini.

121. CORBETT, W. J., "Elizabethan Village Surveys," *Transactions of the Royal Historical Society*, 1897.
122. *Corpus Inscriptionum Latinarum* (Berlin), Vol. 8.
123. CORTES, MARTIN (*fl.* 1540), *Breve compendio de la sphera y de la arte de navegar* (Seville, 1551).
124. COURANT, R., AND ROBBINS, H., *What Is Mathematics?* (New York, Oxford University Press, 1941).
125. COURT, T., AND VON ROHR, M., "A History of the Development of the Telescope," *Transactions, The Optical Society*, Vol. 30, 1928-1929, pp. 207-260; Vol. 32, 1930-1931, pp. 113-122.
126. CUNINGHAM, WILLIAM (*fl.* 1550), *The Cosmographical Glasse* (London, 1559).
127. CURTZE, M. *See* Savasorda; Mainardi of Cremona; Hugo Physicus; Dominicus Parisiensis.

128. DALTON, O. M., "The Byzantine Astrolabe at Brescia," *British Academy Proceedings*, Vol. 12, 1926, pp. 133-146.
129. DANFRIE, PHILIPPE (d. 1606), *Déclaration de l'usage du graphomètre* (Paris, 1597).
130. DANTI, IGNAZIO (1537-1586), *Trattato dell'uso et della fabbrica dell'astrolabio* (Florence, 1569).
131. DARBY, H. C., "The Agrarian Contribution to Surveying in England," *The Geographical Journal*, Vol. 82, 1933.
132. DAREMBERG AND SAGLIO, *Dictionnaire des antiquités grecques et romaines* (Paris, 1837).
133. DATTA, A. B., *The Science of the Sulba. A Study of Early Hindu Geometry* (Calcutta, 1932).
134. DAVIS, JOHN (*c.* 1550-1605), *The Seamans Secrets* (London, 1595).
135. DAY, J., *Principles of Navigation and Surveying* (New Haven, Conn., 1817).
136. DAY, J., *Trigonometry* (New Haven, Conn., 1815).
137. DEIMAL, P., "Die Vermessung der Felder bei den Sumeren um 3000 v. Chr.," *Orientalia*, Vol. 5, 1922, pp. 56-63; Vol. 7, 1924, pp. 1-43.
138. DELLA CORTE, M., "Pompeii Groma, 1912," *Reale accademia nazionale dei lincei*, Vol. 28, 1922.
139. DES BORDES, GIOVANNI (*fl.* 1560), *La déclaration et usage de l'instrument nommé conomètre* (Paris, 1570).
140. DIESTERWEG, A., *Leitfaden für den ersten Unterricht in der Formen-Grössen und raumlichen Verbindungslehre* (Elberfeld, 1822).
141. DIGGES, LEONARD (*fl.* 1555), *A Booke named Tectonicon* (London, 1556).
142. DIGGES, LEONARD, *A Geometrical Practise named Pantometria* (London, 1571, 1591). Published by his son, Thomas Digges.
143. DIGGES, THOMAS (*fl.* 1570), *An Arithmeticall Militare Treatise named Stratioticos* (London, 1572).
144. DIOGENES LAERTIUS, *The Lives and Opinions of Eminent Philosophers*, Translated by C. D. Yonge (London, 1853).
145. DOMINICUS PARISIENSIS, *Practica Geometriae, Zeitschrift für Mathematik und Physik*, Vol. 40, Hist. Liter. Abt, p. 161. Edited by M. Curtze.
146. DORN, B., "Drei astronomische Instrumente," *Mémoires de l'académie impérial des sciences de St. Petersbourg*, 1865.
147. DOU, JAN (*fl.* 1600), *Tractat vant maken ende gebruycken eens nien gheordenneerden mathematischen instruments* (Amsterdam, 1612).

148. Dou, Jan, and Sens, Johann, *Practijck des Landmeten* (Leyden, 1600).
149. Drecker, J., "Das Planisphärium des Claudius Ptolemaeus," *Isis*, Vol. 9, 1927, pp. 255-278.
150. Drecker, J., "Des Johannes Philoponus Schrift über das Astrolab," *Isis*, Vol. 11, 1928, pp. 15-44.
151. Drecker, J., "Hermannus Contractus, über das Astrolab," *Isis*, Vol. 16, 1933, pp. 200-219.
152. Dudley, Robert (1574-1649), *Dell' Arcano del mare* (Florence, 1646).
153. Dümmler, E., "Ekkehart IV von St. Gallen," *Zeitschrift für deutsches Altertum und deutsche Litteratur*, Vol. 14, 1869.

154. Eden, Richard (fl. 1550), *The Arte of Navigation* (London, 1561).
155. Edgar, N., *Elementary and Constructional Geometry* (New York, 1902).
156. Edwards, P. D., "What Specialized Knowledge Should the Teacher Training Program Provide in the Field of Geometry?" *The Mathematics Teacher*, Vol. 34, 1941, pp. 113-118.
157. Eggar, W. D., *Practical Exercises in Geometry* (London, 1903).
158. Eisenlohr, A., *Ein mathematisches Handbuch der alten Ägypter* (Leipzig, 1877).
159. Engelmann, M., "Die Habermelschen Instrumente in Dresden," *Mitteilung aus dem sächsische Kunstsammlung*, No. 4, 1913.
160. Errard de Bar-le-Duc, Jean (fl. 1590), *La Géométrie et pratique géneralle d'icelle* (Paris, 1594).
161. Euclid, *L'optique et la catoptrique*, French Translation by Verecke (Paris, 1938).
162. Evans, L., "Some European and Oriental Astrolabes," *The Archaeological Journal*, Vol. 58, 1911.
163. Ewing, A., *A Synopsis of Practical Mathematics*, Fourth Edition (London, 1799).
164. *Eyn wolgeordent und nutzlich Büchlin wie man Bergwerck suchen und finden soll* (1505).

165. Fabri, Ottavio (fl. 1585), *L'uso della squadra mobile* (Padua, 1615).
166. Faleiro, Francesco (fl. 1510), *Tratado del esphera y del arte del marear* (Seville, 1535).
167. Falke, J., *Propadeutik der Geometrie, eine Bearbeitung der geometrischen Formenlehre nach einer neuen Methode gegrundet auf praktische Aufgaben aus der Geodäsie* (Leipzig, 1866).
168. Feldhaus, F. M., *Die Technik der Antike und des Mittelalters* (Berlin, 1931).
169. Ferguson, J., "The Margarita Philosophica of Gregorius Reisch—a Bibliography," *The Library*, Series 4, Vol. 10, 1930.
170. Fernandez de Navarrete, M., *Coleccion de los viages y descubrimientos que hicieron por mar los Espanoles desde fines del siglo XV* (Madrid, 1825-1837), 5 vols.
171. Fettweiss, E., "Über die erste Entstehung der einfachten geometrischen Formen," *Archiv für Geschichte Mathematik, Naturwissenschaften und der Technik*, New Series 3, Vol. 12, 1929.
172. Finch, J. K., "Lowering the Level of the Alban Lake," *Civil Engineering*, Vol. 4, 1934, pp. 328-330.
173. Finch, J. K., "Our Indebtedness to the Old Surveyor," *The Military Engineer*, July-August, 1925.

174. FINAEUS, ORONTIUS (1494-1555), *De re et praxi geometrica, libri tres* (Paris, 1556).

175. FINAEUS, ORONTIUS, *Protomathesis* (Paris, 1532).

176. FISCHER, J., *Ptolemaei Geographiae Codex Urbinas Graecus* (Leipzig, 1932).

177. FITZHERBERT, ANTHONY (1470-1538), *The Boke of Surveyinge* (London, 1523).

178. FITZPATRICK, B., *Ireland and the Foundations of Europe* (New York, 1927).

179. FLAMSTEED, JOHN, *Historia Coelestis Britannica* (London, 1712).

180. FLEMING, A. P., AND BROCKLEHURST, H. J., *A History of Engineering* (London, 1925).

181. FLINT, A., *Geometry and Trigonometry* (Hartford, Conn., 1806).

182. FLINT, A., *Surveying* (Hartford, Conn., 1804).

183. FORDHAM, H. G., "Christopher Saxton of Dunningley (*c.* 1542-*c.* 1616): His Life and Work," *The Publications of the Thoresby Society*, Vol. 28, 1928, pp. 361-384.

184. FORDHAM, H. G., *Some Notable Surveyors and Map-Makers of the 16th, 17th, and 18th Centuries and Their Work* (Cambridge, Cambridge University Press, 1929).

185. FORESTANI, LORENZO (d. 1623), *Pratica d'arithmetica e geometria nuovamenta posta in luce* (Venice, 1603).

186. FOULLON, ABEL (1513-1563), *Usaige et description de l'holomêtre* (Paris, 1551). Italian Edition by S. Ziletti (Venice, 1564).

187. FOURNIER, GEORGE, S.J. (1595-1662), *Hydrographie, contenant la théorie et la pratique de toutes les parties de la navigation* (Paris, 1643).

188. FRANK, J., "Die Verwendung des Astrolabs nach al Chwārizmī," *Abhandlung zur Geschichte der Naturwissenschaften und der Medizin*, Heft 3, 1922.

189. FRÈRES DES ÉCOLES CHRÉTIENNES, LES, *Géométrie, Cours élémentaire* (Paris and Tours, Undated). *Manuel d'arpentage pour les écoles primaires* (Paris and Tours, Undated).

190. FRONTINUS, S., *De Aquis Urbis Romae*, English Translation by C. Herschel in *Frontinus and the Water Supply of the City of Rome*, Second Edition (Boston, Longmans, Green and Co., 1913).

191. GALILEI, GALILEO (1564-1642), *La operazioni del compasso geometrico e militare* (Padua, 1596).

192. GALLUCCI, GIOVANNI (1538-*c.* 1621), *Della fabrica et uso de diversi stromenti di astronomia et cosmographia* (Venice, 1598).

193. GANDOLFO, J. H., "Tracing the Engineer in Early Egypt and Assyria," *Civil Engineering*, Vol. 1, 1931, pp. 632-637.

194. GANDZ, S., "Die Harpedonapten oder Seilspanner und Seilknüpfer," *Quellen und Studien zur Geschichte der Mathematik*, Abt. B, *Studien*, Bd. 1, Heft 3, 1930, pp. 256-277.

195. GANDZ, S., "The Origin of Angle-Geometry," *Isis*, Vol. 12, 1929, pp. 452-481.

196. GANGULI, S., "Notes on Indian Mathematics," *Isis*, Vol. 12, 1929, pp. 132-145.

197. GELLIBRAND, HENRY (*fl.* 1630), *A Discours Mathematical on the Variation of the Magneticall Needle* (London, 1635).

198. GENTILINUS, E. (*fl.* 1585), *Instruttione de bombardieri* (Venice, 1592).

199. *Geometria Culmensis, Ein agronomischer Traktat aus der Zeit des Hochmeisters Conrad von Jungingen (1393-1407)*, Edited by M. Mendthal (Leipzig, 1886). Latin and German texts.

200. GERBERT, "Gerberti . . . Geometria," Edited by P. B. Pez, Published in Migne, *Patrologiae Cursus Completus*, Vol. 139, 1853, pp. 84-134.

201. GERBERT, *Gerberti postea Silvestri II Papae Opera Mathematica.* Edited by N. Bubnov (Berlin, 1899). *See also* Würschmidt, J.
202. GERBERT, *Oeuvres de Gerbert,* Edited by A. Olleris (Paris, 1867).
203. GIBSON, R., *A Treatise of Practical Surveying* (London, 1767).
204. GILBERT, WILLIAM (1540-1603), *De Magnete* (London, 1600).
205. GILES, H. A., "The Mariner's Compass," *Adversaria Sinica* (Shanghai, 1918), pp. 107-115, 217-222.
206. GILLESPIE, W. M., *A Treatise on Surveying,* Revised Edition (New York, D. Appleton-Century Co., Inc., 1904).
207. GINSBURG, A., "Description of the Astrolabe," *Bulletin of the Museum of Science and Industry* (New York).
208. GOMEZ-PEREZ, F., "Mexican Irrigation in the Sixteenth Century," *Civil Engineering,* Vol. 12, 1942, pp. 24-27.
209. GORE, J. H., *Geodesy* (Boston, Houghton Mifflin Co., 1891).
210. GOUGAUD, DOM LOUIS, O.S.B., *Gaelic Pioneers of Christianity,* Translated by V. Collins (Dublin, M. T. Gill Co., 1923).
211. GRAS, N. S., *A History of Agriculture in Europe and America,* (New York, F. S. Crofts and Co., 1925).
212. GRASSMAN, G., *Raumlehre für Volkschulen* (Berlin, 1824).
213. GREGORY, JAMES (1638-1675), *Exercitationes Geometricae* (London, 1668).
214. GRIZZELL, E. D., *Origin and Development of the High School in New England before 1865* (Philadelphia, University of Pennsylvania Press, 1922).
215. GÜNTHER, S., "Die Erfindung des Baculus geometricus," *Bibliotheca Mathematica,* New Series 4, Vol. 3, 1890, pp. 73-80.
216. GÜNTHER, S., *Geschichte des mathematischen Unterrichts im deutschen Mittelalter bis zum Jahre 1525* (Berlin, 1887).
217. GUMMERE, J., *Surveying* (Philadelphia, 1814).
218. GUNN, B. G., AND PEET, B. T. E., "Four Geometrical Problems from the Moscow Mathematical Papyrus," *Journal of Egyptian Archeology,* Vol. 15, 1929.
219. GUNTER, EDMUND (1581-1628), *Description and Use of the Sector, Crosse-Staffe and Other Instruments* (London, 1624).
220. GUNTHER, R. T., *Early Science in Oxford* (Oxford, Clarendon Press, 1923), Vols. I, II.
221. GUNTHER, R. T., *First Book of Digges' Pantometria,* Old Ashmolean Reprints, IV (Oxford, Oxford University Press, 1927).
222. GUNTHER, R. T., *The Astrolabes of the World* (Oxford, Oxford University Press, 1932), 2 vols.
223. GUNTHER, R. T., "The Great Astrolabe and other Scientific Instruments of Humphrey Cole," *Archaeologia,* Series 2, Vol. 26, 1927, pp. 272-317.
224. GUNTHER, R. T., "The Uranical Astrolabe and other Inventions of John Blagrave of Reading," *Archaeologia,* Series 2, Vol. 28, 1929, pp. 55-72.
225. GUTMANN, JOHANN (*fl.* 1565), *Feldmessung, gewiss, richtig und kurz gestellt* (Heidelberg, 1574).

226. HALLIWELL, J., *Rara Mathematica* (London, 1839).
227. HALLOCK, W., AND WADE, H., *The Evolution of Weights and Measures and of the Metric System* (New York, The Macmillan Co., 1906).
228. HALMA, W., *See* Ptolemy, Claudius.
229. HAMMER, E., "Über die Genauigkeit einiger antiker Absteckungen," *Zeitschrift für Vermessungswesen,* Vol. 40, 1911, pp. 573-586.

230. HAMMER, VON, J., "Extracts from the Mohīt," *Journal of the Asiatic Society of Bengal*, Vol. 3, 1834, pp. 544 ff.; Vol. 7, 1838, pp. 767 ff.; Vol. 8, 1839, pp. 823 ff.

231. HAMMERTON, J. A., *Wonders of the Past* (New York, G. P. Putnam's Sons, 1924).

232. HAMMOND, J., *The Practical Surveyor* (London, 1749).

233. HANNLOSER, H., *Villard de Honnecourt* (Vienna, 1935).

234. HARNISCH, W., *Die Raumlehre oder die Messkunst gewöhnlich Geometrie genannt* (Berlin, 1821).

235. HASE, H., "Joannis Alexandri, Cognomine Philopoi, de usu astrolabi eiusque constructione libellus," *Rheinisches Museum für Philologie*, Vol. 6, 1839.

236. HASKINS, C. H., *Studies in the History of Medieval Science* (Cambridge, Mass., Harvard University Press, 1924).

237. HASKINS, C. H., AND LOCKWOOD, D. D., *The Sicilian Translators of the Twelfth Century*, Harvard Studies in Classical Philology, Vol. 21.

238. HEADLAM, J., "The Guns, Gunners and Gunnery of the English Renaissance," *The Journal of the Royal Artillery*, Vol. 66, 1939, pp. 469-488.

239. HEATH, T., *A History of Greek Mathematics* (Oxford, Oxford University Press, 1921).

240. HEATH, T., "Mathematics and Astronomy," *The Legacy of Greece*, Edited by R. Livingstone (Oxord, The Clarendon Press, 1921).

241. HEATH, T., *The Thirteen Books of Euclid's Elements* (Cambridge, Cambridge University Press, 1908).

242. HEATHCOTE, N. H., "Christopher Columbus and the Discovery of Magnetic Variation," *Science Progress*, July, 1932, pp. 83-103.

243. HEDRAEUS, BENEDICTUS (*c.* 1608-1659), *Nova et accurata astrolabii geometrici structura* (Leyden, 1643).

244. HEE, VAN, L., S.J., "La classique de l'ile maritime, ouvrage chinois du IIIe siècle," *Quellen und Studien zur Geschichte der Mathematik*, Abt. B, Bd. 2, 1932-1933, pp. 255-280.

245. HEE, VAN, L., S.J., "The Great Treasure House of Chinese and European Mathematics," *American Mathematical Monthly*, Vol. 33, 1926, pp. 502-506.

246. HEIBERG, J. L., *Mathematics and Physical Science in Classical Antiquity*, Translated by D. C. MacGregor (Oxford, The Clarendon Press, 1922).

247. HELLMANN, G., *Neudrucke von Schriften und Karten über Meteorologie und Erdmagnetismus*, No. 10, 1898.

248. HELLMANN, G., Über die Kenntnis der magnetischen Deklination vor Christoph Columbus," *Meteorologische Zeitschrift*, April, 1906, pp. 145-149.

249. HENNIG, R., "Die Frükenntnis der magnetischen Nordweisung," *Beiträge zur Geschichte der Technik und Industrie*, Vol. 21, 1931-1932, pp. 25-42.

250. HENRION, DENIS (1590-1640), *Collection ou recueil de divers traictéz mathématiques* (Paris, 1621).

251. HENRION, DENIS, *L'Usage du mecomêtre* (Paris, 1630).

252. HENRION, DENIS, *Usage du compass de proportion* (Paris, 1618).

253. HERBERMANN, C. G., *The Cosmographiae Introductio of Martin Waldseemüller*, United States Catholic Historical Society, Monograph 4 (New York, 1907).

254. HERMANN CONTRACTUS (*fl.* 1040), *Tractatus Astrolabii*, Edited by P. B. Pez, Published in Migne, *Patrologiae Cursus Completus*, Vol. 143, pp. 379-412. See also Drecker, J.

255. HERODOTUS, *History*, Translated by H. Cary (London, 1847).

256. HERON OF ALEXANDRIA. See Schöne, Vincent, Skyring-Walters, Jones.

257. HERSCHEL, C. *See* Frontinus.
258. HIRTH, F., *Ancient History of China* (New York, The Columbia University Press, 1911).
259. HOFMANN, HENRY (*fl.* 1600), *De Octantis Instrumenti* (Jena, 1612).
260. HOGBEN, L., *Mathematics for the Million* (New York, W. W. Norton and Co., 1940).
261. HONNECOURT, DE, V., *Facsimile of the Sketch-book of Vilars de Honecort, an Architect of the Thirteenth Century*, French Edition by M. Lassus and M. Quicherat, English translation by R. Willis (London, 1859). *See also* Hannloser, H.
262. HOOD, THOMAS (*fl.* 1585), *The Use of the Cross-Staff* (London, 1590).
263. HOOKE, ROBERT, *Posthumous Works* (London, 1708).
264. HOOPS, J., *Reallexikon der germanischen Altertumskunde* (Strassburg, 1911), Vol. 2. Article "Geometrie" by A. A. Bjornbo.
265. HOOVER, H. C., AND HOOVER, L. H. *See* Agricola.
266. HOPTON, ARTHUR (*fl.* 1600), *The Topographical Glass* (London, 1611).
267. HORSBURGH, E. M., "The Cross-staff and Its Uses in Navigation," *Scottish Geographical Magazine*, Vol. 46, 1930, pp. 92-100.
268. HUBBARD, H. D., "The Romance of Measurement," *Scientific Monthly*, October, 1931, pp. 356 ff.
269. HUGO PHYSICUS, *Practica Geometriae*, Edited by M. Curtze, *Monatschefte für Mathematik* (Leipzig, 1897), Heft 8.
270. HULSIUS, LEVINUS (d. 1606), *De Quadrante Geometrico* (Nürnberg, 1594).
271. HULSIUS, LEVINUS, *Tractati Instrumentorum Mechanicorum* (Frankfurt a.M., 1603-1615).
272. HULTSCH, F., "Winkelmessungen durch die Hipparchische Dioptra." *Abhandlungen zur Geschichte der Mathematik*, Heft 9, 1899, p. 120.
273. HUTTON, C., *A Course in Mathematics in Two Volumes, Composed for the Use of the Royal Military Academy*, Amended by Olinthus Gregory, Twelfth Edition with Additions by Thomas S. Davies (London, 1841).
274. HUTTON, C., *The Compendious Measurer*, Second Edition (London, 1790).

275. IBN-AL-'AUWĀM. *See* Wiedemann, E.
276. IBN-SĪNĀ. *See* Wiedemann, E.
277. International Congress of Mathematicians, Cambridge, England, 1912, "Summary of Report on the Teaching of Mathematics in Secondary Schools," *L'Énseignement mathématique*, Vol. 14, 1912.

278. JESS, Z., *A Compendious System of Practical Surveying* (Wilmington, Del., 1799).
279. JOÃO DE LISBOA, *Regimento dos longitudes* (Lisbon, 1514).
280. JOHANNES PHILOPONUS. *See* Drecker, J.; Hase, H.
281. Joint Commission of The Mathematical Association of America and The National Council of Teachers of Mathematics, "The Place of Mathematics in Secondary Education," The National Council of Teachers of Mathematics, *Fifteenth Yearbook* (New York, Bureau of Publications, Teachers College, Columbia University, 1940).
282. JORDAN, W., *Handbuch der Vermessungskunde* (Stuttgart, 1897).

283. KÄSTNER, A. G., *Anfansgründe der Arithmetik, Geometrie, eben und sphärischen Trigonometrie* (Göttingen, 1758).

284. KARPINSKI, L. C., *Bibliography of Mathematical Works Printed in America through 1850* (Ann Arbor, Mich., University of Michigan Press, 1940).
285. KAYE, G. R., *Indian Mathematics* (Calcutta, 1915).
286. KAYE, G. R., "Notes on Indian Mathematics," *Journal of the Asiatic Society of Bengal*, New Series, Vol. 4, 1908, pp. 128 ff.
287. KENNEY, J., *Sources of Early Irish History* (New York, The Columbia University Press, 1929). 2 vols.
288. KHANIKOFF, N., "Analysis and Extracts of the Book of the Balance of Wisdom by al Chāzinī," *Journal of the American Oriental Society*, Vol. 6, 1860.
289. KIMBLE, G. H., "Some Notes on Medieval Cartography," *Scottish Geographical Magazine*, Vol. 49, 1933, pp. 91-98.
290. KINGMAN, E. D., "Roger Sherman, Colonial Surveyor," *Civil Engineering*, Vol. 10, 1940, pp. 514-515.
291. KIRBY, R. S., "Some Engineering Beginnings," *Civil Engineering*, Vol. 7, 1937, pp. 735-739.
292. KIRBY, R. S., "Specifications and Plans of Ancient Times," *Civil Engineering*, Vol. 11, 1941, pp. 393-396.
293. KIRBY, R. S., AND LAURSON, P. G., *The Early Years of Modern Civil Engineering* (New Haven, Conn., Yale University Press, 1932).
294. KIRCHER, ATHANASIUS, S.J., *Magnes sive de Arte Magnetica* (Rome, 1641).
295. KLAPROTH, J., *Lettre à M. le Baron Humbolt sur l'invention de la boussole* (Paris, 1834).
296. KLEIN, F., AND SCHIMMACK, R., *Vorträge über den mathematischen Unterricht an den höheren Schulen* (Leipzig, 1907).
297. KÖBEL, JAKOB (1470-1533), *Geometrie von künstlichen Feldmessen* (Frankfurt a.M., 1531).
298. KOKOMOOR, F. W., "The Teaching of Elementary Geometry in the Seventeenth Century," *Isis*, Vol. 11, 1928, pp. 85-110.
299. KRÖGER, M., *Leitfaden für den Geometrie-Unterricht im Mittelschulen* (Hamburg, 1889).
300. KUCHARZEWSKI, F., "Sur quelques niveaux du seizième siècle," *Bibliotheca Mathematica*, Series 3, Vol. 1, 1900, pp. 60-63.

301. LA CROIX, S. F., *Élémens de géométrie* (Paris, 1794).
302. LA HIRE, DE, PHILIPPE (1640-1718), *L'École des arpenteurs* (Paris, 1689).
303. LA HIRE, DE, PHILIPPE, *Sur une nouvelle form de boussole* (Paris, 1689).
304. LANCASTER-JONES, E., "Criticism of Heron's Dioptra," *The Geographical Journal*, Vol. 69, 1927.
305. LANCASTER-JONES, E., *Geodesy and Surveying. Catalogue of the Collections in The Science Museum, South Kensington* (London, 1925).
306. LANE, E. W., "Ingenuity of the Ancient Chinese," *Civil Engineering*, Vol. 1, 1931, pp. 17 ff.
307. LAUSSEDAT, A., *Recherches sur les instruments, les méthodes et le dessin topographiques* (Paris, 1898).
308. LECKY, J., "The Valencia Astrolabe," *Kerry Archaeological Magazine*, March, 1913, pp. 74-79.
309. LE CLERC, SEBASTIEN (1637-1714), *Pratique de la géométrie sur le papier et sur le terrain* (Paris, 1669).
310. LE CLERC, SEBASTIEN, *Traité de géométrie* (Paris, 1690).

311. LEGNAZZI, E. N., *Del catastro romano e di alcuni strumenti antichi del geodesia* (Padua, 1885).

312. LEIGH, VALENTINE (*fl.* 1555), *Treatise of Measuring All Kinds of Lands* (London, 1562).

313. LEONARDO PISANO (Fibonacci), *Scritti di Leonardo Pisano,* Edited by B. Boncompagni (Rome, 1862). 2 vols.

314. LEPSIUS, K. R., "Über eine hieroglyphische Inschrift im Temple von Edfu," *Preussische Akadamie der Wissenschaften zu Berlin. Abhandlungen* (Berlin, 1855).

315. LEVI BEN GERSON. *See* Günther, S.

316. LEYBOURN, WILLIAM (1626-1700), *The Compleat Surveyor* (London, 1653; Second Edition, 1657; Third Edition, 1674).

317. LIETZMANN, W., "Über einige 'Legenden' aus der Geschichte der Mathematik," *Zeitschrift für mathematischen und naturwissenschaftlichen Unterricht aller Schulgattungen,* Vol. 71, 1940, pp. 25-30.

318. LIPPMANN, VON, E. O., "Geschichte der Magnet-nadel bis zur Erfindung des Kompasses (Gegen 1300)," *Quellen und Studien zur Geschichte der Naturwissenschaften und der Medizin,* Vol. 3, No. 1, 1932.

319. LOVE, JOHN (*fl.* 1680), *Geodasia, or The Art of Surveying* (London, 1688).

320. LUCAR, CYPRIAN (*fl.* 1580), *A Treatise named Lucarsolace* (London, 1590).

321. LYONS, H., "Ancient Surveying Instruments," *The Geographical Journal,* Vol. 69, 1927.

322. McCULLOUGH, E., *Practical Surveying* (New York, D. Van Nostrand Co., 1915).

323. MAINARDI OF CREMONA, *Practica Geometriae,* German translation by M. Curtze in *Abhandlung zur Geschichte der mathematischen Wissenschaften* (Leipzig, 1902), Heft 13.

324. MAITLAND, F. W., *Domesday Book and Beyond* (London, 1897).

325. MANLEY, G., "Saxton's Survey of Northern England," *The Geographical Journal,* Vol. 83, 1934, pp. 308-316.

326. MARKHAM, C. R., "The History of the Gradual Development of the Groundwork of Geographical Science." *The Geographical Journal,* Vol. 46, 1915.

327. MARTIN, P., AND SCHMIDT, C., *Raumlehre für Mittelschulen* (Berlin, 1896-1898).

328. Mathematical Association, *A Second Report on the Teaching of Geometry in Schools* (London, 1938).

329. Mathematical Association, "Report on the Teaching of Mathematics in Public and Secondary Schools," *The Mathematical Gazette,* Vol. 11, 1919.

330. Mathematical Association, *The Teaching of Geometry in Schools* (London, 1923).

331. MEDINA, DE, PEDRO (*c.* 1493-*c.* 1567), *Arte de navegar* (Vallodolid, 1545).

332. MEITZEN, A., *Siedelung und Agrarwesen* (Berlin, 1895).

333. MENDTHAL, M. *See Geometria Culmensis.*

334. MERCKEL, C., *Die Ingenieurtechnik im Altertum* (Berlin, 1899).

335. MERRIMAN, A. C., "A Greek Tunnel of the Sixth Century B.C.," *School of Mines Quarterly,* Vol. 6, 1885.

336. METIUS, ADRIAN (1571-1635), *Arithmeticae libri duo et geometriae libri sex* (Batava, 1625).

337. METIUS, ADRIAN, *Genuino Usu utriusque Globi Tractatus* (Francarae, 1611).

338. METIUS, ADRIAN, *Mensura Geographica et Usus Globi Terrestris* (Francarae, 1624).

339. METIUS, ADRIAN, *Primum Mobile* (Amsterdam, 1633).

340. Meyerhoff, M., "Science and Medicine." *The Legacy of Islam*, Edited by T. Arnold and A. Guillaume (Oxford, Oxford University Press, 1931).

341. Middleton, R. J., *The Teaching of Elementary Geometry*, Records of the Education Society, New South Wales, No. 10, 1911.

342. Mirick, G. R., *An Experimental Course in Plane Geometry* (New York, 1941).

343. Mitchell, A. C., "Chapters in the History of Terrestrial Magnetism," *Terrestrial Magnetism and Atmospheric Electricity*, Vol. 27, 1932, pp. 105-146.

344. Moette, Thomas (*fl.* 1690), *L'École des arpenteurs* (Paris, 1692).

345. Mohīt. See Hammer, von, J.

346. Moitoiret, A., *Nouveaux élémens de géométrie pratique concernant l'arpentage* (Rouen, 1700).

347. Montauzan, de, C. G., *Essai sur la science et l'art de l'ingénieur aux premiers siècles de l'empire romain* (Paris, 1909).

348. Moore, E. H., *On the Foundations of Mathematics*, The National Council of Teachers of Mathematics, *First Yearbook* (New York, Bureau of Publications, Teachers College, Columbia University, 1926).

349. Moore, S., *An Accurate System of Surveying* (Litchfield, Conn., 1796).

350. Morley, W. H., *Description of a Planispheric Astrolabe* (London, 1856).

351. Morley, W. H., *Description of an Arabic Quadrant* (London, 1860).

352. Mortet, V., "Un nouveau texte des traités d'arpentage et de géométrie d'Epaphroditus et de Vitruvius Rufus," *Notices et extraits des manuscrits de la bibliothèque impériale*, Vol. 35, 1896.

353. Moscow Papyrus. See Struve, W. W.; Thomas, W. R.

354. Müller, K. O., *Die Etrusker* (Stuttgart, 1877).

355. Münster, Sebastian (1489-1552), *Rudimenta Mathematica* (Basel, 1551).

356. Muirhead, J., *The Mechanical Inventions of James Watt* (London, 1855). 3 vols.

357. Nallino, C. A., *Al Battānī sive Albatenii, Opus Astronomicum* (Mediolani, 1903).

358. National Education Association, *Final Report of the National Committee of Fifteen on Geometry Syllabus* (Chicago, University of Chicago Press, 1912).

359. National Education Association, *Report of the Committee of Ten on Secondary School Studies* (New York, 1894).

360. Nau, M. F., "Le Traité sur l'astrolabe plan de Sévère Sebokt," *Journal asiatique*, Series 9, Vol. 13, 1899.

361. Neckam, A., *De Naturis Rerum*, Edited by T. Wright in the Rolls Series (London, 1863).

362. Neckam, A., *De Utensilibus*, Edited by T. Wright in *A Volume of Vocabularies* (London, 1857).

363. Neuburger, A., *The Technical Arts and Sciences of the Ancients*, Translated by H. L. Brose (Berlin, 1930).

364. Neugebauer, O., "Die Geometrie der ägyptischen mathematischen Texte," *Quellen und Studien zur Geschichte der Mathematik. Quellen*, Abt. B, Bd. 1, 1929, pp. 413-451.

365. Neugebauer, O., "Mathematische Keilschrift-Texte," *Quellen*, Abt. A. Bd. 3; Pts. I and II (1935), Pt. III (1937).

366. Neugebauer, O., "Vorlesungen über Geschichte der antiken mathematischen Wissenschaften," Vol. 1, "Vorgriechische Mathematik," *Die Grundlehren der mathematischen Wissenschaften*, Vol. 43, 1934.

367. NEUGEBAUER, O., AND SACHS, A., *Mathematical Cuneiform Texts*, The American Oriental Society and The American School of Oriental Research (New Haven, Conn., 1945).

368. NEUMANN, J., *Neue Beyträge zur praktischen Geometrie* (Munich, 1800).

369. NORDEN, JOHN (1548-1625), *Speculum Brittaniae* (London, 1593).

370. NORDEN, JOHN, *The Surveyor's Dialogue* (London, 1607).

371. NORMAN, ROBERT (*fl.* 1570), *The Newe Attractive* (London, 1581).

372. NORMAN, ROBERT, *The Safeguard of Saylers, or Great Rutter* (London, 1584).

373. NORWOOD, R., *Epitome, or The Doctrine of Triangles* (London, 1659).

374. NOWOTNY, E., "Groma," *Germania*, Vol. 7, 1923, Pt. I, pp. 22-29.

375. NUÑEZ, PEDRO (1502-1578), *De Arte Atque Ratione Navigandi* (Coimbra, 1546).

376. NUÑEZ, PEDRO, *De Crepusculis* (Lisbon, 1542).

377. NUÑEZ, PEDRO, *Tratado da sphera* (Lisbon, 1537).

378. NUNN, P., "Notes on the Place of Similarity in School Geometry," *The Mathematical Gazette*, Vol. 22, 1938, pp. 234-249.

379. NYE, NATHANAEL (*fl.* 1640), *The Art of Gunnery* (London, 1647).

380. ODDI, MUZIO (1589-1639), *Dello Squadro* (Milan, 1625).

381. OHM, G. S., *Grundlinien zu einer zweckmässigen Behandlung der Geometrie* (Erlangen, 1817).

382. OLDS, E. G., "The Use of Applications for Instructional Purposes," *The Mathematics Teacher*, Vol. 34, 1941, pp. 78-83.

383. OLLERIS, A. *See* Gerbert.

384. ORNUM, VAN, J. L., "Topographical Surveys, Their Methods and Value," *Bulletin of the University of Wisconsin*. Engineering Series, Vol. 1, No. 10, 1896.

385. OZANAM, JACQUES (1640-1717), *Usage du compass de proportion* (Paris, 1688).

386. PACIOLI, LUCA (*c.* 1445-*c.* 1509), *Suma de Arithmetica, Geometria Proportioni et Proportionalita* (Venice, 1494).

387. PARSONS, W. B., *Engineers and Engineering in the Renaissance* (Baltimore, Williams and Wilkins Co., 1939).

388. PAULY-WISSOWA, *Realenzyklopädie der klassischen Altertumswissenschaften* (Stuttgart, 1912), Vol. 7.

389. PEET, B. T. E., "Egyptian Mathematics," *Bulletin of the John Rylands Library*, Vol. 15, 1931. *See also* Gunn, B. G.

390. PEET, B. T. E., *The Rhind Mathematical Papyrus* (Liverpool, 1923).

391. PELETIER, JACQUES (1517-1582), . . . *de Usu Geometriae* (Paris, 1572).

392. PENTHER, J. F., *Praxis Geometriae* (Augsburg, 1732).

393. PEREGRINUS, PETRUS, *Epistola Petri Peregrini de Maricourt ad Sygerum de Foucaucourt militem de Magnete* (Lucera, 1269; First printed at Augsburg, 1558). English translations: Silvanus Thompson, Limited Edition (Chiswick Press, London, 1902). Br. Arnold, F.S.C. (New York, McGraw Book Co., 1904).

394. PEZ, P. B. *See* Gerbert; Hermann Contractus.

395. PHILIPPI, F., *Zur Reconstruction der Weltcarte des Agrippa* (Marburg, 1880).

396. PICARD, JEAN (1620-1682), *Mesure de la terre* (Paris, 1669).

397. PITISCUS, BARTHOLOMEW (1561-1613), *Trigonometriae* (Frankfurt a.M., 1600).

398. PLATO, *The Republic*, Loeb Library Edition, English Translation by P. Shorey (Cambridge, Mass., Harvard University Press, 1935).

399. PLINY, *Natural History,* English Translation by Bostock and Riley (London, 1855).

400. POMODORO, GIOVANNI (*fl.* 1590), *La Geometria Prattica* (Rome, 1599).

401. PORTER, A. K., "The Earliest Geodetic Triangulation," *Empire Survey Review,* Vol. 1, 1931-1932, pp. 100-109.

402. POWER, M., "Medieval Irish Treatise on the Astrolabe," *Irish Texts Society,* Vol. 14, 1912. English and Irish texts.

403. PROCLUS DIODOCHUS, *Hypotyposis Astronomicarum Positionum,* Edited by C. Manitius (Leipzig, 1909).

404. PROGRESSIVE EDUCATION ASSOCIATION, *Mathematics in General Education* (New York, D. Appleton-Century Co., Inc., 1940).

405. PTOLEMY, CLAUDIUS, *Almagest,* French Translation by M. Halma (Paris, 1813). *See also* Drecker, J.

406. PTOLEMY, CLAUDIUS, *Handbuch der Astronomie,* Edited by C. Manitius (Leipzig, 1912).

407. PUEHLER, CHRISTOPHER (*fl.* 1560), *Ein kurze und gründliche Anlaytung zu dem rechten Verstand der Geometrie* (Dillingen, 1563).

408. PURBACH, GEORG (1423-1461), *Quadratum Geometricum* (Nürnberg, 1516-1517).

409. RAISZ, E., *General Cartography* (New York, McGraw-Hill Book Co., 1938).

410. RAMUS, PETER (1515-1572), *Arithmeticae libri duo, Geometricae septem et viginti* (Basel, 1559).

411. RAMUS, PETER, *Scholarum Mathematicorum libri unus et triginta* (Basel, 1569).

412. RATHBORNE, AARON (*fl.* 1600), *The Surveyor* (London, 1616).

413. RAVENSTEIN, E. G., *Martin Behaim, His Life and His Globes* (London, 1908).

414. RAYNER, W. H., "From Columbus' Compass to the First Transit," *Civil Engineering,* Vol. 9, 1939, pp. 661-664.

415. RAYNER, W. H., "Surveying in Ancient Times," *Civil Engineering,* Vol. 9, 1939, pp. 612-614.

416. RECORD, ROBERT (*c.* 1510-1558), *The Pathwaie to Knowledge* (London, 1551).

417. REEVES, E. A., *Maps and Map-making* (London, 1910).

418. REGIOMONTANUS. *See* Schöner, Johann.

419. REGNIER, GEMMA FRISIUS (1508-1555), *De Astrolabio Catholico liber* (Antwerp, 1556).

420. REGNIER, GEMMA FRISIUS, *De Radio Astronomico et Geometrico* (Antwerp, 1545).

421. REGNIER, GEMMA FRISIUS, *Libellus de Locorum Describendorum Ratione,* in Apian's *Cosmographia,* Antwerp Edition (Antwerp, 1533).

422. REHM, A., "Griechische Windrosen," *Sitzbericht der Königlich Bayerischen Akademie der Wissenschaften,* Jahrgang, 1916).

423. REINHOLD, ERASMUS (1511-1553), *Gründlicher und wahrer Bericht vom Feldmessen* (Saalfeld, 1574).

424. REISCH, GREGOR (*c.* 1465-1523), *Margarita Philosophica* (Freiburg, 1503). *See also* Ferguson, J.

425. RENSBERGER, NICOLAS, *Geometria* (Augsburg, 1568).

426. REPSOLD, J. A., *Zur Geschichte der astronomischen Messwerkzeuge von Purbach bis Reichenbach. 1450-1830* (Leipzig, 1908).

427. RHIND PAPYRUS. *See* Peet, B. T. E.; Chace, A. B., Manning, H. P., and Archibald, R. C.; Thomas, W. R.; Eisenlohr, A.

428. RITTER, FRANZ (d. 1640), *Instructio Instrumentalis Quadrantis Novi* (Nürnberg, 1599).

429. ROBERT ANGLICUS. *See* Tannery, P.

430. RODMAN, H., "The Sacred Calabash," *Proceedings, United States Naval Institute,* Vol. 53, 1927, pp. 867-872.

431. ROJAS, DE, JACQUES (*fl.* 1540), *Commentarium in Astrolabium, quod Planisphaerium vocant* (Paris, 1550).

432. ROSSI, G., *La groma e lo squandro ouvero storia dell'agrimensura italiana* (Turin, 1877).

433. RYFF, PETER (1552-1629), *Questiones Geometriae in Euclidis et P. Rami* (Frankfurt a.M., 1600).

434. RYFF, WALTER (*fl.* 1550), *Der furnembsten notwendigsten der gantzen Architectur angehörigen mathematischen und mechanischen Kunst* (Nürnberg, 1547).

435. SAAVEDRA; R., "Note sur un astrolabe arabe," *Atti del IV congresso internazionale degli orientalizi* (Florence, 1880).

436. SANTBECH, DANIEL (*fl.* 1550), *Problematum Astronomicorum et Geometricorum* (Basel, 1561).

437. SARTON, G., *History of Science and the New Humanism* (New York, Henry Holt and Co., 1931).

438. SARTON, G., *Introduction to the History of Science* (Baltimore, Williams and Wilkins Co., 1927), Vol. 1.

439. SAVASORDA (Abraham bar Chiia, *fl.* 1100), *Liber Embadorum*, Latin Translation by Plato of Tivoli; Latin Text with German Translation, Edited by M. Curtze, *Abhandlungen zur Geschichte der mathematischen Wissenschaften,* Vol. 12, 1902.

440. SCHEIL, V., O.P., *Une saison de fouilles à Sippar* (Paris, 1902).

441. SCHMALZL, P., *Zur Geschichte des Quadranten bei den Araben* (Munich, 1929).

442. SCHMIDT, F., *Geschichte der geodätischen Instrumente und Verfahren im Altertum und Mittelalter* (Neustadt an der Haardt, 1935).

443. SCHMIDT, W., "Haben Vitruv und die römischen Feldmesser aus Heron geschöpft?" *Bibliotheca Mathematica,* 1900, pp. 297-318.

444. SCHNELLER, H., "Beiträge zur Geschichte der Technik in der Antike und bei den Araben," *Abhandlungen zur Geschichte der Naturwissenschaften und der Medizin,* Vol. 6, 1922.

445. SCHOEN, E., *Geschichte des deutschen Feuerwerkswesens* (Berlin, 1936).

446. SCHÖNE, H., *Herons von Alexandria Vermessungslehre und Dioptra* (Leipzig, 1903).

447. SCHÖNER, JOHANN (1477-1547), *Scripta clarissimi mathematici M. Johannis Regiomontani de torqueto, astrolabio armillari . . . aucta necessariis Johannis Schoneri Carolostadii additionibus, item libellus M. Georgii Purbachi de quadrato geometrico* (Nürnberg, 1544).

448. SCHOTT, CASPER, S.J. (1608-1666), *Pantometrum Kircherianum* (Herbipolensi, 1660).

449. SCHOY, C., "Abhandlung über die Ziehung der Mittagslinie," *Annalen der Hydrographie und Maritinem Meteorologie,* Vol. 10, 1922.

450. SCHÜCK, A., "Das Blatt der Kompassrose," Geographische Gesellschaft in München, *Jahresbericht,* Vol. 13, 1890, pp. 20-59.

451. SCHÜCK, A., "Der Jakobstab," Geographische Gesellschaft in München, *Jahresbericht,* Vol. 16, 1893.

452. Schück, A., *Der Kompass* (Hamburg, 1915).
453. Schück, A., "Gedanken über die Zeit der ersten Benutzung des Kompasses im nördlichen Europa," *Archiv für die Geschichte der Naturwissenschaften und der Technik,* Vol. 3, 1910.
454. Schück, A., "Zur Einführung der Kompass in die nordwest-europäische Nautik," *Archiv für die Geschichte der Naturwissenschaften und der Technik,* Vol. 4, 1911.
455. Schwenter, Daniel (1585-1636), *Geometricae practicae novae et auctae, Libri IV* (Nürnberg, 1618).
456. Scott, D. A., "Evolution of Mine-Surveying Instruments," *Transactions, American Institute of Mining Engineers,* Vol. 28, 1898.
457. Scultetus, Bartholomew (1540-1614), *Gnomonice de Solariis* (Görlitz, 1572).
458. Sédillot, J. J., *Traité des instruments astronomique des Arabs* (Paris, 1834).
459. Sédillot, L. A., "Mémoire sur les instruments astronomiques des Arabs," *Mémoires présentes par divers savants à l'académie royale des inscrites et belles lettres,* Series 1, Vol. 1, 1844.
460. Seeman, H., "Die Instrumente der Sternwarte zu Marāgha nach al 'Urdī," *Sitzungsberichte der physikalisch-medizinischen Sozietät in Erlangen,* Vol. 60, 1928.
461. Severus Sebokt. *See* Nau, M. F.
462. Seybold, R. F., "The Evening School in Colonial America," *Bureau of Educational Research,* University of Illinois, *Bulletin* No. 31, 1925.
463. Shaw, W., *First Lessons in Observational Geometry* (London, 1903).
464. Shoen, H. H., "The Making of Maps and Charts," National Council for the Social Studies, *Ninth Yearbook* (Cambridge, Mass., 1938).
465. Shuster, C. N., *A Study of the Problems in Teaching the Slide Rule* (New York, Bureau of Publications, Teachers College, Columbia University, 1940).
466. Shuster, C. N., and Bedford, F. L., *Field Work in Mathematics* (New York, American Book Co., 1935).
467. Siddons, A. W., "Progress (History of School Mathematics in England)," *The Mathematical Gazette,* Vol. 20, 1936, pp. 7-26.
468. Skyring-Walters, R. C., "Greek and Roman Engineering Instruments," *Transactions, The Newcomen Society for the Study of Engineering and Technology,* Vol. 2, 1921.
469. Sloley, R. W., "An Ancient Surveying Instrument," *Ancient Egypt,* Vol. 3, 1926, pp. 65-67.
470. Smiles, S., *History of the Invention by John Harrison of the Marine Chronometer* (London, Undated).
471. Smith, D. E., *History of Mathematics* (Ginn and Co., Boston, 1923), 2 vols.
472. Smith, D. E., "Unsettled Questions Concerning the Mathematics of China," *Scientific Monthly,* Vol. 33, 1931, pp. 244-250.
473. Snell, Willebrod (1581-1626), *Erastosthenes Batavus seu De Terrae Ambitu* (Leyden, 1617).
474. Speleers, L., *Recueil des inscriptions de l'Asie antérieure des musées royaux du cinquantenaire à Bruxelles* (Brussels, 1925).
475. Stamper, A. W., *A History of the Teaching of Elementary Geometry* (New York, Bureau of Publications, Teachers College, Columbia University, 1909).
476. Stark, W. E., "Measuring Instruments of Long Ago," *School Science and Mathematics,* Vol. 10, 1910, pp. 48 ff., 126 ff.

477. STEINSCHNEIDER, M., "Die Mathematik bei den Juden," *Bibliotheca Mathematik,* New Series 10, 1896, No. 3, *et seq.*

478. STEVENSON, E. L., *Portolan Charts* (New York, Hispanic Society of America, 1911).

479. STEVIN, SIMON (1548-1620), *Mathematicorum Hypomnematum,* Tomus Secundus, *De Geometriae Praxi* (Leyden, 1605).

480. STOEBER, E., *Die römischen Grundsteuervermessungen* (Munich, 1877).

481. STÖFFLER, JOHANN (1452-1531), *Elucidatio Fabricae Ususque Astrolabii* (Tübingen, 1511).

482. STRUVE, W. W., "Mathematischer Papyrus des staatlichen Museums der Schönen Künste in Moskau," *Quellen und Studien zur Geschichte der Mathematik,* Abt. A, Bd. 1, 1930.

483. STURM, JOHANN C. (1635-1703), *Mathesis Compendiaria sive Tyrocinia Mathematica Tabulis Matheseos Generalis* (Nürnberg, 1670).

484. STURM, JOHANN C., *Mathesis Juvenilis* (Nürnberg, 1699).

485. STURMY, SAMUEL (b. 1633), *The Mariners Magazine,* Fourth Edition (London, 1700).

486. SUBERVILLE, DE, HENRY (*fl.* 1590), *L'Henry-mètre, instrument royal et universel* (Paris, 1598).

487. SULVASŪTRAS. *See* Bürk, A.; Datta, A. B.; Thibaut, G.

488. SŪRYA-SIDDHĀNTA. *See* Burgess, E.

489. SUTER, H., "Das Buch der geometrischen Konstruktionen von Abū'l Wefā," *Abhandlungen zur Geschichte der Naturwissenschaften und der Medizin,* Vol. 3, 1922.

490. SUTER, H., *Die Mathematik auf den Universitäten des Mittelalters* (Zurich, 1887).

491. SUTER, H., "Die Mathematiker und Astronomen der Araber und ihre Werke," *Abhandlungen zur Geschichte der mathematischen Wissenschaften,* Vol. 10, 1900.

492. SWEEDLER, E., "The Mathematics Club at Curtis High School," *The Mathematics Teacher,* Vol. 29, 1936, pp. 394-395.

493. TANNERY, P., "Le Traité du quadrant du maître Robert Anglais," *Notices et extracts de la bibliothèque nationale,* Vol. 35, 1897.

494. TANNERY, P., *Traité de l'astrolabe universel ou Saphea d'Arzachel par Guillaume l'Anglais. (Guillielmus Anglicus, 1231)* (Paris, 1897).

495. TARTAGLIA, NICOLO (*c.* 1506-1557), *General Trattato di Numeri e Misure* (Venice, 1556).

496. TARTAGLIA, NICOLO, *Nuova Scienza* (Venice, 1537).

497. TARTAGLIA, NICOLO, *Quesiti et Invenzioni Diversi* (Venice, 1546).

498. TAWNEY, R. H., *The Agrarian Problem in the Sixteenth Century* (London, 1912).

499. TAYLOR, E. G. R., "A Regional Map of the Early Sixteenth Century," *The Geographical Journal,* Vol. 71, 1928, pp. 473 ff.

500. TAYLOR, E. G. R., *Late Tudor and Early Stuart Geography* (London, Methuen and Co., 1934).

501. TAYLOR, E. G. R., *Tudor Geography* (London, Methuen and Co., 1930).

502. TAYLOR, H. O., *The Medieval Mind* (London, Macmillan & Co., 1911).

503. TAYLOR, H. O., *Thought and Expression of the Sixteenth Century* (New York, The Macmillan Co., 1920).

504. THEVENOT, MELCHISEDECH (*c.* 1620-1692), *Machine nouvelle pour conduire les eaux* (Paris, 1666).

505. THEVENOT, MELCHISEDECH, *Recueil des voyages* (Paris, 1681).

506. THIBAUT, G., "On the Sulvasutras," *Journal of the Asiatic Society of Bengal,* Vol. 44, 1875.

507. THOMAS, W. R., "Moscow Mathematical Papyrus, Problem 14," *Journal of Egyptian Archeology,* Vol. 17, 1931, pp. 50 ff.

508. THOMPSON, J. W., "The Introduction of Arabic Science into Lorraine in the Tenth Century," *Isis,* Vol. 12, 1929.

509. THOMPSON, S., "The Rose of the Winds," *Proceedings, British Academy,* Vol. 14, pp. 179-209. *See also* Peregrinus, Petrus.

510. THORNDIKE, L., *Sciençe and Thought in the Fifteenth Century* (New York, The Columbia University Press, 1929).

511. THORNDIKE, L., "The Historic Background of Modern Science," *Scientific Monthly,* Vol. 16, 1923, pp. 487-496.

512. THULIN, C., *Die Handschriften des Corpus Agrimensorum* (Leipzig, 1913).

513. THUREAU-DANGIN, F., *Rituels accadiens* (Paris, 1921).

514. TROPFKE, J., *Geschichte der Elementar-Mathematik* (Leipzig, 1923).

515. ULM, VON, CONRAD (*fl.* 1570), *Geodasia* (Strassburg, 1579).

516. VENTURI, J. B., *Il Traguardo di Erone* (Bologna, 1814).

517. VERNIER, PIERRE (1580-1637), *La Construction, l'usage et les propriétéz du quadrant nouveau de mathématique* (Brussels, 1631).

518. VINCENT, A. J. H., "Extraits des manuscrits rélatifs à la géométrie pratique des Grecs: Le traité de la dioptre de Héron d'Alexandrie," *Notices et extraits des manuscrits de la bibliothèque impériale,* Vol. 19, Pt. 2, 1858.

519. VINCI, DA, LEONARDO, *Il codice atlantico, nella biblioteca ambrosiana di Milano* (Milan, 1894-1904). Facsimile of his notes.

520. VITRUVIUS, *De Architectura, Libri Decem,* English Translation by M. H. Morgan (Cambridge, Mass., Harvard University Press, 1914).

521. VOGEL, K., "The Truncated Pyramid in Egyptian Mathematics," *Journal of Egyptian Archeology,* Vol. 16, 1930, pp. 242 ff.

522. WAGHENAER, LUCAS (*fl.* 1580), *Speculum Nauticum* (Amsterdam, 1586).

523. WALSH, J. J., *The Thirteenth the Greatest of the Centuries* (New York, Catholic Summer School Press, 1907).

524. WEHNER, H., "Die Kenntnis der magnetischen Missweisung im Mittelalter," *Weltall,* 1905, No. 11.

525. WEIDNER, E., "Ein babylonisches Kompendium der Himmelskunde," *American Journal of Semitic Languages and Literature,* Vol. 40, 1923.

526. WEIDNER, E., *Handbuch der babylonischen Astronomie* (Leipzig, 1915).

527. WEISSENBORN, H., *Beiträge zur Kenntnis der Mathematik des Mittelalters* (Berlin, 1888).

528. WELBON, M. C., "Lotharingia as a Center of Arabic Influences," *Isis,* Vol. 16, 1931, pp. 188-189.

529. WHITTLESEY, C., "Origin of the American System of Land Surveys," *Journal of the Association of Engineering Societies,* Vol. 3, July, 1883, pp. 275-280.

530. WIEDEMANN, E., "Al Mīzān," *Encyclopaedia of Islam* (Leyden, 1913), Vol. 3.

531. WIEDEMANN, E., "Beiträge zur Geschichte der Naturwissenschaften," *Sitzungsberichte der physikalisch-medizinischen Sozietät in Erlangen,* 1904 *et seq.*

532. WIEDEMANN, E., AND FRANK, J., "Die Gebetzeiten im Islam," *Sitzungsberichte der physikalisch-medizinischen Sozietät in Erlangen,* Vol. 58, 1926.

533. WIEDEMANN, E., AND FRANK, J., "Vorrichtungen zur Teilung von Kreisen und Geraden nach al Bīrūnī," *Zeitschrift für Instruments-Kunde,* Vol. 41, 1921, pp. 225-229.

534. WILKINSON, J., *Manners and Customs of the Ancient Egyptians* (London, 1878).

535. WILLIAM ANGLICUS. *See* Tannery, P.

536. WILLIAMS, K. P., AND COON, R. H., "Sixteenth Century Gunnery," *The Field Artillery Journal,* Vol. 19, 1929, pp. 128-135.

537. WILSON, H., *Surveying* (London, 1731).

538. WINTER, H., "Seit wann ist die Missweisung bekannt?" *Annalen der Hydrographie und Maritimen Meteorologie,* September, 1935, pp. 352-363.

539. WINTER, H., "What Is the Present Stage of Research in Regard to the Development and Use of the Compass in Europe?" *Research and Progress,* Vol. 2, 1936, pp. 225-233.

540. WINTER, H., "Who Invented the Compass?" *The Mariner's Mirror,* Vol. 23, 1937, pp. 95 ff.

541. WOLF, A., *A History of Science, Technology and Philosophy in the 16th and 17th Centuries* (New York, The Macmillan Co., 1935).

542. WOLFF, G., "The Abstract and the Concrete in the Development of School Geometry," *The Mathematics Teacher,* Vol. 29, 1936, pp. 365-373.

543. WOLFF, G., "The Development of the Teaching of Geometry in Germany," *The Mathematical Gazette,* Vol. 21, 1937, pp. 82 ff.

544. WOLKENHAUER, A., *Beiträge zur Geschichte der Kartographie und Nautik des 15 bis 17 Jahrhunderts* (Munich, 1904).

545. WOLKENHAUER, A., "Über die ältesten Reisekarten von Deutschland aus dem Ende des 15 und dem Anfang des 16 Jahrhunderts," *Deutsche geographische Blätter,* Vol. 26, 1903.

546. WORSOP, EDWARD (*fl.* 1570), *Errors of Landemeaters* (London, 1582).

547. WRESZINSKI, W., *Atlas zur altägyptischen Kulturgeschichte* (Leipzig, 1923). 2 vols.

548. WRIGHT, R. R., *The Book of Instruction in the Elements of the Art of Astrology,* Translated from al-Bīrūnī (London, 1934).

549. WRIGHT, T. *See* Neckam, A.

550. WÜRSCHMIDT, J., "Geodätischen Messinstrumente und Messmethoden bei Gerbert und bei den Araben," *Archiv der Mathematik und Physik,* Series 3, Vol. 19, 1912.

551. YOUNG, J. W., "Some Recent French Views on Concrete Methods of Teaching Mathematics," *The School Review,* Vol. 13, 1905, p. 279.

552. ZIMMER, H., "Über die Bedeutung des irischen Elements für die mittelalterliche Cultur," *Preussiche Jahrbücher,* 1887.

553. ZIMMERMANN, G. R., *Ratpert, der erster Zürcher Gelehert* (Basel, 1878).

554. ZONDERVAN, H., *Allgemeine Kartenkunde* (Leipzig, 1901).

555. ZUBLER, LEONARD (*fl.* 1600). *Fabrica et Usus Instrumenti Chorographici* (Zurich, 1607).

556. ZUBLER, LEONARD, *Novum Instrumentum Geometricum* (Basel, 1607).

557. ZWEIG, S., *Conqueror of the Seas—The Story of Magellan,* English Translation by E. and C. Paul (New York, The Viking Press, 1938).

Index